AT ABOUKIR
A STORY OF NAPOL
OF EG
BY

G. A. HE
Author of "The Dash for Khartoum" "By Right of Conquest"
"In Greek Waters" "St. Bartholomew's Eve" &c.

BLACKIE & SON LIMITED
LONDON AND GLASGOW

PREFACE

With the general knowledge of geography now possessed we may well wonder at the wild notion entertained both by Bonaparte and the French authorities that it would be possible, after conquering Egypt, to march an army through Syria, Persia, and the wild countries of the northern borders of India, and to drive the British altogether from that country. The march, even if unopposed, would have been a stupendous one, and the warlike chiefs of Northern India, who, as yet, were not even threatened by a British advance, would have united against an invading army from the north, and would, had it not been of prodigious strength, have annihilated it. The French had enormously exaggerated the power of Tippoo Sahib, with whom they had opened negotiations, and even had their fantastic designs succeeded, it is certain that the Tiger of Mysore would, in a very short time, have felt as deep a hatred for them as he did for the British.

But even had such a march been possible, the extreme danger in which an army landed in Egypt would be placed of being cut off, by the superior strength of the British navy, from all communication with France, should alone have deterred them from so wild a project. The fate of the campaign was indeed decided when the first gun was[Pg vi] fired in the Bay of Aboukir, and the destruction of the French fleet sealed the fate of Napoleon's army. The noble defence of Acre by Sir Sidney Smith was the final blow to Napoleon's projects, and from that moment it was but a question of time when the French army would be forced to lay down its arms, and be conveyed, in British transports, back to France. The credit of the signal failure of the enterprise must be divided between Nelson, Sir Sidney Smith, and Sir Ralph Abercrombie.

CHAPTER I.
MAKING A FRIEND.

Two lads were standing in one of the bastions of a fort looking over the sea. There were neither guards nor sentinels there. The guns stood on their carriages, looking clean and ready for action, but this was not the result of care and attention, but simply because in so dry a climate iron rusts but little. A close examination would have shown that the wooden carriages on which they stood were so cracked and warped by heat that they would have fallen to pieces at the first discharge of the guns they upheld. Piles of cannon-balls stood between the guns, half-covered with the drifting sand, which formed slopes half-way up the walls of the range of barracks behind, and filled up the rooms on the lower floor. Behind rose the city of Alexandria, with its minarets and mosques, its palaces and its low mud-built huts. Seaward lay a fleet of noble ships with their long lines of port-holes, their lofty masts, and network of rigging.

"What do you think of it, Sidi?"[Pg 12]

"It is wonderful!" his companion replied. "How huge they are, what lines of cannon, what great masts, as tall and as straight as palm-trees! Truly you Franks know many things of which we in the desert are ignorant. Think you that they could batter these forts to pieces?"

The other laughed as he looked round. "One of them could do that now, Sidi, seeing that there is scarce a gun on the rampart that could be fired in return; but were all in good order, and with British artillerists, the whole fleet would stand but a poor chance against them, for while their shot would do but little injury to these solid walls, these cannon would drill the ships through and through, and if they did not sheer off, would sink them."

"But why British artillerists, brother, why not our own people?"

"Because you have no properly trained gunners. You know how strong Algiers was, and yet it was attacked with success, twice by the French, twice by ourselves, and once by us and the Dutch; but it is a rule that a strongly defended fort cannot be attacked successfully by ships. If these forts were in proper condition and well manned, I don't think that even Nelson would attack them, though he might land somewhere along the coast, attack and capture the town from the land side, and then carry the batteries. Successful as he has been at sea, he has had some experience as to the difficulty of taking forts. He was beaten off at Teneriffe, and although he did succeed in getting the Danes to surrender at Copenhagen, it's well known now that his ships really got the worst of the fight, and that if the Danes had held on, he must have drawn off with the loss of many of his vessels."

"I know nothing of these things, brother, nor where the towns you name are, nor who are the Danes; but it seems to[Pg 13] me that those great ships with all their guns would be terrible assailants. As you say, these forts are not fit for fighting; but this is because no foes have ever come against us by sea for so many years. What could an enemy do if they landed?"

"The Mamelukes are grand horsemen, Sidi, but horsemen alone cannot win a battle; there are the artillery and infantry to be counted with, and it is with these that battles are won in our days, though I say not that cavalry do not bear their share, but alone they are nothing. One infantry square, if it be steady, can repulse a host of them; but you may ere long see the matter put to proof, for I hear that the officers who came on shore this morning asked if aught had been heard of the French fleet, which had, they say, sailed from Toulon to conquer Egypt. It is for this that the English fleet has come here."

"Their bones will whiten the plains should they attempt it," the other said scornfully. "But why should they want to interfere with us, and why should you care to prevent them doing so if they are strong enough?"

"Because, in the first place, we are at war with them, and would prevent them gaining any advantage. In the second place, because Egypt is a step on the way to India. There we are fighting with one of the great native princes, who has, they say, been promised help by the French, who are most jealous of us, since we have destroyed their influence there, and deprived them of their chance of becoming masters of a large portion of the country."

The conversation had been carried on in Arabic. The speakers were of about the same age, but Edgar Blagrove was half a head taller than his Arab friend. His father was a merchant settled in Alexandria, where Edgar had been born sixteen years before, and except that he had spent[Pg 14] some two years and a half at school in England, he had never been out of Egypt. Brought up in a polyglot household, where the nurses were French or Italian, the grooms Arab, the gardeners Egyptians drawn from the fellah class, and the clerks and others engaged in his father's business for the most part Turks, Edgar had from childhood spoken all these languages with equal facility. He had never learned them, but they had come to him naturally as his English had done. His mother, never an energetic woman, had felt the heat of the climate much, and had never been, or declared she had never been—which came to the same thing—capable of taking any exercise, and, save for a drive in her carriage in the cool of the evening, seldom left the house.

Edgar had, from the first, been left greatly to his own devices. His father was a busy man, and, as long as the boy was well and strong, was content that he should spend his time as he chose, insisting only on his taking lessons for two hours a day from the Italian governess, who taught his twin sisters, who were some eighteen months younger than himself; after that he was free to wander about the house or to go into the streets, provided that one of the grooms, either Hammed or Abdul, accompanied him. When at thirteen he was sent to England to stay with an uncle and to go through a couple of years' schooling, he entered a world so wholly unlike that in which he himself had been brought up, that for a time he seemed completely out of his element.

His father had an excellent library, and during the heat of the day the boy had got through a great deal of reading, and was vastly better acquainted with standard English writers than his cousins or school-fellows, but of ordinary school work he was absolutely ignorant, and at first he[Pg 15] was much laughed at for his deficiencies in Latin and Greek. The latter he never attempted, but his knowledge of Italian helped him so greatly with his Latin that in a very few months he went through class after class, until he was fully up to the level of other boys of his age. His uncle lived in the suburbs of London, and he went with his cousins to St. Paul's. At that time prize-fighting was the national sport, and his father had, when he sent him over, particularly requested his uncle to obtain a good teacher for him.

"Whether Edgar will stay out here for good, Tom, I cannot say, but whether he does or not, I should like him to be able to box well. In England every gentleman in our day learns to use his fists, while out here it is of very great advantage that a man should be able to do so. We have a mixed population here, and a very shady one. Maltese, Greeks, Italians, and French, and these probably the very scum of the various seaports of the Mediterranean, therefore to be able to hit quick and straight from the shoulder may well save a man's life. Of course he is young yet, but if he goes regularly for an hour two or three times a week to one of the light-weight men, I have no doubt that when he returns he will be able to astonish any of these street ruffians who may interfere with him.

"Even if he is never called upon to use his fists, it will do him a great deal of good, for boxing gives a quickness and readiness not only of hands, but of thought, that is of great service; and moreover, the exercise improves the figure, and is, in that respect, I think, fully equal to fencing. Please put this matter in hand as soon as he arrives. As to his studies, I own that I care very little; the boy speaks half-a-dozen languages, any one of which is vastly more useful to a resident here than Latin and Greek together.[Pg 16] Naturally he will learn Latin. Of course his Italian will facilitate this, and it is part of a gentleman's education to be able to understand a quotation or turn a phrase in it. Still, it is not for this that I send him to England, but to become an English boy, and that your Bob and Arthur and his school-fellows will teach him."

Edgar was quite as much surprised at his cousins and school-fellows as they were with him. The fact that he could talk half-a-dozen languages was to them amazing, while not less astonishing to him was their ignorance of the affairs of Europe except, indeed, of the French Revolution—their vagueness in geography, and the absolute blank of their minds as to Egypt. It was not until three months after his arrival that he had his first fight, and the instructions he had received during that time sufficed to enable him to win so easy a victory, that it was some months before he had again occasion to use his fists in earnest. This time it was in the streets. He was returning home with his cousins, when a pert young clerk thought it a good joke to twitch off his cap and throw it into a shop, and was astounded when, before the cap had reached the floor, he himself was prostrate on the pavement.

He was no coward, however, and leapt up, furious, to punish this boy of fourteen, but in spite of his superior strength and weight, he was no match for Edgar, whose quickness on his legs enabled him to avoid his rushes, while he planted his blows so quickly and heavily that in ten minutes the clerk was unable to see out of his eyes, and had to be led away amid the jeers of the crowd. This success increased Edgar's ardour to perfect himself in the art. If he could so easily defeat an English lad of seventeen, he felt sure that after another year's teaching he need not fear an attack by the greatest ruffian in Alexandria.[Pg 17] His uncle had taken advice on the subject, and, desirous of carrying out his brother's instructions to the fullest, changed his master every six months; so that during the two years and a half that he was in England Edgar had learned all that the five most skilled light-weight pugilists in England could teach him.

"Yes, he is going in for it thoroughly," his uncle would say to his friends. "Of course, I shall have my own boys taught in another three or four years, for I think that every gentleman should be able to defend himself if assaulted by a street ruffian; but in his case he has to learn when quite young or not at all, and I think that it will be very useful to him, as all these foreign fellows draw their knives on the least occasion."

When Edgar returned to Alexandria, nine months before the time when he and Sidi were watching Nelson's fleet, his father was well pleased with the change that had taken place in him. He had been tall for his age before he left, now he had not only grown considerably, but had widened out. He was still far from being what may be called a squarely-built boy, but he was of a fair width across the shoulders, and was a picture of health and activity. The muscles of his arms, shoulders, and loins were as tough as steel, his complexion was fresh and clear, and he had scarce an ounce of superfluous flesh upon him.

"Save for your complexion, Edgar, you might well pass as a young Bedouin if you were to wrap yourself up in their garb. I see you have profited well by your teachers' instructions. Your uncle wrote to me a year ago that you had administered a sound thrashing to a fellow seventeen years old who had meddled with you, and as, no doubt, you have improved in skill and strength since that time, I should think that you need have no fear of holding your[Pg 18] own should you get into trouble with any of these street ruffians."

"I should hope so, father; at any rate I should not mind trying. I know that I could hold my own pretty fairly with young Jackson. They call him the 'Bantam'. He is the champion light-weight now, though he does not fight above nine stone, so there is not much difference between us in weight."

"Good! and how about your school work?"

"Oh, I did pretty well, father! I was good in Latin, but I was nowhere in figures."

"Not grown quarrelsome, I hope, on the strength of your fighting, Edgar?"

"No, sir, I hope not. I never had a fight at school except the one I had three months after I got there, and I only had that one row you speak of with a clerk. I don't think it would be fair, you see, to get into rows with fellows who have no idea how thoroughly I have been taught."

His father nodded.

"Quite right, Edgar. My ideas are that a man who can box well is much less likely to get into quarrels than one who cannot. He knows what he can do, and that, if forced to use his skill, he is able to render a good account of himself, and therefore he can afford to put up with more, than one who is doubtful as to whether he is likely to come well out of a fight if he begins one."

Edgar found on his arrival at Alexandria that his mother and sisters were about to leave for England. Mrs. Blagrove had become seriously indisposed, the result, as she maintained, of the climate, but which was far more due to her indolent habits, for she never took any exercise whatever. Her general health was greatly impaired, and the two Italian doctors who attended her—there being no English medical[Pg 19] men resident there—had most strongly advised that she should return home. They had frankly told Mr. Blagrove that a colder climate was absolutely necessary to her, not only because it would brace her up and act as a tonic, but because she would probably there be induced to take a certain amount of exercise. The two girls were to accompany her, in order that they should, like Edgar, enjoy the advantage of going to an English school and mixing with English girls of their own age. They, too, had both felt the heat during the preceding summer, and Mr. Blagrove felt that a stay of two or three years in England would be an immense advantage to them.

Mrs. Blagrove was to stay with her father, a clergyman in the west of England, for a few months, when her husband intended himself to go over for a time. The war had much reduced business, the activity of the French privateers rendered communication irregular and precarious, the rates both for freight and insurance were very high, the number of vessels entering the port were but a tithe of those that frequented it before the outbreak of the war, and as no small part of Mr. Blagrove's business consisted in supplying vessels with such stores as they needed, his operations were so restricted that he felt he could, without any great loss, leave the management of his affairs in the hands of his chief assistant, a German, who had been with him for twenty years, and in whom he placed the greatest reliance.

Edgar would be there to assist generally, and his father thought that it would even benefit him to be placed for a time in a responsible position. It was, of course, a great disappointment to Edgar to find that his mother and the girls were on the point of returning. Their departure, indeed, had been decided upon somewhat suddenly owing to a strongly-armed English privateer, commanded by an old[Pg 20] acquaintance of Mr. Blagrove, coming into port. She had been cruising for some time, and had sent home a number of prizes, and was now returning herself to England for another refit and to fill up her crew again. As she was a very fast vessel, and the captain said that he intended to make straight home and to avoid all doubtful sail, Mr. Blagrove at once accepted the offer he made to take his wife and daughters back to England, immediately he heard that his friend was looking for a passage for them. Accordingly for the next week there was much packing and confusion. At the end of that time the three ladies, after a tearful adieu, sailed for England, and things settled down again.

Edgar felt the absence of his sisters keenly. There were but a handful of English traders in the city, and none of these had boys who were near enough to his own age to be companions. However, it had the effect of enabling him, without interruption, to settle down steadily to work with his father, and to make himself acquainted with the details of the business. This he did so industriously that Mr. Blagrove said more than once: "You are getting on so well, Edgar, that I shall be able to go home for my holiday with the comfortable conviction that in yours and Muller's hands matters will go on very well here, especially as business is so slack."

It was about three months after his return that Edgar had an opportunity of finding the advantage of his skill in boxing. He had, on the day after he came back, had a sack of sawdust hung up in his room, and every morning he used to pummel this for half an hour before taking his bath, and again before going to bed, so that he kept his muscles in a state of training. Moreover, this exercise had the advantage that it enabled him to stand the heat of the climate much[Pg 21]better than he would otherwise have done, and to save him from any of that feeling of lassitude and depression so usual among Englishmen working in hot climates. He was returning one day from a ride; dusk had fallen, and when just beyond the limits of the town he heard shouts and cries, and saw a scuffle going on in the road. Cantering on, he leapt from his horse, dropped the reins on its neck, and ran forward.

Two of the lowest class Maltese or Greeks were dragging a young Arab along, holding his hands to prevent him getting at his knife, and beating him about the head with their disengaged hands. It was evident that he was not one of the dwellers in the city, but an Arab of the desert. His horse stood near, and he had apparently been dragged from it.

"What is the matter? what are you beating him for?" he asked in Italian.

"This Arab dog pushed against us with his horse, and when we cursed him, struck at us."

"Well, if he did, you have punished him enough; but perhaps his story is a different one."

"Go your way, boy," one exclaimed with a Greek oath, "or we will throw you into that fountain, as we are going to do him."

"You will, eh? Unloose that lad at once or it will be worse for you."

The man uttered a shout of rage. "Hold this young Arab wolf's other hand, Giaccamo, so that he cannot use his knife. I will settle this boy;" and his companion seized the lad's other wrist.

He rushed at Edgar, waving his arms in windmill fashion, thinking to strike him down without the least difficulty, but he was astounded at being met with a terrific blow on the[Pg 22] nose, which nigh threw him off his balance, and this was followed an instant later by another on the point of his chin, which hurled him back, half-stunned, to the ground, with a vague impression in his mind that his head was broken into fragments. Before he even thought of rising, Edgar sprang at his companion, who, releasing the Arab boy's hands, grasped his knife, but before he could draw it, a blow, given with all Edgar's strength and the impetus of his bound forward, stretched him also on the ground, his knife flying from his hand.

The Arab boy had drawn his knife also, but Edgar exclaimed to him in his own language, "No, no, pick up the other knife, and then stand over him, but don't stab him." Then he turned to his first assailant, who was rising to his feet, still confused and bewildered. He had instinctively drawn his knife.

"Drop your knife, drop it!" Edgar cried. But with an oath the man sprang at him. His eyes, however, were full of tears, his ears sung, and his head buzzed, partly from the blow on the jaw, partly from the force with which he had come in contact with the ground. Edward lightly sprung aside and avoided the cut aimed at him, and then delivered a blow with all his force just in front of the ear, and the man dropped again as if shot. In a moment Edgar had wrenched the knife from his hand, then he turned to the young Arab.

"That is enough," he said; "they have both got more than they wanted; they are harmless now, we have their two knives."

The Arab, who was panting from his exertions, and who had evidently restrained himself with difficulty from plunging his knife into his fallen assailant, turned round towards him.[Pg 23]

"Who are you, brother, whose blows fell men like strokes of lightning?"

"My name is Edgar Blagrove. I am the son of a merchant, whose place of business is in the great square. Who are you, and how did this business begin?"

"My name is Sidi Ben Ouafy. I am the son of a chief. My father's tribe live in the oasis ten miles east of the old lake. I was riding from the town when these two men, for whom there was, as you see, plenty of room in the road, staggered suddenly against me, whether with evil intent or merely to enjoy the pleasure of seeing me rolling in the dust, I know not. They nearly unseated me from the suddenness of the attack, and as I recovered I certainly struck at them with my whip. One seized me by the foot and threw me off my horse, and then, as you saw, they fell upon me, beat me, and were dragging me to the fountain to throw me in when you came up. Had they not heard your horse coming along they would, I believe, have killed me. Henceforth you are my brother; my horses and all that I have are yours, and every sword of our tribe would leap from its scabbard in your defence were it needed. To-morrow I will ride in again, and my father himself will assuredly come with me. I cannot speak of my gratitude now, my head is still dizzy with the blows they gave me; even yet I cannot understand how it was that these two men have thus fallen before you, and you with no weapon in your hands. Are they dead?"

"Not they," Edgar said scornfully; "they are wondering what has happened to them, and fear to move, not knowing that their own knives might not be driven into their hearts did they venture to rise. Well, good-bye, Sidi; I will see you off first; and I should advise you, when you ride into the town again, to bring your pistols with you. Like[Pg 24] enough these scoundrels will try to get revenge for this defeat."

"I will do so. I know not why I did not carry them to-day. I will not only bring them, but two of my tribesmen shall ride with me. But methinks that you will be in greater danger than I shall, brother."

"I shall be on the look-out, and will, for a time, carry pistols with me; but I do not often go out after dark, and have no occasion ever to enter the streets where rogues of this sort live. As to an open attack, I have no fear of it; but I have no doubt that either of those scoundrels would plant a knife between my shoulders if they had a chance to do so."

Both the lads mounted their horses, and after a few words of farewell rode off in different directions. Not until the sound of the horses' hoofs died away did the two figures in the road move, then they sat up.

"What has happened, Zeno?"

"I know not, save that my head is ringing. I feel as if my jaws were broken, and my nose is so swelled that it seems as big as my head."

"And I can scarcely see from my eyes," the other said. "Cospetto, never before have I been thus handled!"

"We will kill him!" the other said furiously.

"That of course; I know not who he was, but we shall doubtless find out. I can hardly believe even now that it was with his hand that he struck us—it was done so quickly. He was there—then I struck at him, when—paff!—and it seemed to me that the air was full of stars; then, paff again! my jaws cracked, I fell backwards, there was a crash, and the world seemed to have come to an end. And you, Giaccamo, what did he do to you?"

"It was like that, except that I only had one blow, and[Pg 25] there was an end of it. I was drawing my knife when it came—how, I know not. My knife flew from my hand—there was a flash of fire from my eyes, and I was on the ground, and thought it best to lie there, lest that accursed young Arab should take it into his head to sheathe my knife in my body. The next time we will give the young fellow no chance to try those strange tricks upon us."

"You are right, Giaccamo; I would sooner fight against even Thomasso, who is the best knife-player in Alexandria, than face that fellow again. Who can he be, I wonder?"

Edgar rode home, and after seeing his horse taken into the stable, went into the house.

"I have found my boxing of use, father."

"How is that, Edgar?"

The lad told him what had happened.

"You were quite right to strike, my boy," his father went on when he had heard the story; "'tis likely enough that those ruffians would have killed the lad. There are fellows here who would do murder for the sake of a few copper coins; and, doubtless, those men thought that the young chief would have some trinkets about him that would pay them for their trouble. I am sorry that you did not let the Arab put his knife into them; it would have been a good riddance, for the town abounds with rascals of that kind—the scum of the Mediterranean, men who have made their native towns too hot to hold them, and have committed crimes untold.

As it is, you will have to be careful; fellows of this kind are not of a forgiving nature, and will be patient enough to wait for their revenge, but sooner or later they will attempt to take it."

"It was so dark, father, that they can scarcely have seen my face."

"Perhaps not, but no doubt they were able to make out[Pg 26] your figure, and there are very few better-class young Europeans here. You will have to be on your guard, lad; you had better always carry pistols with you. Clever as you may be with your fists, if you were attacked by half-a-dozen fellows with knives, you would stand but little chance with them. Don't be out after dusk; in daylight you are fairly safe. At any rate, you would be, if you avoid the rookeries, where the lower class of European inhabitants live. I have a brace of short-barrelled pistols up-stairs I will give you. I carried them at one time when things were very unsettled here. You have made two bitter enemies, but, on the other hand, you have made a friend who may be useful. These Arabs, when they once form a friendship, are as true as steel, and in the event of any fanatical troubles here, you would find a sure refuge among them. The lad's father, Aboo Ben Ouafy, I know a little of, as he has made purchases of me. His tribe is not a large one, but he himself is a fine fellow. As the lad told you, their head-quarters are in an oasis some eight or ten miles, I believe, east of the old site of Lake Mareotis. They, of course, like all those people, are frequently absent on hunting or plundering expeditions."

The next day Sidi and his father, followed by half a dozen tribesmen, halted in front of Mr. Blagrove's place of business, and the two former dismounted and entered. The Bedouin chief saluted the merchant gravely, while Sidi went up to Edgar, who was sitting at a table, for he now worked for some hours a day in his father's office, and who rose at the lad's approach, and held out his hand in English fashion.

"You are none the worse for our scrimmage last night, Sidi?" he said heartily.

"No harm was done," Sidi replied gravely. "I am glad of what happened, for it has given me a friend, a brother."[Pg 27]

"I am glad too," Edgar replied, "for I too am happy to have gained a friend."

In the meantime his father was saying to Mr. Blagrove, "I have come, effendi, to thank you and your son for the assistance he rendered to my boy yesterday. I have no doubt that he saved his life, and that at the peril of his own. It is wonderful what my son tells me, that, with his hands alone he beat to the ground the two men who had attacked him, though they were armed with knives. I know not how it could be done, but since it was done 'tis plain that he must possess skill unknown to us. Sidi has called him brother, and henceforth I shall regard him as a son, and my tribe will be his should he need their services. I doubt not that the attack was made in order to gain the horse my son rode, which is one of famous breed, and would sell at high price at Cairo or any other of the large towns. I feel sure that they would have killed him in order that they might carry the horse away without search being made for it, for before we found that Sidi had been slain the horse would have been a hundred miles away."

"I know that your tribe is famous for having some of the best Arabian blood in the country, sheik, and I think it probable that you are right. The fellows may have seen your son ride into the town and determined to waylay him on his return."

"Your son did wrong not to kill them," the Arab said, "he will be in danger from them. I have called not only to thank him, but to ask him to come and bide with us for a time; he will assuredly be in danger here. Were I governor of the town I would chop off the heads of all those people who breed disorders and are a curse to it. 'Tis well that Franks like yourself should settle among us, and should trade with us, buying our goods and selling[Pg 28] to us those of Europe, but these thieves and cut-throats, these ruffians who neither trade nor work, but live by ill-doing, should be rooted out."

"I should be glad for my son to stay with you for a short time, sheik. I share your opinion that these men will try to avenge themselves, and it were well that he should be away for a time. Doubtless they will watch narrowly to see if they can find the young fellow who interfered with them, but if they meet with no one like him they may well think that he has left the town."

"It is well!" the Arab said. "I am going now to the governor to lay a complaint against these men. My son will go with me to tell him what they are like; the son of a sheik is not to be assaulted by town ruffians with impunity. We may be kept some time, but when we have done we will return hither. Will your son be ready to ride with us?"

"Certainly, sheik; it will not take him five minutes to make his preparations."

"He will not need a horse," the sheik said; "I have brought one with me for him."

Edgar had listened with delight to this conversation (which was in Arabic, which his father spoke fluently). The idea of going to stay for a time in an Arab encampment was exciting indeed, for he had already begun to find the life monotonous after the two years spent at school and in the lively companionship of his cousins.

"It were well that you should come out and see your horse," the sheik said to him, "and make friends with him while we are away, for he is not accustomed to Europeans, and might give you trouble were you to mount him at once."

Edgar and his father both went out. One of the Arabs[Pg 29] was standing at the horse's head, rubbing its nose and talking to it as if it had been a human being.

"That is the horse," the sheik said gravely. "Only to one, whom I regard as a son, would I part with him. On his back you may scoff at pursuit by any foes, for outside my encampment there is not a horse in Egypt which it could not distance. Now it is yours to do with as you like, save to sell it, for I would not that his blood should run in any veins save those of the horses of my tribe."

"This is, indeed, a princely gift, sheik," the merchant said warmly. "'Tis a noble horse, and one that a king might ride. My son is indeed indebted to you, and will value it beyond all price."

Edgar was warm in his expressions of gratitude and admiration, although, indeed, he was unable to appreciate at its full value the points of the animal. It was a gray, and, to English eyes, would have looked light and wanting in bone, and fit rather for a lady's use than for a man's, with its slender limbs and small head; but one accustomed to Arab horses, as Mr. Blagrove was, could see at once that it was of the purest strain and highest breeding.

"Come with me," the sheik said to Edgar. "At present, you see, he is not accustomed to your white face, but he will soon come to love you, and answer to your call."

The horse, indeed, had laid back his ears, distended his dilated nostrils, and stepped back a foot or two; but as the sheik approached it gave a little whinny of pleasure, and, advancing, laid its muzzle against his cheek.

"This is your new master, Beauty," he said, as he stroked its glossy neck. "He will keep you well, and you will be as one of his children, and you must be a good friend and servant to him."

Edgar now stroked the animal. A quiver as of fear ran[Pg 30] through it as he touched it, but as he continued, this died away; and as Edgar spoke quietly to it in Arabic, it was not long before it responded to his caresses, and after taking a good look at him with its soft liquid eyes, it put its head on his shoulder.

"You are friends now," the sheik said, with a tone of pleasure. "It is to few, even of my tribesmen, whom he would give such a greeting. He recognizes you already as his friend. Give him a handful of sweetmeats, and the bargain will be sealed."

The merchant at once sent one of the native boys out to buy a bag of sweetmeats. The sheik waited until he saw the horse taking these out of Edgar's hands and munching them contentedly, then, leaving one of his tribesmen in charge of the horse, he mounted, and rode off with his son and the rest of his followers. Edgar stood for some time talking to the horse, and then, leaving it to the native, went into the house to make his preparations for the journey.

"You have, indeed, done well for yourself, Edgar," his father said as he came in. "'Tis in every way fortunate. The Turks love us little, and though they put up with us, as they need the goods that we sell, still there may at any moment be a fanatical rising, and it is well, indeed, to have made friends with one of the desert tribes, among whom you can find a safe refuge. You little know the value of the horse he has given you. The breed is a famous one, and the sheik has been offered a fabulous sum for one of his steeds, but nothing could tempt him to part with one. An Arab prizes a valuable horse beyond all his earthly possessions, and, save under the pressure of the direst want, nothing could persuade him to part with it. In presenting it to you, therefore, the chief has shown his friendship in[Pg 31] the most striking manner possible, and that he regards you, as he says, as one of his family."

CHAPTER II.
A BEDOUIN TRIBE.

It was two hours before the sheik returned.

"We have been fortunate," he said, as Mr. Blagrove and Edgar came out into the court-yard as he entered. "The men have had their punishment. The governor, after hearing my story, sent to the head of the police, and charged him to take four men down with him into the quarter where men of this sort are generally to be found. When my son described the men to him, and said that he thought that one of them was a Maltese named Giaccamo, and the other was a Greek called Zeno, he spoke to some of his men, and they said they knew two fellows who generally went about together that answered to the description. They were, he said, notorious ruffians, but except for rioting and wounding among their compatriots, with which the police did not concern themselves, they had been able to find nothing against them, though they strongly suspected that they were concerned in many crimes. We went down with them to that quarter, and the police soon found out the place where they lived, but on enquiry were assured that both men were ill, the old woman who came to the door declaring that they had been in bed for some days. However, the police insisted upon entering, and speedily brought them down. Sidi recognized them at once, and indeed they had scarcely lied in saying that they were ill, for the eyelids of one were so swollen and[Pg 32] blackened that he could not see out of them, while the other's nose was well-nigh as big as the rest of his face.

"They were at once taken before the cadi. He heard my son's evidence, and then said that had it been proved they attempted to steal the horse, he would have had their heads smitten off, but that though this was doubtless their intention, they had not done so. He sentenced them to a hundred blows with a stick, and to be expelled from the town and neighbourhood, warning them that should they be found near the town again, they would assuredly be punished with death. I waited and saw the blows administered, and although I felt angry that the cadi had not ordered them to execution, I admit that the punishment was severe enough, and the wretches howled like whipped curs. I trust that there will be no more trouble from them. Still, I hope that this will not prevent your son coming to visit us."

"Certainly not, sheik. He is prepared and ready to go, and he is looking forward to his stay with you with so much pleasure that even did I wish it I could not now deprive him of the enjoyment of it. Still, I am heartily glad that the two fellows have been expelled the town, for I should never have felt easy as to Edgar's safety so long as they were here."

A few minutes later the party set out. Edgar's valise was fastened to the saddle of one of the sheik's followers. The road ran along the sandy dunes that divided the low country, formerly covered by Lake Mareotis, from the sea, and as soon as they were well out from the town the horses were broke into a gallop. While in point of actual speed even the best Arab horses cannot hold their own against a moderate English race-horse, whose greater height and longer stride gives him an advantage, they are greatly[Pg 33] superior in last, and possess extraordinary endurance and stamina. Brought up as if belonging to the family of their owners, their intelligence has been cultivated as has that of dogs. They are exceedingly docile and affectionate. Their pace is a very easy one, and Edgar was delighted indeed at the manner in which his new acquisition flew along without any apparent exertion, continuing the pace without a check until they reached the Arab encampment in an hour and twenty minutes from leaving Alexandria.

Here they leapt from their horses in front of a group of black tents. The oasis was of small extent, extending but two hundred yards across. In the centre was a group of thirty or forty palm-trees. Near these the herbage was thick, gradually dwindling away until it became lost in the sand. In the centre, near the tents, was a well, an irregularly-shaped pit some five-and-twenty feet deep, with a rough path down to it by which the women went to get water both for their own use and for that of the horses. A score of these were tethered on the grass.

"You are welcome to our tents," the sheik said; "may your visit be a fortunate one! Mulick," he called to one of the Arab boys, "take Beauty; but first," he went on to Edgar, "it were best that you talked to him a little, and gave him some sweets. He will soon get to love you, and it is well that he should hear your voice as often as possible."

"I will lead him out myself," Edgar replied, "and then Mulick can tether him. I shall know another time how to do it myself."

Then he patted the Arab's glossy neck, rubbed its ears, and praised it, giving it a handful of sweets while he did so. Beauty evidently appreciated the attentions, and replied to him by a low whinny. Then he took off its saddle and led it to a spot Mulick pointed out, and then watched[Pg 34] the boy tether it, and took off the bridle and carried it back to the tents. A woman came out from the largest of these. She was not veiled, for except when they go into the towns the Bedouin women seldom conceal their faces.

"Ayala," the sheik said, "this is the young white lord who saved Sidi from those who attacked him; henceforth he is as one of our tribe."

"May the blessings of Allah fall upon you!" the woman said. "Sidi is our only child. Had he been taken from us our lives would have been desolate indeed."

"I am very glad that I happened to come along at the time," Edgar said. "It has been a most fortunate occurrence for me, as much indeed as for Sidi. I have no friends of my own age, and it will be great pleasure to me to have him as a sort of brother. I am sure that we shall get on capitally together. Besides which, your husband has given me a grand horse, such as I could never have obtained for money. Sidi will be able to teach me Arab ways, and I daresay I shall be able to show him something of our customs and life."

Edgar was now shown a tent that had been newly erected for his use. The furniture was simple, consisting only of a handsome Eastern carpet, which covered the ground, and a pile of rugs for sofa and bed. Hanging from one of the sticks that supported the tent was a porous jar of water. When he had hung up his rifle and pistols, powder-horn and bullet-pouch, its furnishing was complete.

"Is this all your tribe?" he asked Sidi, as he came out from his tent.

"Oh, no! our tribe dwells in a large oasis a hundred miles to the south, and fifty miles west of Cairo. There are other portions of the tribe dwelling not far from the same spot, and we can ride five hundred strong when we go to fight the[Pg 35] Berbers of Morocco. But my father is only sheik of his section. There are generally but six tents left here to keep possession, and we are often away for months. We find that we can buy such goods as the tribe requires cheaper at Alexandria than at Cairo, where, indeed, we do not often go, for ill-blood exists between us and the authorities there, who ventured on some complaint to send out a party of Mamelukes against us. We beat them back handsomely, but had to leave our oasis for a time, as we could not withstand the force they would be sure to send against us. That was thirty years ago. They filled up our wells and cut down our palm-trees. The wells were soon cleared out again, and the palm groves have grown up. They have not interfered with us again, but even now we care not to visit Cairo, though it may be that the matter is altogether forgotten there."

Edgar remained a fortnight with his new friends, and enjoyed the life much. He took lessons from Sidi in hurling a lance, and discovered that it would need a long practice indeed to enable him to do so with the accuracy shown by the Arabs. He also practised with his rifles and pistols. When he left he gave a warm invitation to Sidi to come and stay with him. This, however, the Arab lad declined.

"I should not be comfortable in your European dwelling," he said. "I should be miserable, sitting on one of those chairs. Your father is busy, and so are you; I should be altogether out of my element."

"But I might have said the same thing here, Sidi?"

"Oh, no! it is easy to fling off restraint, to throw yourself on the sand, to ride and shoot and hurl the spear. Those are sports that you can enjoy as much as I do. I will come over often and see you, but do not ask me to stay."[Pg 36]

Edgar saw that it was better not to press the matter, at any rate for the present. In time, when Sidi became more accustomed to European ways he might perhaps come to stay, but if he came now it would be a penance rather than a pleasure. After that time the young Arab rode over frequently, leaving his camp at daybreak and arriving in time to spend a long day with Edgar. Sometimes they rode together, sometimes walked along the sea-shore, and Sidi soon learned to enjoy as much as his friend a row or a sail on the water, which to him was at first altogether a novelty. The merchant possessed several boats, which he used in his business, and a pretty gig which carried a sail, in which he himself went off to visit ships which brought goods for him. This was at other times at Edgar's service. He had learned, even before going to school, to manage it, and it therefore was unnecessary to take anyone with them.

Sidi at first did not take kindly to an oar. Trained to hard exercise on horseback and in the sports of the tribe, he had yet a great aversion to anything like steady labour, and was unable even to understand Edgar's willingness to exert himself at an oar when he could have had men to row him about. In time, however, when he had mastered the initial difficulties of the art, he took to the exercise, and they often spent the whole day in the boat, either coasting along Aboukir Bay, or, more often, shooting on the lakes.

The arrival of the British fleet had created quite an excitement in Alexandria, and the news they brought, that a large French fleet had left Toulon, carrying many thousands of troops, destined, it was believed, to operate in Egypt, had caused an intense feeling of dismay among the British merchants settled there, and a corresponding exultation among the French.[Pg 37]

"Will the French fleet be stronger than this?" Sidi asked, as he and Edgar leant on the parapet and looked at the long line of British ships.

"There may be more of them—very likely there are," Edgar said carelessly; "but that makes no matter, we are sure to thrash them. In the first place, we always do so somehow; and in the next, as our fleet is commanded by one of the best admirals we have, there is no fear of their being beaten. The only fear is that the fleet mayn't fall in with the French until they have landed their troops."

"The troops could not stand against our Mamelukes," Sidi said scornfully. "They would soon drive them into the sea."

"I am not so sure of that," Edgar said. "No doubt the Mamelukes are splendid horsemen. I suppose they are as good as any in the world; but horsemen cannot win a battle alone. The French infantry are very fine, and I doubt whether any number of horsemen could break their squares. Then their artillery is immensely superior to that of the Egyptians; that will give them a very great advantage."

"But if your fleet meets theirs and beats it, how could they ever get back again?"

"I expect they mean to stay here and hold the country," Edgar said. "I don't know what good it would do to them; still I suppose they think it would, or they would not take the trouble to come over. But if they should take the country, it would be very bad for men like my father, for they would be sure to put all the English in prison, and it would be the ruin of their business."

"Would they put you in prison?"

"I don't know; I expect so. They would hold all the English as prisoners."

"You would come out to us. You will be quite safe[Pg 38] there. If their soldiers came, they would never catch us; we could move about anywhere, we know all the places where water is to be found, and they would only die of thirst if they went after us into the desert."

"Well, I hope that it is not going to be so, Sidi; but if the French should land here I should like it very much. I suppose you would fight against the French."

"If they came to take Egypt, of course we should, and then you could see it all, and fight with us against them."

"It would be very jolly, Sidi, and I should like nothing better; but of course I shall have to do as my father tells me. I expect he would shut up his place, and get all his goods on board a ship and go away till it was all over, if he was able. No doubt he would want me to go with him."

That evening Edgar learned that he had rightly guessed the steps that his father would take in case a French army landed.

"It is an awkward business, lad," he said. "Of course if Nelson comes up with the French fleet, we may hope that it will come out right; but if, before he catches it, they manage to land twenty or thirty thousand troops, our position here would be a most serious one. I intend to charter the *Petrel*, which has just discharged the cargo she brought here. I shall put all my most valuable goods on board at once, especially all the Egyptian carpets and other oriental work, so that within a few hours of hearing that their fleet was off the coast, I should be ready to sail for England. Of course there would be an end to the business here, so long as the French remained in Egypt; and no doubt any British subjects they could lay their hands on would be thrown into prison, just as was the case when they occupied Holland.

"I should not, however, propose to shut up the house altogether, for although we, as English, would be seized, and[Pg 39] thrown into prison, and the place closed, France is not at war with Germany, and Muller could carry on the shipping business without interruption, his own name being substituted for mine. I should instruct him to do no trade with the interior; everything will be turned topsy-turvy, and all trade of that sort would be at an end. On the other hand, with the French masters here, a considerable number of French and Italian ships will be coming in with stores of all kinds, these will often need supplies, repairs, and so on; and as we have men capable of doing anything in the way of refitting, Muller could keep things going, and carry on a business that should pay all expenses, and would probably leave a margin of profit. At any rate, the house would not go to wreck and ruin, and the business be entirely lost.

"I don't think the French occupation would be likely to last very many months. You may be sure that there would be great efforts made at home. A tremendous fleet would be sent out here, and the difficulties of bringing in stores and reinforcements for the army would be enormous. Possibly we too may land an army. Certainly we could nowhere fight the French so advantageously as here; it would be the case of India over again, as long as we are superior at sea, as we could bring troops here more safely and more expeditiously than they could. However, that seems to me the best arrangement we can make if the French land. To me it would make no great difference, for, as you know, I had arranged to sail in three weeks for England.

"The only alteration would be that you must accompany me instead of staying here. Even putting aside the fact that you would be made a prisoner, you would, if you stayed here, be a hindrance rather than a help to the business. Muller would carry it on as a purely German firm, while if[Pg 40] you were here it would be evident that I had merely left temporarily, and that you were my representative. That would be fatal to Muller doing business with the French."

"I see that, father, although I must say that I would rather stop to see the fun."

Mr. Blagrove smiled.

"I don't suppose you would see much of it in any case, Edgar. However, that is out of the question. I daresay my correspondents in London will be able to take you into their office, or get you a situation of the same kind elsewhere, so that if you stop in England a year you will not be wasting your time. However, the French have not come yet, and I can hardly think that they can intend to undertake an expedition, where, even if our fleet is not strong enough to do so at once, it will ere long certainly be raised to a point when it will completely cut them off from France."

"But even if they come, father, they may not succeed in conquering Egypt. Don't you think that the Mamelukes will be able to make head against them?"

"We don't know how strong the French are, but even if they come in great force, if the Mamelukes were well handled, Edgar, they ought to be able to prevent them from advancing far inland. They ought to hang in clouds round them, driving in their cavalry whenever they ventured to leave the shelter of their infantry fire. They ought to harass them night and day, and prevent them obtaining supplies of any sort. I am afraid that nothing of that kind will be done. The Mamelukes have been spoilt, and they are so puffed up that they believe themselves to be invincible, and that they have only to make a grand charge to sweep the French away.

"However, it will make no great difference to us when[Pg 41] we are once fairly away, for of course I shall not think of returning here until matters have settled down again. The French traders have had a bad time of it since the war began, and most of them left long ago, for it was so seldom that a vessel got through our cruisers that they could not rely upon any regular supplies of goods. Of course, there are many small shopkeepers who take their goods of me, and retail them out to the natives, but all the importers left. I am afraid it is going to be our turn now; that is, unless Nelson manages to intercept their fleet—no very easy matter, for they might land anywhere along the coast between this and Syria. But I imagine that their descent will take place near this town, for from it they could follow the fresh-water canal to the point where it flows from the Nile, and so on to Cairo.

"They may, however, land at either the Damietta or Rosetta mouths of the river; still, I think that they are more likely to come here, seeing that the ships could more closely approach the shore."

The British fleet remained but a few hours off Alexandria. The short Peace of Campo-Formio had caused the greater portion of the British fleet to be recalled from the Mediterranean; and it was not until the French preparations were almost complete that the news reached England that a vast number of transports had been collected by the French at various ports, that provisions of all kinds were being put on board, and it was rumoured that an army was about to embark for some unknown destination.

Nelson was at once sent off with a fleet to blockade Toulon, from which port it was evident that the men-of-war intended to guard this great fleet of transports would start. It arrived there on the first of June, only to learn that the French fleet had set out three days previously.[Pg 42] The idea that Egypt was its destination had not entered the minds of the British ministers, and although Nelson had been furnished with instructions as to the course to be taken in the case of almost every contingency, this had never been even discussed.

The French fleet consisted of 13 vessels of the line, 9 frigates, and 11 corvettes and despatch-boats. All of these, with the exception of a few of the smaller vessels, were furnished by Toulon. Here, too, 20,500 men had embarked in 106 transports. They were to be joined by 30 transports from Marseilles, 20 from Corsica, 35 from Genoa, and 41 from Civita Vecchia, bringing up the total to 232 transports, carrying 32,300 men.

In one arm the army was extremely deficient, as only 680 horses could be put on board. Of these 300 were for the cavalry,—all of whom, however, took with them saddles and bridles,—the rest were for the artillery and train.

Nelson started at once in search of the enemy, but having no clue to the direction they had taken he was able to obtain no news of their whereabouts until he heard that they had captured, without resistance, the island of Malta. Then he returned with all speed, imagining for the first time that possibly Egypt was the object of attack, and made for Alexandria. On his arrival there he heard that nothing was known of the French movements, although in fact their fleet was on that day lying at anchor off Cape Harzet, twenty leagues to the west.

Supposing, therefore, that they must after all have sailed for the coast of Syria or Constantinople, he steered for Alexandretta, and learning that, after having captured Malta, the French fleet had sailed to Candia, he left for Rhodes, searched everywhere through the islands of the Archipelago, and it was only when he anchored off Cape Matapan, the[Pg 43] southern extremity of the Morea, that he first learned that the French army had landed in Egypt a month before.

The object of the French expedition was a vast one, but the means with which it was undertaken were insufficient for its execution, and the difficulties in the way were infinitely greater than had been supposed in

Paris. Bonaparte had been chosen for its command principally because the directory feared that the great popularity of the victorious general would render him formidable to themselves. They knew already that he was by no means favourably disposed towards them, and they were therefore anxious to remove him from the public eye.

Napoleon, on his part, was perfectly aware of the reason for which he was appointed to the command, but he accepted it under the belief that a vast amount of glory was to be gained, and that, should the plans of the directory be entirely carried out, and India wrested from the English, his name would be placed by the side of Alexander in history. Already negotiations had been carried on for some time with Tippoo Sahib. Commissioners had been despatched to him, and an alliance proposed against the British. His power had been greatly overrated by the French, and but a feeble idea was entertained of the enormous difficulties of the scheme they proposed, which was that, after completely subduing and organizing Egypt, they should march through Syria and Damascus, thence to the head of the Persian Gulf, and thence down through India.

No account had been taken of the enormous difficulties of the journey. There was no thought of the powerful and warlike people of Northern India. The only idea was to revenge the total overthrow of the French power in India by the British, to re-establish it on a firmer and wider base[Pg 44] than ever, and so not only to humiliate the pride of England, but to obtain a monopoly of the trade of the East.

The news that possibly a French fleet might at any moment appear before the port spread the greatest dismay throughout Alexandria; the native population were furious, and foreigners scarcely dared to show themselves in the streets. Mr. Blagrove and Edgar were busy from morning till night on the day after the British fleet had left, in transporting the goods from the store to the ship that had been chartered.

"It is quite possible that all this is needless," the merchant said to Edgar when they sat down to a hasty meal late in the evening. "I think myself that it is almost absurd, although I do not mean to leave anything to chance; but it is purely a surmise that the French expedition is intended to operate against Egypt. It seems to me that either Greece or Syria is much more likely to be its destination. I have just had a letter put into my hand, brought by the captain of a small Maltese trader. It is from a correspondent in Malta. He states that the French fleet has appeared off the island and summoned the knights to surrender, and that it is thought probable that the demand will be acceded to. He said that he sent me a line by a little coaster that intended to sail late that evening, and was taking a cargo of grain for Alexandria.

"That certainly looks as if the expedition is intended to operate farther east, for Malta is altogether out of the way for a fleet coming from Toulon hither. Still it is just as well to continue our work. There is, naturally enough, a violent ferment among the native population, and this may not improbably find vent in a fanatical attack upon the

Christians. At any rate, we will get the rest of our goods of any value on board, and then await events."[Pg 45]

By the next evening their preparations were completed. The ferment had now somewhat cooled down, and people were beginning to think that the excitement roused by a mere vague report was absurd. The next morning at breakfast Mr. Blagrove said to his son:

"I think, Edgar, that as things have quieted down, and we are all beginning to hope that the scare was altogether unfounded, it would be just as well that you should ride over to your friends in the desert, stay the night there, and come back to-morrow. They would think it strange and discourteous if we were to leave suddenly without communicating with them; and as I hope our absence will be of short duration, I should be very sorry to give people so well-disposed towards you any ground for offence. But return by to-morrow evening. In the extremely remote possibility of a French fleet being made out before that time, I must embark at once, if only for your mother and sisters' sake. It would be madness to wait here—simple madness. Even putting aside the certainty of captivity for a very long period, it is by no means improbable that there would be a sudden rising on the part of the population, and a massacre of foreigners.

"I consider the contingency so remote, that it is scarcely worth speaking of; but if the French fleet should arrive during the thirty-six hours that you will be away, and I am obliged to embark and sail off, you must stay with your Arab friends. You see, I have some £8000 worth of goods on board the *Petrel*, and the loss would be an extremely heavy one for me; and I have besides £2000 in cash. I shall leave £1000 in Muller's hands, which will be ample for his needs, as there is a very heavy stock of ships' stores in the warehouse. I shall, of course, instruct him to supply you with any money that you may require.[Pg 46] You understand that I regard all this as extremely improbable, but it is just as well to make arrangements for every contingency. And then, should the French fleet come in sight, I can embark on board the *Petrel*, and set sail without any great anxiety on your account. More to relieve my mind than because I think there is any reasonable ground for thinking it necessary, here are fifty pounds in gold; you had best sew them up securely in the band of your trousers to-night; it will be no great trouble, and they will be safer there than if loose in your pocket."

As Edgar rode away the next morning, he could not help thinking that it would be great fun if the French were to arrive before he returned. The thought of a year or two passed in a stuffy office in London was not an agreeable one; while, were he to stay with the Bedouins, he might have a life of excitement and adventure. No doubt they and the other tribes would all fight against the invaders; impelled in the first place by their intense love of independence, and in the second, because the invaders were Christians. The thought of dashing charges, of skirmishing with the French cavalry, of pursuit, of flight, was very fascinating to a high-spirited lad of seventeen, and after indulging in these fancies for some time, he sighed, as he thought how small was the chance of their becoming reality.

He was heartily welcomed on his arrival at the oasis. The news that Sidi had brought of the visit of the British fleet, and the fact that they were in search of a great French fleet carrying an army that might possibly be intended for the invasion of Egypt, had created great excitement in the camp.

"Do you think it can be true," the sheik asked him, "that so wild an idea can have come to these people, as to think that they could conquer our country?"[Pg 47]

"That I cannot say," Edgar replied. "If they did come, they would be very formidable opponents, for they have conquered many countries in Europe; their soldiers are well trained and disciplined, and they will have great numbers of guns; but my father thinks that they can hardly intend to come here, for if they landed we should soon have enough ships-of-war here to prevent their return, and they would be cut off from France altogether. There is no news of their fleet, except that they have arrived at the island of Malta. Whither they sailed thence we know not. Our fleet has gone in search of them, and will fight them when they find them. But if they should escape, and should really come hither, my father and I will embark on board a ship which he has loaded with his most valuable goods, and we shall at once sail for England. It is for this reason that I have ridden over this morning. If we should go, our departure will be very sudden, for we should get up anchor as soon as the French fleet was made out in the distance, or, at any rate, as soon as it became dark enough to hide our departure; and I should have been sorry indeed to go without saying good-bye to you."

"But for how long will you go, brother?" Sidi asked.

"Until the trouble was over here, which might be only two or three months, but which might be as many years."

"And will you be glad to go back to your own country?" the sheik asked.

"No, indeed. There I should have to work in an office in London, which would be very dull, while here my work is light, I have amusements, and I have my friends here."

"Why not stay behind with us until your father returns? You know that you would be most welcome, and that it would gladden all our hearts to have you with us."

"I should like it above all things, sheik," Edgar said[Pg 48] warmly, "and I thank you most heartily for the invitation, but of course I must do as my father wishes, and he thinks it best that we should go to England if the French come, for they would keep us both as prisoners, and would seize all our goods and merchandise. However, it does not seem to him likely that the French will really come here, and it was only because he considered that it was just possible they might do so that he himself suggested that I should come over and stay here until to-morrow afternoon, lest, if we should have to leave suddenly, you might not think that we had forgotten you in our haste to be off. For myself, I wish that I could stay here. I suppose that if the French came you would fight, and I could fight with your tribe?"

"Assuredly we will fight," the sheik said. "Why should these Franks come here to molest us? I love not the Turkish rule much, but we are in no way molested. Assuredly every Arab through the desert will ride against them and aid the Mamelukes to drive them into the sea. How great an army would they bring against us?"

"We hear from the officers of our fleet that the news received in England said that some 30,000 men were preparing to embark for some unknown destination."

"Thirty thousand!" the sheik said scornfully; "why, there are 10,000 Mameluke cavalry and fully 20,000 infantry, janizaries, and spahis, besides the levy of the whole population, and the desert tribes can put 5000 horsemen into the field. They will never dare to come against us unless with a force very much larger than you speak of. No, it is not against Egypt that the expedition can have sailed."

"That is what my father thinks," Edgar said; "not because of the force you could bring against them, but[Pg 49] because they would know that they might be cut off at any time from returning by our fleet, and their position would then become desperate. We have long blockaded them in their own ports, and if they are not strong enough to get out of these, still less would they be able to leave Egypt."

"Let us not talk more of them," the sheik said contemptuously. "They are dogs; if they come hither we shall know how to deal with them."

CHAPTER III.
LEFT BEHIND.

The sheik spoke a few words to two of his followers, who at once mounted their horses and rode off.

"They will bring us news if anything happens," he said; "they will go into Alexandria."

It was late in the evening when they returned.

"You have news?" the sheik said, as they came up to the fire by which he was sitting. The moon was shining brightly, lighting up the wide expanse of sand round the grove.

"The Franks have come," one said.

Edgar sprung to his feet with an exclamation of surprise and alarm.

"When did they come?" the sheik asked.

"When we reached the city all was quiet," the man said, "except that soldiers were working at the fortifications. When we asked why this was, they said that some Bedouins had come in two hours before with the news that the sea near Cape Harzet was covered with ships, and that they were sailing this way. Many did not believe the story, but all the people and the soldiers were ordered to work on the[Pg 50] fortifications, to bring up shot for the great guns, to carry stones to mend the walls where they were broken, and to prepare for the defence. The sun was nigh half down when we saw a great many white dots on the edge of the sea. They were still some leagues away, when everyone pointed and cried out, 'It is the enemy!' and worked harder than ever. It was not for two hours that we were sure that they were ships. When we were so, we went, as you bade us, to the English merchant's. He was busy directing men, who were going backwards and forwards to a ship in the harbour. We said to him, 'Master, our sheik has sent us to carry him news should the fleet of the Franks come here. He told us to come to you if it did so, as you might wish to send for your son.'

"'It is too late,' he said; 'too late for my son to come to me. I am on the point of starting now, as you see. Many of the ships have already put to sea, and the captain has sent to say that he cannot risk his vessel by staying longer. The French will be here within two or three hours, and although they will not venture to enter the harbour till daybreak they could capture all vessels going out. Tell my son that I regret much that I let him go away for the day, but had no thought that the enemy would come so soon. Bid him not be uneasy about me, for it will be dark in an hour, and the French will not be up until two hours later, and they will have their hands full without trying to catch the craft that are putting out from here. Here is a letter for him; I was going to leave it here in case he returned.'

"Five minutes afterwards he took his place in a boat and was rowed off to the ship. We saw the men getting up the anchor, and then the sails were spread, and she sailed out of the harbour. Then, not wishing to be shut up in the[Pg 51] town, we went out through the gates and rode to the mound by the sea-shore that is called Marabout. Then we got off our horses to see what would happen. It was dark when the Franks' vessels came along; some of them sailed on towards the harbour, but most of them anchored and let down their sails, and presently one could see vast numbers of boats rowing towards the shore."

When the man had finished, Edgar opened the note that was handed to him. It was written in pencil.

My dear Edgar,—In face of all probabilities the French fleet is in sight. They will be here soon after it is dark. The city is in a state of mad excitement. The captain of the 'Petrel' has just come in, saying that the French are coming along the coast from the west, and that I must be on board before it is dark. For some reasons I regret that you are not with me, but I believe that you will be quite safe with your Arab friends, and possibly this may be more to your liking than a long stay in London. Take care of yourself, lad. God bless you!—Your affectionate father.

Edgar's first thought at hearing the news had been regret that he could not accompany his father, but this was very speedily succeeded by a feeling of delight that he would be enabled to witness stirring events.

"Are you glad or sorry?" the sheik asked.

"I am much more glad than sorry," he replied. "My father, no doubt, is disappointed that I am not returning home with him. I should on no account have remained behind had it been possible to join him in time. As it is, it is neither my fault nor his, but, as I think, a stroke of good fortune. And now, chief, I can accept your kind offer of hospitality, and hope that if there is any fighting that I shall ride by the side of Sidi."[Pg 52]

The Arab smiled gravely. "That assuredly you shall do. It is, as you say, no one's fault, but the will of Allah, that has left you in my charge, and I doubt not that good fortune will befall us thereby. Now, what think you that is meant by the Franks landing at Marabout instead of sailing on to attack the port?"

"It means, no doubt, that they are going to assault the city by land. They probably do not know how weak are the fortifications, and fear that the fleet might suffer much injury from their guns, and may therefore prefer to attack from the land side."

"But can they take the city that way?"

"I have no doubt that they can. Their guns could blow in the gates in a very short time. Moreover, from the high ground near Pompey's Pillar they could harass the defenders of the wall, or, if they chose, make a breach in it. The wall is very old, and in many places in a bad state of repair."

"Could we go into the city and aid in the defence?" the sheik asked.

"There will be no entering from this side, sheik. The French army will be between us and Alexandria, and, moreover, the guns from their war-ships will be able to sweep the sands. We might pass round by the south and enter the city from the other side; but your forty men would add but little strength to the defence, and would be far more useful as horsemen when the French begin their advance."

"How long will it take them, think you, to capture the town? Help can come down from Cairo in a week."

"I think that the French will lose but little time, sheik. So long as the town holds out, the fleet might be attacked by Nelson, should he come back this way, while as soon as[Pg 53] they have captured the town all the light-draught vessels would find shelter in the harbour. You may be sure that they would lose no time in mounting guns from the ships on the forts, and render themselves perfectly safe from attack. They say that Bonaparte is in command of the French. He is their ablest general, and very active and enterprising. I should not be surprised if he captures the place before sunset to-morrow."

The sheik made no reply. It seemed to him that Edgar's opinion that the city which had withstood many sieges could be captured in a few hours was too absurd to need argument.

"There is nothing to be done now," he said; "let us sleep. To-morrow, before sunrise, we will make a detour round the south side of the city and approach the eastern gate, and then decide whether to enter the town or not."

In a few minutes there was silence in the camp, but long before the sun rose everyone was astir. The women were to be left with the boys and old men. The preparations were of the simplest character; each of the thirty-eight men going hung a bag of dates at his saddle-bow, looked to his firearms, and mounted. As the oasis was situated to the south-west of the city, they did not strike the old bed of Lake Mareotis until half-way along what had been its south shore. At present all was silent in the distant city, and the sheik said shortly, "We will wait till we see what is going to be done." Presently two or three Arabs were seen galloping across the cultivated ground. They belonged to the Henedy tribe, one of the wildest and most savage of the people of the desert. When they saw the group of horses they made their way towards them. As the sheik advanced a few paces, one of them leapt from his saddle and came up to him.

"What has happened, brother?" Ben Ouafy asked.[Pg 54]

"Last evening the Franks began to land, and all night they continued to come ashore. At midnight Koraim, the commander of the town, went out to see what they were doing, at the head of twenty Mamelukes, and fell upon a company of their skirmishers, charged them, killed many, and carried the head of their captain in triumph into the town. At five this morning our tribe arrived. We rode up near them, and saw that they had neither horsemen nor cannon. They were divided into three columns, and were marching towards the town. We dashed in between the columns and cut down many of their skirmishers, but we were only five hundred, and dared not attack the column, which opened such a heavy fire that we were forced to draw off. Our sheik ordered us to ride south to carry the news to Ramanieb that the Franks had landed. They may have sent the news from the town, but he thought it best to make sure."

"'Tis well!" the sheik said, and the Arab threw himself into the saddle again, and with his companions rode south at a gallop. "You see," the sheik went on to Edgar, "the Franks cannot mean to attack the town. What could they do without cannon?"

"It would assuredly be a desperate enterprise, sheik, but I think that they may attempt it, seeing that it is all-important to them to obtain possession of the port before our fleet can return."

The party remained sitting, with the patience of their race, until the sheik should give orders for them to mount. Edgar got up several times, and walked backwards and forwards. He was less accustomed to waiting, and was burning for action. Just at eight o'clock there came suddenly to their ears an outburst of firing, the boom of cannon, and the sound of a crackling roll of musketry.[Pg 55]

"The French have lost no time in beginning," he said.

The young Arab nodded. A flush of excitement glowed through the olive skin, his hand tightly grasped his spear, and his eyes were fixed on the distant city. Suddenly the sheik raised the vibrating battle-cry of the Arabs, in which the whole of his followers joined, and then at a wild gallop they dashed forward, the horses seeming to share in the excitement of their riders. After maintaining the pace for a couple of miles they reined in their horses somewhat, and at a canter swept along the neck that divided in old time the lakes of Aboukir and Mareotis, slackened down into a walk as they approached the fresh-water canal, where they stopped for a few minutes to allow their horses to drink, and then continued at a leisurely pace until they mounted the high ground at Ramleh. From here they obtained a view of the eastern side of

Alexandria. They could hear the din of battle on the other side of the town, and could see the great fleet anchored, a mile from shore, some two miles to the west of the town. The wind, which had been blowing strongly the night before, and had seriously hindered the work of disembarkation of the French troops, had now subsided. Some of the men-of-war were engaging the forts, but at so great a distance that it was evident that it was a demonstration to distract the attention of the besieged rather than a serious attack. Four or five ships, under the shortest sail, were cruising backwards and forwards parallel with the shore eastward of the town, and occasionally a white puff of smoke burst out from one or other of them, and a shot was sent in the direction of scattered bands of horsemen near the shore.

After gazing at the scene in silence for some minutes, the sheik turned his horse and rode back to a spot near the canal, where the moisture, permeating through its banks,[Pg 56] had given growth to a luxuriant crop of grass. Here all dismounted and tethered their horses. Four of the Arabs were appointed to watch over their safety, and the rest reascended the mound, and squatted down on the sands. Gradually the other parties of horse gathered there, and the sheiks gravely consulted together. All had a conviction that Alexandria would hold out until help came from Cairo. The question of entering the town was discussed. Presently the sound of cannon ceased, but the rattle of musketry continued unabated.

"Why have the guns ceased firing, think you?" the sheik asked Edgar.

"It is one of two things, sheik. Either the French have got so close up to the walls that the cannon can no longer be brought to fire upon them, or they have stormed the walls and the fighting is now in the streets of the town."

"But there are two walls," the sheik said; "the one known as the Arab wall, and the inner defences. It is impossible that they can have carried both."

"It would seem so," Edgar agreed; "but as the musketry is as hot, or hotter, than ever, it is evident that fighting is going on at close quarters, and that either the guns cannot be fired, or they have been captured. You see the walls were in many places weak, and the attempts that have been made during the past three or four days to repair the breaches that existed were very incompletely done. I am very much afraid that it is as I said, and that the French have gained an entrance."

Half an hour later, a number of horsemen, followed by a crowd of people on foot, poured out from the eastern gate. One of the leading horsemen drew rein for a moment as he passed the group of Arabs.[Pg 57]

"The town is lost," he said; "the Franks have won their way into the streets, and Koraim has surrendered."

An exclamation of fury broke from the Arabs.

"It will be our turn next," Ben Ouafy said, shaking his spear towards the city. "This is but the beginning of the work. They may take a city, but the sands will devour them."

As they knew that the French had no cavalry the Arabs remained quiet; the stream of fugitives continued to pour past them, men, women, and children.

"We will return," Ben Ouafy said at last. "We will move south and join the rest of the tribe, and then see what the government of Cairo are going to do."

The capture of the town had not been effected without loss. Menou's column had attacked on the right, Kleber in the centre, Bon had moved round south of the town. The Arab wall was obstinately defended, Kleber and Menou were both wounded as they led the grenadiers to the assault; Bon, however, had met with less resistance, and had captured the inner wall before the other columns succeeded in doing so. For some time the battle had raged in the streets, but the captain of a Turkish vessel had been sent by Napoleon to the governor, pointing out that further resistance would bring destruction upon the town, while if he yielded, the French troops, who came as friends to deliver them from the tyranny of the Mamelukes, would do no harm to anyone. Koraim thereupon capitulated. He was at once attached to the general staff, and charged with maintaining order in the town and disarming its inhabitants.

Proclamations were at once sent out through the country, declaring that the French had come to destroy the Mameluke domination, and that they were friends of the Sultan of Turkey. Protection was offered to all the villages that[Pg 58] submitted; those that did not do so would be burnt. Seven hundred Turkish slaves, who had been delivered at the capture of Malta, and who had been extremely well treated, were at once sent to their homes in Tripoli, Algiers, Morocco, Syria, Smyrna, and Constantinople, being provided with ample sums of money to support them on their way. These measures had an excellent effect. Koraim sent out messengers to the Arab tribes of the neighbourhood. His influence among them was great, and their sheiks for the most part went at once into Alexandria, and agreed to keep the road open from Alexandria to Damanhour, and to sell and deliver within forty-eight hours 300 horses, 500 dromedaries, and 1000 camels. They were presented with dresses of honour and money. By this time the transports had all entered the old port of Alexandria, and were busy discharging their cargo and the troops they carried, and in a short time the whole French army was on shore.

Scarce a word was spoken among Ben Ouafy's party on their homeward ride. The sheik gave his orders on his arrival.

"We will wait for a day or two," he said to Edgar as they dismounted. "The French have no cavalry, and would not come out here. Let us see what the other tribes are going to do; we are but a small body."

When, two days later, a messenger arrived from Koraim, the sheik, after reading the contents of the proclamation, indignantly tore it in pieces.

"Tell Koraim," he said to the messenger, "that hitherto I have regarded him as an honourable man, now I spit upon him as a traitor. Whatever others may do, I will fight against the Franks till the last."

As soon as the messenger had departed, he gave orders for the tents to be struck.[Pg 59]

"We must be going, Sidi," he said; "some of the tribes may be taken in by these promises, and may give aid to the enemy; in that case they would doubtless obey orders to attack those who refuse to do so. Three of them can each put four or five hundred spears into the field. We will move away at once. With fifty men we cannot fight two thousand."

The process of packing-up occupied but a short time. As soon as the tents were made into bundles the thirty camels were brought in and loaded. The women and children took their places on the top of the baggage, and then the men mounted their horses, and the cavalcade started across the desert.

"Which way do we travel, Sidi?"

"We are not going direct. There are but few wells, and the distances are long between. Mounted men alone can do the journey without difficulty, but it is a painful one with women and children, and we never go that way unless in case of great necessity. We shall travel towards the south-east, keeping near the edge of the cultivated country until we reach the Nile, and then follow along the river bank until within a few miles of Cairo, thence it is three days' journey to the south-west. There is a well half-way."

After proceeding some ten miles, they perceived a party of Arabs galloping in the direction of Alexandria. They changed their course, however, and soon came up with the Ben Ouafy caravan. Two of the sheiks of the party rode forward and exchanged salutations with the chief.

"Whither are you journeying, Ben Ouafy?"

"I am going south to join my tribe; and you—are you going to Alexandria?"

"I am going there at once."[Pg 60]

"Hast not the news reached you that the Franks have captured it?"

"Truly we have heard so, and a messenger came to us but this morning, saying that they had come to deliver us from the Turks, and inviting us to go in thither and see them. Have you not received a message also?"

"I received such a message, indeed, but its words were idle. For the Turks and their Mamelukes I have no great love. They prey upon the land, and enrich themselves at our expense; but the Franks would doubtless do the same, and I would rather be fleeced by those of the true faith than by kaffirs."

"But they come as our friends."

Ben Ouafy smiled. "Why should they come as our friends, Chief of Oulad A'Ly; what have we done for them? Why should they cross the sea in their ships at great expense and much danger, to save those whom they know not, from the Turks? You might as well expect the lion to come to rescue a deer attacked by a jackal. He might, it is true, drive it away, but it would only be that he might himself slay and devour the stag. We have heard of these Franks, how they have taken Italy and other countries; and think you, that if they should overpower the Osmanlis and defeat the Mamelukes, that they will say, 'We have accomplished our purpose, we have freed you from your oppressors, now we will sail back to France and leave you to manage your own affairs'?"

"He promises to respect our religion," the sheik said, "to buy horses and camels from us at fair prices, to give us rich presents, and to treat us with honour."

"No doubt, no doubt. 'Tis easy to speak soft words when one needs aid, but such promises are forgotten when the object is attained. To-day he is the friend of the Arabs,[Pg 61] to-morrow he will be their master, and if we aid these kaffirs against the followers of the Prophet, we shall well deserve whatever may befall."

"Then you will not go in to the gathering to which he invites us?"

"Assuredly not. Even were it for no other reason, I would wait and see what comes of the matter. We know not yet that he will conquer the Mamelukes, and if he fails to do so, assuredly their vengeance will afterwards fall upon all who have assisted these people."

The sheik cast his eye over Ben Ouafy's cavalcade, as if estimating its strength. He saw, however, that it contained as many armed men as he had with him, and if the idea had entered his mind of commencing the campaign by plundering it, he concluded it must be at once abandoned.

"I have no intention," he said, "of taking part with the Franks against the government. I am going to sell horses and camels. Frank money is as good as Turkish, and, moreover, they threaten to attack and destroy those who refuse to aid them. Your tribe lives far away, though, indeed, you may abide here at times, and there is nothing of yours that they can destroy. I have my people to think of, their villages, their flocks and herds and horses; therefore, I shall go and see this great man, and hear what he says, and shall, if I can, keep on terms of peace with him. An army so strong and so fierce that it has captured Alexandria after four hours' fighting is too formidable for an Arab chief to resist; but, assuredly, I have no thought of fighting on his side against my countrymen."

The sheik bowed courteously.

"Every man has his own way of looking at things, and in a matter like this each must do as seems best to him. Go in peace, and may good fortune attend you!"[Pg 62]

The formal salutation was returned, and the sheiks rejoined their parties, and each kept on their course as before they met.

"There, my son," Ben Ouafy said to Sidi, "you see how the desire for gain influences men to evil deeds. In order to sell a few hundred horses and as many camels, the Oulad A'Ly are going to assist the Franks against true believers. It is true that they may not be going to fight for them, but the animals that they sell to them will enable them to fight, which comes to the same thing. Of course he professes that he is thinking of saving his villages from destruction, but he must know well enough that the Franks have other things to think of than to spread over the country here, and give ample time to the Mamelukes to prepare for their coming. Moreover, as it is clear that the French have no cavalry, they could not make excursions, for if they seized all the horses in Alexandria, these would not suffice to mount a party strong enough to assail a tribe like the Oulad A'Ly, who can put nigh a thousand horsemen into the field."

The party travelled without haste. Before arriving on the Nile, Edgar suggested to the sheik that it would be as well were he to discard his European dress for an Arab one.

"When we were at Damanhour," he said, "I marked how the people scowled at me as I rode through the streets; and as no doubt you will ride into Cairo ere long, it would save trouble were I to be so attired that I should escape notice."

"It would be a good plan," the sheik agreed. "I daresay Sidi can supply you with a suit."

"I can purchase what is needed at the next place we come to," Edgar said, "I have money for any necessity[Pg 63] that may arise. Even putting aside the trouble of being constantly questioned, I should prefer the Arab dress, for under this baking sun I think it would be a good deal more comfortable than these English clothes."

Accordingly, at the next town they passed through, Sidi and Edgar went together to the bazaar, and the latter purchased, after the usual amount of bargaining, clothes similar to those worn by his friend. The expense was but small, for the costume of an Arab chief differed but little from those of his followers, except that his burnoose was of finer cotton, and his silken sash of brilliant colours, richer and more showy. With this exception the whole costume was white, and although some of the Arab sheiks wore coloured burnooses, Edgar chose a white one, as both his friend and his father wore that colour. He bought two or three changes of clothes, for he knew that water was often scarce, and that washing of garments could not be indulged in frequently. That night when the camp was pitched he donned his new costume, and placed his pistols in his sash in Arab fashion. Sidi wound his turban for him, and gave him instructions how the clothes were to be worn. Those he had taken off were made into a bundle so that they could be resumed if necessary. He felt rather awkward as with his friend he sallied out from the tent which they now shared between them.

"You look well, Edgar," the sheik said approvingly, "but you will need to stain your arms and legs, and it will be better for you to stain your face and neck also, for you would attract quite as much attention as a white Arab as you would in your European dress."

"I was thinking so myself, sheik; it will be much pleasanter for me to be able to pass anywhere without comment."[Pg 64]

"You are taller than I thought," the sheik said; "it had not struck me that you were much taller than Sidi, but I see now that you are as tall as I am."

"I suppose the flowing garments make one look taller," Edgar said. "I have often been surprised, when standing near a native who looked to me a good deal taller than myself, to find that he was really not above my own height."

"My wife shall make a stain for you as soon as she can get the material. There will be no difficulty about that, for we often dye our burnooses brown, especially when we are starting on a long journey."

The sheik's wife and the other women were voluble in their expressions of satisfaction at the change in Edgar. They had been but little in the towns, and the comparatively tight-fitting European garments were, in their eyes, ugly and unbecoming. Seen in the more graceful dress of the Arabs they recognized for the first time that their guest was a good-looking young fellow, tall, active, and not ungraceful in figure, and that he could even compare not unfavourably with Sidi, who was a favourite with the whole camp. Even the men, impassive as they usually were, uttered a few words of satisfaction at Edgar having adopted an Arab costume, and at his appearance in it. On the following day the sheik, taking his son, Edgar, and two of his followers, left the caravan and rode on to Cairo, leaving the others to travel by easy stages to join the rest of the tribe.

"Doubtless we shall find many other sheiks assembled there," he said as they rode along; "the government is sure to have sent orders already for all the Bedouin tribes to hold themselves in readiness to gather there to oppose the advance of the French. The levies of the city and the neighbourhood will also be called out, not so much perhaps to[Pg 65] fight as to labour at the fortifications. That they will not ask of the Arabs, for no Arab would work like a fellah. We will fight, but we will leave it to the peasants to work. The Mamelukes will, however, in the first place oppose the Franks. I love them not. They are the oppressors of Egypt, but the lions of the desert are not more courageous. They are proud of themselves, and believe themselves to be invincible. They will not believe that the Franks can stand for a moment against them, and you know that the night that the Franks landed, twenty Mamelukes rode out against them, killed many, and brought in their heads in triumph. They would not ask us to charge with them, but would deem it shame to ask for aid in such an encounter, but they will be willing enough to accept our help in cutting off the fugitives and in preventing others who may land from spreading over the country."

"Then you still feel sure that the Mamelukes will defeat the French?" Edgar said.

"If it be the will of Allah, my son. The Mamelukes are not like the people who defended Alexandria; they are warriors. We Arabs are brave, we do not fear death; but when, from time to time, a tribe refuses to pay its annual tribute, and a band of Mamelukes is sent against them, truly the sons of the desert cannot withstand them in combat, even when much more numerous, and are either destroyed or forced to make their submission. These men regard themselves not as simple soldiers; it is an army of emirs. Each has his two or three slaves to wait upon him, to groom his horse and polish his arms. Their dresses are superb; their arms and trappings are encrusted with gold and gems. Each carries his wealth on his person, and there are few who cannot show a hundred pieces of gold, while many can exceed that by ten times. It is true that they are the op[Pg 66]pressors of the people, and that Egypt has been drained of its wealth for their support, yet we, who suffer from them, cannot but feel proud of them. Are they not followers of the Prophet? They are men like those whom the great Sultan Saladin led against the Christian hosts who strove to capture Syria. We have tales how brave these were, and how they rode, clad in steel from head to foot; and yet their bones whitened the sands, and the true believers remained in possession of their lands. The Mamelukes are men such as those were, and until I see the contrary I shall not believe that they can be defeated by these Franks."

"I hope that it may be so, sheik, and I doubt in no way their valour; but it is the guns and the discipline of the French that will, I fear, decide the conflict."

CHAPTER IV.
THE BATTLE OF THE PYRAMIDS.

The little party had ridden but a few miles when they saw a party of five or six hundred Arab horse approaching. The sheik rode to meet them, and after a short conversation with their leaders, returned.

"We need go no farther for orders," he said. "Mourad Bey, with 3000 Mamelukes and as many Janizaries, is within a few miles. Orders have been sent to all the Arab tribes to hasten to oppose the march of the enemy, and from all parts they are riding hither. Doubtless my brother, who is the great sheik of the tribe of which we are a branch, is already on his way to join him. We will at once ride and bring back all our fighting men. The caravan can proceed without guard. Even a hostile tribe would respect it[Pg 67] at the present time, when all are engaged with the enemy. We shall speedily overtake them. They would not have started for an hour after we mounted, and cannot have gone many miles before we come up with them."

Riding at full gallop, they soon overtook the caravan. The Arabs received with shouts of satisfaction the orders their leader gave them to retrace their steps. The old men, who were to proceed with the caravan, were told that in the event of meeting with any parties hastening towards Ramanieh, to tell them that the orders were to harass the French as they advanced, and to say that all the sheik's fighting men were already engaged in the work. Then, after a brief adieu to the women, the Arabs rode at full gallop towards the river.

It was on the morning of the 29th of June that the French had taken Alexandria, and on the 6th of July that they commenced their march. General Dugua, with Kleber's division, had been taken by water to Rosetta, which they occupied without difficulty, and with a large flotilla of boats carrying provisions and stores, proceeded up the Nile as far as Damanhour, at which town the main portion of the army arrived after two days' painful march.

The French met with no resistance, owing to the fact that almost all Bedouins near the coast had accepted Napoleon's tempting offers. Nevertheless the troops were already discouraged. They had expected to find a rich and fertile country, with palm-trees, lovely towns, and an abundance of supplies of all kinds; but the Nile was now at its lowest, and during the previous season it had not, as usual, overflowed its banks and fertilized the country, consequently their march lay through a sandy waste. The dust rose in clouds under their feet, the sun beat down upon them; they suffered agonies of thirst, and many dropped from[Pg 68]exhaustion. And their disappointment was great when they found that, instead of a rich and prosperous town, Damanhour was but a collection of huts, affording neither means of subsistence nor booty of any kind. Beyond the town large bands of Arabs had gathered, and the French army were obliged to keep their ranks as they marched, to maintain a constant watchfulness, and to travel at a slow pace in order that they might not be separated from their baggage. General Muireur was seized with a serious fever, the result of heat, thirst, and disappointment. He mounted his horse on the morning after his arrival there, and rode out beyond the outposts. He had gone but a short distance when a party of Arabs, hiding among some bushes, sprang to their feet and poured in a volley. He fell dead, and his body was stripped, and the Arabs, mounting their horses, rode off before the outposts could arrive on the spot.

From this time the French dared not straggle. Every man who left the ranks or lagged behind was killed. The Arabs were seldom seen, but they lay concealed behind every inequality of the ground, every clump of bushes. Occasionally, when there seemed to be an opening, a horde of Arabs would sweep down, but these always recoiled from the steady fire of the French infantry, and on the 10th of July the leading French division, that commanded by Desaix, reached Ramanieh, on the Nile. Here, after their terrible march, the French troops were seized with a delirium of pleasure at seeing the verdure on the banks of the river, and the water.

Disregarding all orders, they broke their ranks and rushed wildly to the stream, into which thousands of them plunged in their uniforms. In the cultivated fields great quantities of melons were found, affording a delightful food, for since they had left Alexandria there had been nothing to eat but[Pg 69] the biscuits they had brought with them. Many paid dearly for over-indulgence in the fruit, numbers being prostrated with colic, while not a few died. Next day the army rested, the horses needing the halt even more than the men, for they had not recovered from the long confinement of the voyage when they started from Alexandria, and the scanty supply of water, the clouds of dust, and the heaviness of the passage across the deep sand had caused the death of a large number, and had rendered the rest all but unserviceable.

They had learnt from the natives that Mourad, with a large number of Mamelukes, was in front of them; and, indeed, on the day of their arrival there they appeared in such force that the French formed in order of battle outside the town. The Mamelukes rode backwards and forwards in front of the line brandishing their weapons and threatening a charge. A few rounds of artillery, however, speedily taught them the power of the French guns, and they retired to Chebreisse, and the French were not disturbed the next day. Here the army had the satisfaction of being rejoined both by Dugua's division, with its flotilla, and by another fleet of boats from Alexandria.

The Bedouins under the sheik had taken no part in the irregular skirmishes. There were already as many Arabs as sufficed for cutting off stragglers and compelling the French to march in military order, and the sheik determined to hold his small party together until some opportunity for a general encounter presented itself. Sometimes from the crest of the sand-hills he and his followers watched the progress of the dark masses of infantry.

"They march very slowly," he said to Edgar. "Why do they not go on quicker?"

"I fancy that they are keeping pace with the baggage-[Pg 70]train. Their animals must be completely exhausted; and last night as we followed them we came upon many dead horses. They know that their only safety is to keep together, and I doubt not that the men are well-nigh as exhausted as the animals. Even on horseback the heat is terrible, and although we have our water-skins well-filled, I feel it very much, and of course men on foot carrying their muskets and ammunition and knapsacks must feel it very much more. I think they will go on faster after they have left Ramanieh. They will have the Nile by their side, and will have no want of water. The sand is firmer, too, and moreover they will be able to obtain what they require from the boats."

On the evening of the 12th the French arrived at a village near Chebreisse. At sunrise the next morning a battle began between the flotilla and some Egyptian gun-boats that had come down from Cairo, together with some batteries that had been established on the banks. The Mamelukes sallied out from Chebreisse and charged down with such ardour that it seemed as if they were about to hurl themselves on the French infantry. When within a short distance, however, they suddenly stopped their horses, checking them almost instantaneously, then they discharged their carbines, and retired as rapidly as they had come. This they repeated several times, but the shells of the French batteries played havoc among them.

Never before had the Mamelukes encountered a shell-fire, and the destruction wrought by these novel missiles bursting among them caused them to retire at full speed, leaving three or four hundred dead behind them, and abandoning some of the guns they had placed in position before Chebreisse. A large Arab force had been drawn up in front of the town when the Mamelukes charged, in readi[Pg 71]ness to follow the latter as soon as they had broken the French ranks. This was the first opportunity that Edgar had had of seeing any considerable body of this famous cavalry, and he acknowledged that nothing could be more superb than their appearance. The splendour of their dress, the beauty of their horses, and magnificence of their arms and trappings excited his admiration to the highest.

"Now you will see," the sheik said exultingly, "how they will gallop over the Franks!"

Edgar said nothing, but sat watching the splendid array as they swept down upon the French line. Each of the French divisions was formed up in square, with the artillery and dismounted cavalry in the intervals. The volleys of musketry that received the charging Mamelukes was sufficient to quell the ardour of the boldest horsemen in the world. In vain, before drawing off, they circled round and round the French formation, seeking for some weak spot upon which they could hurl themselves, and when at length they drew off, the French soldiers ran out from their ranks to plunder the fallen.

In silence the Arabs followed the Mamelukes, and the chief did not say a word until they had ridden, at a leisurely pace, some distance beyond the town.

"You were right," he said at last to Edgar. "I did not think that any men on foot could have resisted that charge, but the Franks stood as steadily as if it were a flock of sheep that was approaching them. The cannon are terrible. Who would have thought that the balls they shoot would explode and fly into pieces when they reach their mark! How is it done?"

Edgar explained as well as he was able the nature of shells, and how, when they were fired, a fuse was lighted of a length just sufficient to burn down to the powder[Pg 72] within the ball at the time it reached the object at which it was fired.

The fight on the river had been more severe, and had been maintained with great obstinacy. At one time two gun-boats were taken by the Egyptians. These, however, were recaptured, and the admiral's ship burnt. Admiral Perrè, who commanded the first flotilla, was wounded by a cannon-ball, and the loss on both sides was severe.

For eight days the French continued to march forward. They suffered terrible hardships, and at times were almost in a state of mutiny. The interminable extent of sand utterly dispirited them, and they came to believe that all that they had heard of Egypt was false, and that they had been deliberately sent there by the directory to die. They doubted even the existence of Cairo. Some, in their despair, threw themselves into the river and were drowned. Many died on the march, less from sunstroke and exhaustion than from despair. At last the Pyramids came in sight, and their spirits rose again, for here, they were told, the whole army of Mamelukes, Janizaries, and Arabs were assembled to give battle, and they hoped therefore to terminate the campaign at a blow.

During the whole march they were harassed by the Arabs, and many were cut off and killed. Marches were always performed at night, and at ten o'clock in the morning they halted for the day, preparing themselves for slumber by a dip in the Nile. On the 21st of July they advanced from Omdinar, and at ten o'clock made out the enemy drawn up in line of battle. They had constructed a large entrenched camp, with forty pieces of ancient cannon incapable of movement. In this camp were 20,000 infantry, Janizaries, Spahis, and militia from Cairo. On the right were the Mameluke cavalry, some 10,000 strong, with one or two[Pg 73] foot-soldiers to each horseman. To the left of the Mamelukes, and between them and the Pyramids, were some 3000 Arab horse.

The French army was drawn up in the same order as in their last fight, in great squares of divisions, the left resting on the Nile, and the right on a large village. Napoleon, with his staff, reconnoitered the enemy's entrenched camp, and by means of telescopes discovered that the cannon were not upon field-carriages, but were simply heavy ship guns that had been taken from their flotilla, and were served by the sailors. They, therefore, could not be moved, and it was evident that if the infantry left the camp they must do so without guns. The entrenchment itself was not formidable; it had been begun but three days before, and although it might be impracticable for cavalry, it would offer no serious obstacle to an attack by infantry.

The discovery that the cannon were immovable, decided Napoleon in his dispositions for the battle, and he gave orders that his army should move across to his right, and should thus be concentrated for the attack upon the Mamelukes and Arabs. Mourad Bey, seeing Napoleon's object, at once ordered two-thirds of his cavalry to charge the French while they were in motion, while the others were to remain near the entrenched camp. So rapidly did they sweep down, that the French squares fell into some confusion, and Desaix, with his division, which formed the head of the column, had difficulty in maintaining themselves, their ranks being somewhat broken by a grove of palm-trees through which they were passing. They, however, received the Mamelukes with so terrible a fire of musketry and grape-shot that the charge was not pressed home. The Mamelukes, however, fought with desperate courage, sweeping round the French squares, and even endeavouring to[Pg 74] back their horses into the line of bayonets, in hopes of breaking the wall of steel.

At length, however, they could do no more, and Mourad, with 2000 men, rode off towards Gizeh, while the rest, not noticing the way that he had taken, owing to the cloud of dust and smoke, rode back to the entrenchment. The French now pressed forward with all speed, and a division was thrown across the plain, so as to prevent the horsemen from retreating by the line that Mourad had taken. The latter, seeing what had happened, charged again and again with his Mamelukes, to endeavour to break an opening through the French, by which the rest of his forces could join him. The divisions of Generals Bon and Menon advanced to the attack of the entrenchments; but the infantry, panic-stricken at the defeat of the cavalry, did not await the attack, and after but two or three rounds of shot had been fired by their cannon, deserted the position, and fled in wild confusion to the river.

Here some succeeded in making their way across by boats, while many swam over. The Mamelukes also attempted to swim their horses; a few succeeded, but more were drowned. The total loss on the Egyptian side amounted to some 10,000 men, including infantry, cavalry, and the slaves of the Mamelukes. 1000 prisoners were taken, and some 2000 camels and horses fell into the victors' hands. Great booty was captured by the French soldiers, and for days they occupied themselves in recovering the bodies of the drowned Mamelukes, which amply repaid their trouble, as four or five hundred pieces of gold were often found upon them, besides jewels and other valuables. The great bulk of their less portable property they had, however, placed on board sixty boats, and these, when the battle was seen to be lost, were set on fire, and their contents destroyed.[Pg 75]

The Arabs had taken little share in the battle. When the Mamelukes charged, they had been ordered to remain in reserve, and only to charge when the latter had broken the French squares. Burning with impatience they watched the mighty torrent of horse sweep across the plain, then came the roar of artillery and the incessant rattle of musketry. Then they saw with astonishment the cavalry recoil; they witnessed charge after charge, and then saw them sweeping round the squares, while the plain, where they had first attacked, was strewn thickly with the bodies of men and horses right up to the bayonets of the French line. The Arabs burst into cries of dismay.

"Nothing can stand such a fire as that," Edgar said to Sidi; "the musketry and grape from the cannon are mowing them down like grass—it is terrible!"

For a time the Mamelukes were hidden from sight by the cloud of smoke and by the dust raised by their horses' hoofs, then they were seen to emerge.

"There is Mourad's banner!" the sheik exclaimed; "they are making for Gizeh, but surely all cannot be there—there are not more than 2000 with him."

Then another body of about equal strength broke out from the dust of the battle, and went towards the entrenchments.

"Let us join them there," the Arab shouted; and at full gallop they rode across and joined the Mamelukes. Then, heralded by a tremendous artillery fire, the French line advanced, pouring heavy volleys of musketry into the cavalry, and upon the defenders of the entrenchments. In two or three minutes the infantry were seen to be throwing away their guns, leaping from the entrenchments, and flying in a disordered crowd towards the river. Had the French possessed any cavalry, not one of the fugitives could have[Pg 76] escaped. The Mamelukes, seeing that all was lost, had ascertained that Mourad had ridden towards Gizeh, and now started to endeavour to rejoin him; while among the Arabs the cry rose, "To the desert!" and, turning their horses, they galloped away, passed the foot of the Pyramids, and out into the desert, where they halted, seeing that once out of reach of the fire of the French guns, there was no fear whatever of their being pursued.

"It is the will of Allah," the sheik said, as he and his party dismounted. "Truly you were right, friend Edgar; we know not how to fight. Who could have dreamt that men on foot could have withstood the charge of five thousand horsemen? And yet the Mamelukes fought, as always, bravely."

"They did indeed, sheik," Edgar agreed. "They did all that was possible for men to do, but against such a fire of infantry and artillery horsemen are powerless. Had our infantry been as well trained as those of the French, and instead of remaining in the entrenchments, where they could render no assistance whatever, marched against the French infantry and broken their squares, the Mamelukes would then have been able to dash down upon them, and not a French soldier would ever have reached their ships again; but without infantry the horsemen could do nothing."

"Then you think that all is lost, Edgar?"

"Assuredly all is lost for the present, sheik. Mourad Bey and the party with him may get away, but the rest are penned in between the French and the river, and few of them will escape. As for the infantry, they are a mere mob, and even if they get away they will never venture to stand against the French. Napoleon will enter Cairo to-morrow, and there he will remain. Numbers of horses will fall into the hands of the French. They will take many[Pg 77] more in Cairo, and before long they will have cavalry as well as infantry, and then no part of the country will be safe from them."

"Then is Egypt to fall altogether under the rule of the French?"

"Only for a time. Our fleet will soon return, and their troops here will be cut off from their country. They may remain here for some time, but at last they will have to go. I think that we shall send an army out to fight against them. We shall know what their strength is, and that they cannot be reinforced; and they will find in the long run that although they may have captured Egypt, they are themselves but prisoners."

"And what would you advise?" the sheik asked. "You understand the ways and customs of the Franks, while I know no more than a little child. Thus, you see, in this matter you are the graybeard and I but a boy. Therefore speak freely what you think will be best."

"Then I should say, sheik, that your best course would be to return at once to your oasis. The French army will doubtless remain near Cairo. They will send cavalry and light artillery over the country, to search out their enemies, and to reduce all to obedience. Around Alexandria all will be quiet, and so long as French convoys are not attacked, the force there is not likely to interfere with peaceable people. If you return there you will live unmolested. You can wait and see how matters go. If there is any great rising against the French, it will be open to you to take part in it, but at present hostilities against the French would only bring down their vengeance. It may be that the Arabs in the great oasis to the west will continue the war, but in the end they will be sure to suffer by so doing."[Pg 78]

"I think that your advice is good," the sheik said. "Sidi and you shall return home at once with half my followers. I will ride at daybreak with the other half. In one long day's ride I shall reach the spot where the women and baggage have gone, and I will escort them back. The road will certainly be safe from the Franks, who will, for some time, be occupied with Cairo, though it is hardly likely that the town will resist. Ibrahim, after the destruction of the Mamelukes and the defeat of the army, cannot hope to resist a great attack; for the fortifications, like those of Alexandria, have been suffered to decay, and the French would assuredly soon force an entrance. However, after the march that they have made they will need rest, and for a time the roads will be safe. But this is not so with regard to the Arabs. The whole country will be in confusion, and an unarmed caravan might well be plundered by any party of Arabs who met it, though they would not interfere with it were it headed by a sheik with armed followers. Therefore I will go to fetch them. My son will ride fast, and take possession again of our home, lest some of our neighbours, finding it deserted, should occupy it, and then trouble would follow."

Accordingly, the next morning at daybreak the troop divided and rode off in different directions. The greater part of the gathering had scattered the evening before, and determined to return home and wait events. Four days' rapid travelling took Sidi and his companions back to the oasis, which they found exactly as they had left it, the tribes in the neighbourhood having been all too busy in following the French army, and picking up baggage left behind by the break-down of the horses, to attend to other matters.

The next day Sidi and Edgar rode into Alexandria.[Pg 79] Everything there was going on as peacefully as usual; French soldiers lounging about the streets, a number of labourers, under the direction of French officers, were at work restoring the fortifications on the sea face of the town, the shops were all open, the markets were as well supplied as usual. To Edgar's surprise a good many French sailors were to be seen in the streets.

"Their fleet cannot have sailed," he said to Sidi. "Let us ride out through the East gate to Ramleh. It may be, of course, that there is a despatch-boat lying in the port, though I did not see one. I can hardly fancy that the French admiral would have kept his fleet here, for Nelson must sooner or later get the news of what has taken place, and it is certain that when he does he will hurry back at full speed."

From the elevation of Ramleh, however, the French fleet could be made out, lying in Aboukir Bay in a long line.

"Hurrah!" Edgar exclaimed; "there they are. I mean to see this battle, Sidi, if I have to stop here a month. It cannot be long before Nelson arrives. I cannot think why the French admiral should have risked being caught in a trap like this, when a defeat would cut the French army off from Europe altogether."

"But what will you do?"

"I shall go into the town, and buy three or four of your Arab blankets, and put up a little tent here."

"I will share it with you," Sidi replied. "I will send one of our two men back and tell him to return with two more. There will be four of them to look after the horses, and to fetch things out from the town as we may require them. I should like to see the battle too; it must be something terrible to hear the noise of so many great cannon."[Pg 80]

The inaction of the French has never been satisfactorily explained. Admiral Brueys bore a high reputation as a sailor. He was a personal friend and possessed the complete confidence of Bonaparte. The latter had given him the strictest injunctions to sail for Toulon as soon as he had completed the discharge of the stores that he had on board. Instead of doing this, however, he anchored in Aboukir Bay, and there waited. It may have been that he feared that Napoleon might never reach Cairo, or that he might be defeated in a great battle there, and that it might be necessary for him to return to the port and to re-embark his army. No other explanation is possible of his delay in carrying out the imperative orders that he had received.

After the despatch of the messenger the two friends rode along the shore until they could not only make out the exact position of the French fleet, but count the guns in the broadsides of each vessel. It consisted of thirteen line-of-battle ships, comprising the flag-ship the *Orient*, of 120 guns, three of 80, and nine of 74, together with four frigates, four mortar vessels, and a number of gun-boats, while on an island ahead of the line was a battery of guns and mortars. Many parties of Arabs were riding about on the shore, and there were several of their encampments. Some had been attracted to the spot from a considerable distance in order to view the great vessels of which reports had reached them, others again were simply there from the spirit of restlessness that pervaded the population.

The news of the battle of the Pyramids had not yet arrived, and all were in suspense. The belief that the Mamelukes would defeat the French was all but universal. Had this taken place the whole of the Arab tribes would at once have harassed the retreat of the defeated army, and with the Mamelukes pressing upon them it is probable that[Pg 81] not a single Frenchman would have reached the sea. As Edgar and his friend were watching the French fleet a vessel was seen over the spit of sand. She was some three miles out at sea.

"There is another of their ships of war, Sidi. I wonder whether she has been scouting along the coast to gather news as to where our fleet may be at present?"

When she came abreast of the extremity of the bay she changed her course and bore closer in.

"She is coming in to join the others. I wonder what news she brings?"

When, however, she approached within two miles of the French fleet she again changed her course, and bore along parallel with the coast.

"I suppose she is going into Alexandria. She hasn't got any colours flying. That is curious, too; all the ships here are flying theirs. Look! there are men at the mast-heads of several of the ships examining her with telescopes. That is curious, too, for she is not signalling. There she is, turning again and making out to sea. Perhaps she is a British ship sent on ahead by Nelson to discover the position of the French. If it is so we shall most likely have the fleet here to-morrow. Then we shall see a big battle; at least we shall if the French don't run away. See! there is a twelve-oared boat starting from the admiral's ship and rowing right away. They must be going to Alexandria. They are rowing hard, too."

They watched it for some time, and then returned to their tent. Two hours later a number of ships' boats were seen coming out from Alexandria.

"They are men-of-war boats," Edgar said. "I think I must have been right, and that that vessel we saw must have been an English frigate. That boat has been sent to[Pg 82] order all the sailors we saw in the streets of the town to return at once."

For some hours boats continued to pass, all filled with men, but there were no signs of movement on the part of the ships.

"If it was one of our frigates the French admiral must have made up his mind to fight them. They have got a great advantage, covered as they are by those two land batteries. Besides, I know that there is a spit of sand running out there which will make it very awkward for an enemy, not knowing its position, to attack them. There is one thing, the French will find it difficult to sail out if they want to. You see the wind is on shore, and they are all riding head to it. There can't be much water inside them. No doubt they could get out all right if they had plenty of time and no one to interfere with them, but it would be a difficult business to manage if the British fleet were upon them."

At ten o'clock the next morning a number of large vessels were seen in the distance. They bore down towards Alexandria, but the wind was light and they made but slow way, and it was five in the afternoon before, having changed their course, they formed into line of battle and headed for the French fleet. The scene from the shore was intensely exciting. In each fleet there were thirteen battle-ships, but the French ships were the larger and more heavily armed. They carried forty-six more guns, and the weight of their broadside was 14,029 pounds to 10,695 pounds, while they carried 2300 more men, and were 5000 tons heavier. They had, too, in addition, four frigates, besides the mortar vessels, gun-boats, and the battery on the island of Aboukir. Soon after six o'clock, the two leading vessels of the British fleet being within range, the French opened fire, as did the guns[Pg 83] of the battery. Edgar uttered an exclamation of disgust as one of the largest of the English ships was seen to stop suddenly in her course.

"She has run on the shoal!" he exclaimed. "Look, our ships are steering for the head of the French line; they mean to go inside them."

As the British vessels reached the head of the French ships they anchored one after another, each laying itself broadside to broadside against an opponent, and the battle commenced with terrible energy, the tremendous roar of the guns astounding the Arabs who were gathered on the sand-hills. At first the French reply was feeble. They were taken entirely by surprise by Nelson's manœuvre. Believing that he could only attack them from outside, they had prepared only on that hand for the fight, and in clearing the decks for action all the useless gear and fittings had been piled over on the other side, and it was some little time before this could be cleared away and the guns got ready for action. Then for a time their fire was as heavy as that of the British. Nevertheless some of them had suffered terribly before they were able to return a shot, and this contributed in no small degree to the British victory.

The loss of the *Culloden*, which was the vessel which struck on the sands, and of the *Leander*, which went to her assistance, was serious, and had the French rear-admiral, Villeneuve, who commanded the five vessels at the rear of the French line, cut his cables and come to the assistance of his comrades, the eight British ships, engaged with as many French, would have been in a serious position. He did not do so, however, possibly fearing to run his ships aground. Consequently the *Alexandria* and the *Swiftsure* came in to the assistance of the British ships, some of[Pg 84] which were being terribly damaged by the greatly superior weight of the French fire. The *Bellerophon*, dismasted and disabled by the enemy's fire, dropped out of the line, and the *Alexandria* took her place, while the *Swiftsure* attacked the *Franklin*. The *Leander*, seeing how hard was the fight, relinquished her attempt to get the *Culloden* afloat, and, sailing in, engaged in the battle.

For a time the issue was doubtful. The three English seventy-four-gun ships were matched against one of a hundred and twenty and two of eighty-four. Darkness did not put a stop to the engagement, which continued to rage with unabated fury, the battle being practically between twelve British ships and eight French ships of the line and their four frigates and gun-boats. By ten o'clock five of the French van had surrendered, and the great hundred-and-[Pg 85]twenty-gun ship, the *Orient*, was in flames. The excitement of the Arabs as the battle continued was unbounded. It seemed to them that mortal men could not sustain so terrible a conflict, and exclamations of wonder and admiration rose constantly among them.

The light of the burning vessel enabled the whole of the terrible scene to be clearly witnessed. Half the ships were partly or wholly dismasted, the rigging was cut to pieces, and the sails were riddled with balls. The splintered sides, bulwarks shot away, and port-holes blown into one, showed how terrible was the damage inflicted on both sides. Higher and higher rose the flames on board the *Orient*. Men could be seen leaping overboard into the water from the burning ship, and soon after ten she blew up with a tremendous explosion, the concussion of which was so great that many of the Arabs were thrown to the ground. For ten minutes a dead silence succeeded the roar of battle, not a gun was fired on either side. The British vessels near the spot where the *Orient* had lately floated lowered what boats there were uninjured and set to work to rescue the survivors, who were either clinging to spars or were swimming. Several of these, too, were hauled in at the lower port-holes of the ships.

The French ship *Franklin* was the first to recommence firing, but after a few more broadsides from the *Swiftsure* she hauled down her colours. The firing continued without any abatement until three o'clock in the morning. It then died away for a time, but recommenced at six o'clock with fresh fury, and it was not until two in the afternoon that it came to an end. Villeneuve, seeing that all was lost, now woke up and cut his cables. Three of his ships ran aground, but with the *Guillaume Tell* and the *Genereux* and two frigates he made off, there being only one British ship that was in[Pg 86] condition to make sail in pursuit. The two line-of-battle ships and one of the frigates were afterwards captured by a British squadron.

Thus of the thirteen French ships of the line eight had surrendered, one had blown up, two had escaped, and two were on shore. If the *Culloden* could have got into action, it is probable that not one of the French fleet would have left Aboukir Bay. The British loss in killed and wounded was 895. 3105 of the French, including the wounded, were captured, and 5225 perished in the fight. The victory was the most decisive that was ever won at sea.

CHAPTER V.
A STREET ATTACK.

Not until the last gun was fired did Edgar and his Arab friend return to their tent, utterly worn out by excitement and watching.

"I told you what it would be, Sidi," Edgar said as they went along. "I was certain that we should thrash them. It is a tremendous victory, and you see it is as important for you as it is for us, for the French army is now cut off. It will be a long time indeed before the French can fit out another fleet strong enough to have even a chance of fighting ours, and, as far as I can see, the only possible escape for their army is to march all the way round by Syria to Constantinople, and I should think that after this the Sultan will at once declare war with them, for by conquering Egypt they have taken one of his provinces."

This turned out to be the case. The news of the capture of Egypt had filled the Sultan with indignation and rage,[Pg 87] but the fear excited by the success of the French arms in Europe deterred him from declaring war against so formidable a foe until the report of the destruction of their fleet reached Constantinople, when he at once plucked up courage, declared war against France, and ordered two armies to be gathered for the reconquest of Egypt. The news of the destruction of the French fleet caused intense excitement throughout Egypt. It showed that the French were not, as many had been inclined to consider them, invincible, and that it was improbable they would be able to receive any reinforcements from beyond the sea.

A week previously the Arabs had felt completely crushed, now the feeling of independence and hope sprang up again, and the whole situation was at once changed. Sidi had, directly the fight came to an end, sent off one of his followers to meet his father, and to inform him of what had taken place. Four days later the man returned; he had met the chief and his party just as they had reached the river. The latter had resolved at once to rejoin the desert tribesmen, and to escort the caravan back to their oasis; his wife, the women, and the animals were to remain there. The party now at the encampment with Sidi were to join him at once.

"The sheik bids me say," the messenger went on to Sidi, "that he would that you should not wait until the others are ready to start, but, if he is willing, should at once ride with your white friend to Cairo, if he is disposed to go with you; there, from his knowledge of the language of the Franks, he would be able to gain much information as to their designs.

"He bids you regard him as your leader, and to act as he may advise. Two of us are to go with you to look after your horses. He begs that one of you will come to the base of the Great Pyramid on the twelfth day after I[Pg 88] left him, that is in ten days from now, to tell him what news you have gathered and to consult with him. He is convinced that the news you sent him will call all the Arabs to arms again."

"That is just what I should wish," Edgar said. "I have been thinking for the last four days that I should like to be at Cairo. That is the place of interest now."

He and his friend talked the matter over. "It will be better," Edgar said, "that we should go as simple Arabs, and that we should take two horses of less value than those which we now ride. You could send them up by the party that will rejoin your father. As two young Arabs on ordinary horses, we should attract no attention. We could encamp with our two men just outside the town, and go in and out as we pleased; no one would be likely to notice or question us. Or we might even wear the dress of the fellaheen, which would be safer still, for if the Arabs begin to make attacks upon French parties, as they are likely to do, any of them wandering in the streets of Cairo might be regarded with suspicion by the soldiers."

"I will do just as you advise, Edgar. I suppose that we had better start at once."

"Certainly, as soon as we have eaten a meal. Will the man who brought the news in be fresh enough to start again at once?"

"Certainly he would," Sidi said in a tone of surprise; "an Arab never feels fatigue on horseback. Of course he must have a fresh horse. I will pick out another man to accompany us, and two horses for ourselves. There are two that would suit us well, for they are both sound and fast, though but poor animals to look at, and no one will cast an eye of envy upon them."

"That is just what we want, Sidi."[Pg 89]

In less than an hour they were galloping across the plain. The journey of 110 miles was accomplished in two days, and the party, without entering the town, encamped on some waste ground outside the walls. Here were many small huts belonging to the poorest class of the population, together with many small shelter tents of black cloth erected by parties of wandering Arabs like themselves. They had, on the previous night, changed their attire, and had nothing to distinguish them from the poorer classes of Arabs, who, having given up the desert life, earned a precarious existence in the towns. The two men with them looked with disdain at their surroundings, and Edgar felt obliged to warn them.

"You must remember," he said, "that the lion couches before he springs, and crawls and conceals himself until he is within reach of his prey, so is it needful also for us to bear ourselves humbly. We are come to see what the French are doing; how they comport themselves, and what is the feeling among the population. We are as spies who come to examine a country before it is attacked, and to carry out our object we must bear ourselves so that suspicion may not fall upon us. If you are questioned, remember that we are four men ready to act as guards to a caravan or on any such service that may present itself."

Leaving the two men to look after the horses, Edgar and Sidi entered the city. The scene was intensely interesting, Cairo being vastly more oriental in its appearance than Alexandria. The narrow streets were crowded; strict orders had been issued against plundering, Napoleon being anxious to win the good-will of the population, and merchandise of all sorts was displayed in the shops. Each trade had its special bazaar, the gold and silversmiths, the dealers in silks, in carpets, richly embroidered garments, tobacco, long pipes[Pg 90] with jewelled mouthpieces, narghiles with their long twisted stems; workers in iron, vendors of the yellow shoes used by the women in walking, the dainty gold-embroidered velvet slippers for indoors, or the pointed upturned shoes of the men, had each its own bazaars scattered throughout the streets.

Women, in their long dark blue garments, and the hideous white linen yakmash covering the whole face below the eyes, and falling to the breast, moved through the crowd, others of higher rank, seated on donkeys and attended by eunuchs, made their way back from the baths, or from visits to their friends. Stout Turkish merchants or functionaries rode along perched on high saddles, looking as if they would bear to the ground the little donkeys, that nevertheless went lightly along with their burden. French soldiers abounded, gazing into the shops, and occasionally making small purchases, chattering and laughing, the fatigues and sufferings of the march being now forgotten.

There were comparatively few of the richer class in the streets, many of these having left the city at the approach of the French, while on the night before the latter entered there had been serious tumults in the city, and the houses of many of the beys had been broken into and sacked. Through all this crowd Edgar and Sidi wandered unnoticed.

"It does not look as if there were any strong feeling against the Franks," Sidi remarked, as they issued into a large square which was comparatively deserted, and seated themselves on a bench in the shade of the trees near a fountain.

"No; but it is not here that one would expect to find any signs of disaffection. No doubt the traders are doing a good business, for every officer and soldier will be sure to spend all his pay in presents for those at home, or in me[Pg 91]mentoes of his stay here, and I am sure the things are pretty enough to tempt anyone. It is in the poorer quarters that trouble will be brewing."

Presently a group of French officers came along and seated themselves at a short distance from the two young Arabs. Having not the slightest idea that these could understand what they said, they talked loudly and unrestrainedly.

"The thing is serious, gentlemen," one of them, who was clearly of superior rank to the rest, said. "Since the news of this most unfortunate affair arrived, there has been a great change in the situation. For the last two days there has not been a single horse brought into the horse-market, and the number of bullocks has fallen off so greatly that the commissariat had difficulty this morning in buying sufficient for the day's rations for the army, but the worst of it is, that assassinations are becoming terribly common, and in the last three days fifty-two men have been killed. There will be a general order out to-morrow that men are not to go beyond certain limits, unless at least four are together, and that they are not, under any pretext whatever, to enter a native house.

"Besides those known to have been killed, there are twenty-three missing, and there is no doubt they too have been murdered, and their bodies buried. The Egyptian head of the police has warned us that there are gatherings in the lower quarters, and that he believes that some of Mourad's emissaries are stirring the people up to revolt. A good many parties of Arabs are reported as having been seen near the city. Altogether I fear that we are going to have serious trouble; not that there is any fear of revolt, we can put that down without difficulty, but this system of assassination is alarming, and if it goes on, the men will[Pg 92] never be safe outside their barracks, except in the main thoroughfares. One does not see how to put it down. An open enemy one can fight, but there is no discovering who these fellows are in a large population like this, and it would be of no use inflicting a fine on the city for every French soldier killed; that would affect only the richer class and the traders. There is no doubt, too, that the news that our fleet has been completely destroyed has dispirited the soldiers, who feel that for the present, an any rate, they are completely cut off from France."

"That is certainly serious, general," one of the officers said, "and there seems only the project of the invasion of India or a march to Constantinople. After our march here, though it was but little over a hundred miles, and the greater portion of the way along the bank of the river, with our flotilla with stores abreast of us, neither of these alternatives look as easy as they seemed to us before we set foot in this country."

"No, indeed, colonel; our campaign at home gave us no idea of what the march of our army would be across these deserts, and it certainly seems to me that the idea of twenty thousand men marching from here to India is altogether out of the question. If our fleet had beaten the English, gone back and brought us twenty thousand more men, and had then sailed round the Cape, and come up to Suez to fetch us and land us in India, the thing would have been feasible enough, and in alliance with the Sultan of Mysore we might have cleared the English out altogether, but the land march seems to be impossible; a small body of men could never fight their way there, a large body could not find subsistence."

"No; I fancy that Constantinople will be the place at which we shall emerge. A march to Palestine will, of[Pg 93] course, be hard, but it is only three or four days from the Egyptian frontier. I don't fancy that there will be any difficulty on the way up through Syria and Asia Minor, and that almost everywhere we shall find cultivated land, and an abundant supply of provisions for the army. As for the Turks, I have no doubt that we shall thrash them, if they venture to interfere with us, as easily as we did the Egyptians. I have no fear for the safety of the army, and if the Egyptians venture on a rising here, before we start, we shall give them such a lesson that a few thousand men left here should have no difficulty in keeping the country in order."

They chatted for some time longer, and then moved off. Edgar repeated to his friend the substance of their conversation, and they then returned to their tent. The next day they wandered through the poorer portion of the town. Groups of men were assembled in many places, talking excitedly; when, as it sometimes happened, a party of French soldiers came along, they broke up, only to assemble at another spot. Sidi and Edgar mingled with them, and gathered that in a short time there would be trouble. It was agreed that so long as the whole French army remained there nothing could be done, but it was regarded as certain that it would soon break up. It was argued that they could not remain at Cairo. Mourad was gathering a large force higher up on the Nile. The Arabs were moving again. Damietta and Rosetta would have to be occupied. There were numbers of the Mamelukes between Cairo and Suez. The French could not remain quietly until the whole country was in arms against them. No doubt columns would be sent off, and as soon as they were gone, the time for a rising would come.

They were going down a quiet lane when two men came[Pg 94] out from a house. One of them looked fixedly at Sidi and exclaimed:

"This is the Arab boy who got us into trouble at Alexandria; now it is our turn."

Paying no attention to Edgar, who was so entirely altered by his disguise as to defy recognition, the two men seized Sidi, and began to drag him into the house. Edgar sprang forward and struck one of them so heavy a blow in the face that he released his hold of Sidi and staggered back against the wall. Then with a shout of fury he drew his knife and rushed at Edgar. The latter also snatched his knife from his girdle, shifted it into his left hand, and threw himself into the usual boxing attitude with his left foot forward. The Maltese paused in his rush. This line of defence was altogether new to him. He had been engaged in many a fierce fray, but his opponents had always, like himself, fought with their knives in their right hands.

The momentary indecision was fatal to him. With the speed of a practised boxer Edgar changed feet. Springing forward with his right foot in advance he caught his opponent's wrist with his right hand, and snatched the man's arm across his body, and plunged his own knife to the hilt under the other's arm. He was but just in time, for the Greek, who, having hurled Sidi into the passage, had turned to the assistance of his comrade, was close upon him, giving vent to a hoarse howl of fury as his comrade dropped. Edgar faced him in the same attitude as that in which he had met the Maltese. The man paused out of reach and then crouched, swaying his body from side to side in readiness for a spring, but he never gave it. Sidi, although thrown heavily down, had leapt up again with the activity of a cat, and with a single bound from the door he reached the Greek and buried his knife between his shoulders. Almost at the same[Pg 95]moment there was a shout from the other end of the street, and two or three men were seen running towards them.

"Through the house, Sidi!" Edgar exclaimed.

They rushed in, closed and fastened the door, and then ran out into the yard behind the house, which was fortunately empty. They were over the wall in a moment into another yard, entered a door that stood open, went noiselessly along the passage, for both were barefooted, opened a door and went out into the lane beyond, pausing for a moment before they did so to see that there were no blood-stains that would attract attention on their dress. As their arms were bare, there were but a few spots of blood to be seen. They wiped the blood from the hands that held the knives on the inside of their dress, and then walked quietly out, pulled the door to, but did not attempt to close it, walked quietly down the lane, took the first turning, turned again four or five times, and then quickened their pace to a fast walk, and in ten minutes emerged from the labyrinth of lanes they had been traversing. Up to this time not a word had been spoken from the moment they entered the house.

"We are well out of that, Sidi," Edgar said. "Who would have thought of our meeting those two scoundrels again? I am sorry that I had to kill that man, but it was his life or mine."

"You have assuredly again saved my life, Edgar. I am sure that they would have murdered me."

"No doubt they would," Edgar said. "But as I was with you, and was not likely to stand and look on while they did it, it was a fight of two against two, and you did your share."

"It was a poor share, brother. You drew off the attention of the man that would have killed me, and I had but[Pg 96] to strike him down without danger to myself. Again you have saved my life."

"That may be, but I think that you in turn saved mine, for I doubt whether I should have got on as well with the second fellow as I did with the first."

"Oh, I have no doubt you would!" the young Arab said confidently. "How did you kill him? I saw nothing of it."

"It was simple enough," Edgar replied, and related how the short conflict had begun and ended.

"You must really teach me these things, Edgar. It is wonderful how quick you are, and with a knife too; for I have heard you say that in England people never fight with knives."

"One learns quickness from boxing," Edgar said carelessly. "That is one of the advantages of it. It teaches one to think quickly and act quickly; and if one can fight with one's fists, of course one can fight with a knife. It was a boxing trick I used, and a very useful one, and more easy than it would be against a good boxer, who would have hit me with his left before I could strike my blow, but of course this fellow had no idea of doing that, so that unless I had failed to grasp his wrist it was a certainty. Did the other hurt you? I heard you go down with a crash."

"I feel stiff," Sidi replied, "and I expect that I shall be a good deal worse to-morrow, for I am sure I am bruised all down the back; but that is no matter. It is a good thing that we have done with those two men; I felt sure that they would try to be revenged on us if they ever fell in with us again."

The next day, the anniversary of the establishment of the republic, was celebrated by a grand review of the troops, and a few days later the news came that Desaix's division, which had set out in pursuit of Mourad on the day[Pg 97] after the battle of the Pyramids, had overtaken him, and another fierce fight had ensued. The charge of the Mamelukes had broken one of the French squares, and for a time great confusion prevailed, but Desaix shouted to the soldiers to throw themselves down on the ground, and then the next square opened so terrible a fire on the Mamelukes that they were forced to retreat. Two days later Kleber marched with his division for Damietta.

In the native quarter the agitation continued, but so far peace had not been broken, and the French took little heed of what was passing, and had no idea that there was any danger of a rising. Had it been their object to provoke such movement, they could hardly have taken steps better calculated to bring it about. They had, in the first place, after their arrival proceeded to largely strengthen and increase the fortifications, and in doing so had altogether disregarded the feelings of the people, had pulled down houses and mosques, had desecrated tombs, and cleared away all buildings on spaces of ground across which the guns would play. This desecration of their sacred places had given rise to the deepest feelings of exasperation among the people.

In the next place, many of the fortifications were converted so that the guns menaced the town instead of the country round, and at the citadel especially, which dominated the whole city, guns were placed to overawe it. The next step was deeply resented by the people, for interfering with their ancient usages. Cairo was divided into fifty quarters, each of which had a wall and gate. These gates were closed at night, or indeed at any time, by the orders of the chief of the quarter, and the interruption caused by these breaks in the line of communication had given rise to many quarrels between the soldiers and the townspeople. The inconve[Pg 98]nience was a distinct one, and the French, without giving any notice of their intentions, sent a strong party of engineers, supported by troops, to demolish all these gateways.

The taxes were onerous in the extreme. By means of a council that had been appointed, consisting of notabilities who had, either by fear or bribery, been brought over to the side of the French, a crushing taxation was imposed, and this rendered the trading and upper classes, upon whom the burden principally fell, as hostile to the French domination as were the lower classes. Thus the French themselves had, by their high-handed conduct and their absolute disregard for the feelings and religious sentiments of the people, prepared a mine that was on the point of exploding.

That afternoon a messenger arrived from the sheik, saying that he should be at the Pyramids on the following morning, at nine o'clock, and that he wished them to meet him there.

"Would you take the men with us, Edgar?"

"No, I think it would be best to leave them. They are well established here now, and have come to be looked upon by those around them as having left the tribe altogether and as intending to work as carriers. I should tell one or other of them to go into the town every day, and see how matters are going on. If your father, as I hope, decides to take no part in any attack on the French here, he can easily send a messenger to recall them."

Accordingly, the next morning they mounted at daybreak, rode down to Boulak, and were, with their horses, ferried across the river; then they mounted again and rode to the Pyramids. An hour later a cloud of dust was seen rising to the south-west, and in a few minutes the sheik, with fifty followers, rode up.

"What is the news?" he asked his son as he leapt from[Pg 99] his horse. "We heard that the people of Cairo are about to rise against the Franks, and numbers of our people have already ridden to join them in the attack."

"The city is in a very disturbed state, father, but as yet the rising has not begun."

"That is good, my son. We were unable to strike a blow at the Franks in the battle here; this time we will do our share, with the aid of Allah.

"You do not think that that is well?" he broke off as he glanced at Edgar.

"It is for you to decide, sheik," Edgar said. "For my part, I do not believe that the rising will be successful. It is true that a large number of the French are absent. Desaix has gone with his division to capture the northern provinces and drive out Mourad Bey and the Mamelukes. Kleber marched yesterday, they say, to Damietta, but there is still a strong force here. I doubt not that the rising will be successful at first. Many French soldiers away from their regiments will be cut down and killed, detached parties may be attacked and overpowered, but I believe that in the end their discipline will triumph. Their cannon will sweep the streets, the guns of the citadel and the new forts that they have armed will shell the town; and although, if a really desperate defence is made, the town can hardly be captured without great loss, Bonaparte is sure to do so sooner or later, for, if necessary, he can call back Kleber and Desaix. It is a matter of life and death to them. Were the country to hear that Cairo had been recovered and the French driven out with heavy loss, there would be a rush to arms. The army would, I believe, be able to fight its way down to Alexandria, but when beleaguered there, unable to obtain any stores from the country round, and their retreat from sea cut off, their position would be desperate."[Pg 100]

"I do not say that you are not right," the sheik said gravely. "You understand the mode of warfare of these Franks much better than I do, and have been right in all your predictions of what would happen; but whatever may be the danger, it is clear to me that it must be faced. Brave men do not shrink from encountering death, and how can a follower of the Prophet shrink from death in battle with infidels. Numbers of my countrymen will assuredly take part in the struggle, and did I ride away without sharing in the conflict, I should not be able to lift up my head again. It may be that it is fated that I shall not return; so be it; if it is the will of Allah that I should die now, who am I to oppose it?

"Let there be no more said on this. I know, my friend, that you are not afraid of danger, and that your counsel is not prompted by any thought of personal fear. I acknowledge that all you say may come to pass, but my mind is made up. Thousands of Arabs will fight there, and I shall not draw back. Sidi will, of course, fight by my side, but it is not your quarrel, and there is no reason why you should risk your life in a struggle that you believe to be hopeless."

"Assuredly, chief, I shall ride with you. You have treated me as one of your tribe, and I have come to regard myself as such. Sidi is as my brother, and were there no other reason, I would ride to battle by his side. Moreover, this is as much my business as yours. My country is at war with France, and if at present Egypt is invaded by them, it is not because France desires to capture Egypt, but because by their occupation of the country they hope to strike a blow at England."

"It is well!" the chief said. "I think not that either you or Sidi will fall. Allah sent you to his aid when he was in danger, and he would hardly have done so had it been his[Pg 101] will that you should both perish so shortly afterwards; but we are all in His hands, and shall die when our time comes, and not before."

Then, as if dismissing the subject, he asked Sidi what had happened in the town, and whether they had been questioned by any as to their business.

"The principal thing, father, that has happened to us is, that we again met the two men who attacked me at Alexandria, and were beaten and turned out of the city, and as it happened then, I should have lost my life had it not been for my brother."

"Tell me about it," the sheik said, his face hardening and his fingers playing with the hilt of the long knife in his sash.

Sidi related the whole adventure.

The sheik stood stroking his beard gravely as Sidi spoke. His eyes turned from his son to Edgar.

"Bishmillah!" he exclaimed, when the story was finished, "Allah must have sent you to be Sidi's protector. Without doubt, he would have lost his life had he been alone. Truly it is a wonderful thing this English science that you possess, and that enables you, though but a lad, to knock down strong men, and although unused to a knife, to slay ruffians accustomed to it from their childhood, with their own weapons. More than ever am I beholden to you, Edgar. Twice have you saved my son's life. Had you been alone, these men would not have recognized you, and it was but because he was attacked that, as on the last occasion, you joined in the fray. Show me, I beg you, how you slew this man."

"It was simple, sheik. Had I fought him in his own fashion he would, I have no doubt, have killed me. But my method was as new to him as his would have been to me. Will you draw your dagger and advance at me as if going to strike? Now, if I have my knife in my right hand[Pg 102] also, you know what to do; you would try to grasp my wrist with your left hand. I should try to grasp yours in the same way. We should struggle, but with your superior strength you would soon wrench your right hand free, and strike me down. Now, you see, I take my closed knife in my left hand, pointing it straight towards you, with my left foot forward; that is the position in which we stand when we use our fists. You, like that Maltese, are puzzled, and stand, as he did, for a moment indecisive; that would have been fatal to you. As, you see, I leap forward, changing my advanced foot as I do so, catch your wrist, and pull your arm with a sudden jerk towards me, and at the same moment strike you under the arm with my left hand."

An exclamation of wonder broke from the Arabs standing round listening to the conversation, as with lightning speed Edgar repeated the manœuvre that had been fatal to the Maltese.

"Bishmillah," the chief ejaculated, "but it is wonderful! It is true I should have been a dead man had your blade been opened, and your movement was so rapid that I could not have avoided it."

"No, because you were not accustomed to it. Had you been an English boxer you would have leapt back as quickly as I leapt forward. I should have failed to grasp your wrist, and should in that case have leapt back again to my former position, for had I remained thus I should have been at your mercy. Had I succeeded in doing so before you struck me, we should have been as we began, and I should have tried some other trick. Certainly as long as I stood with my left arm extended and my knife pointed towards you, you could not have closed with me—for I am much quicker on my feet from the training that I have received—and I could have got back more quickly than[Pg 103] your knife could fall, and even if the blades fell at the same moment you would but gash my shoulder, whereas I should pierce you at a vital point.

"It is with this as with other matters. You have been trained from childhood to sit your horse. You can stoop over while you are galloping at full speed and pick up a stone from the sand. You can twirl your lance round your head and throw it into the air, and catch it as it descends while going at full speed. You can do things that no untrained Englishman could do. So is it with me. I have learned boxing from the best masters in England, I have practised daily for two years and a half, and I have gained a quickness that could not be imitated by one who has not had such teaching and practice."

"It is true," the sheik said. "But it is not the less wonderful in our eyes that, though knowing the use of our weapons, we should be but as children in your hands when thus fighting on foot. I wonder no longer that you should so easily have conquered this man. What say you, my brothers?"

An exclamation of assent broke from the Arabs, who, in spite of Edgar's explanation, henceforth regarded him with an almost superstitious respect. As soon as the troop had arrived, Edgar had gone to see his horse, which, as well as that of Sidi, the sheik had brought with him. It had whinnied with pleasure as he came up to it, and he stood patting it for some time, and giving it some dates. He now went over to it again, and on his return asked the chief:

"Were you thinking of riding that splendid horse of yours?"

"Certainly I was," he replied, in a tone of surprise.

"I do not mean to take mine," Edgar said, "and I think that it would be a great pity if you and Sidi were to[Pg 104] ride yours. I can understand that, in a fight on the plains, it would be a great advantage to be so mounted, for either in pursuit or flight it would be invaluable, but in the narrow streets of Cairo it would be a sin to risk so splendid an animal, and the one I have been riding would be just as useful. We shall be fighting, not against cavalry, but against infantry and artillery, and it would be useless to ride a horse that would outstrip those of the rest of the band; while even if we won the day our satisfaction would be lessened indeed had one to mourn the loss of one's friend."

"You are right," the sheik said gravely. "Were I to lose Zeila it would be like the loss of a child; we love each other dearly. I had not thought of it before. It seemed to me a matter of course that if I rode in the battle she should carry me as she has done a score of times; but, as you say, this will not be like fighting in the desert, when man singles out man, and one's life depends as much upon the intelligence and quickness of the horse as upon one's skill with spear and scimitar. Two of my followers shall take our three horses back to our camp in the desert. You and Sidi are already mounted. One of the men shall give me his horse, and shall ride on Sidi's; each will then have but one to lead. If my son and I are killed, the two horses will be valuable possessions to my wife."

Accordingly the saddle was shifted from the sheik's horse to that of one of his followers, and the latter, with his comrade, was told to start for the oasis as soon as the rest of the party set out for Cairo.

[Pg 105]

CHAPTER VI.
THE RISING IN CAIRO.

As soon as a meal had been eaten the Arabs mounted again, rode to a ferry two miles above the city, crossed there, and joined a large party of their countrymen, who were gathered at a short distance from the city. There was much excitement among them, for one of their number had just returned, bringing news that there was fighting in the town. Napoleon had gone in the morning to examine the ruins of Old Cairo. On hearing that there were armed gatherings in various parts of the town, General Dupres started from the barracks of Birketelfi with a detachment of dragoons. On his approaching one of these gatherings fire was opened upon him. He and some of his dragoons were shot, and the rest galloped with the news to Junot, who was in command, and who at once sent to acquaint Bonaparte with what was taking place.

The latter returned at once, found the first two gates at which he arrived in the hands of the insurgents, and making a detour, entered the town by that of Boulak, and, joining Junot, he ordered the whole of the troops to be concentrated in the great open space known as the Square of El-Esbekieh, where were the headquarters and barracks occupied by a portion of the troops, and the houses in which the staff-officers, servants, and others lodged. Cannon were placed at the mouth of all the streets leading from it, and the troops were ordered to remain under arms all night. The Arabs had, soon after the sheik's party joined them, entered the town by one of the gates that had been seized by the insurgents, and established themselves in one of the large open spaces near the walls. Parties galloped down[Pg 106] into the town, and from time to time brought back news of what was being done.

They reported that no attacks had been made on the troops, but that the whole town was in a state of insurrection; that the keepers of the French restaurants had been, for the most part, killed, and all their houses pillaged; and that the insurgents had gathered in great force in the cemetery, near the Square of El-Esbekieh. The sheik, with his followers and many of the other Arabs, rode down to this spot in readiness to take part in the attack that would, he supposed, be at once made on the French. Finding that nothing was done, the sheik rode to the Mosque of Gama El Ashar, where the leaders of the insurrection were gathered. He dismounted and went in. He found a tumultuous debate going on, a few being ready for instant attack, while the others urged the advisability of waiting until the next morning, when many more Arabs, and the inhabitants of Old Cairo and other places, would have joined them.

The sheik at once took part in the debate, and urged strongly that the attack should be made without an instant's delay.

"You are giving time for the Franks to prepare themselves," he said. "You have already lost the advantage of surprise. After the first shot was fired there should not have been a moment of delay; but no shot should have been fired until you had given us notice. Then together we should have flung ourselves upon them when they were confused and dismayed, and had no time to form plans or to gather themselves in one place. You have already lost that advantage, but do not give them any longer time. You may be sure that already swift horsemen have been sent to order the divisions that have just marched to return at once, and by to-morrow evening they may be here."[Pg 107]

"You have spoken truly," one of the leaders said, "that no shot should have been fired until all was in readiness, and that we should then have attacked at once with all our force. But the impatience of individuals has destroyed our plans. The evil has already been done; the Franks are gathered together. They can receive no reinforcements until to-morrow night, while in the morning we shall be joined by fully 10,000 men; therefore nothing would be gained, and much lost, by attacking to-day."

The majority of those present agreed with this opinion, and the sheik returned to the cemetery.

"You were right," he said to Edgar moodily. "To be successful, such a rising should have been prompt. They should have wasted no time in killing tradesmen and plundering their shops. They should have hurled themselves at once upon the troops and cut them to pieces before they had time to recover from their surprise. Had they acted thus they might have succeeded. Now they have allowed the whole of the French to gather, with their guns, and after what happened in the battle, I fear there can be little doubt of what will occur when we attack them; but this does not alter my determination to do my best towards gaining a victory.

"Even if defeated the affair will not be without advantage. The Franks will begin to see that, easy as was their first victory, the Egyptians are not a flock of sheep to be maltreated and robbed without even venturing to murmur, and that they cannot afford to scatter their forces all over the country. Moreover, the news that Cairo is in insurrection will spread through the country and excite a feeling of resistance. Many will die, but their blood will not have been shed in vain. The French think that they have conquered Egypt—they have, in fact, but marched to[Pg 108] the capital. They only hold the ground they stand on, and it will not be long before they feel that even that is trembling under their feet."

Some sheep that had been brought, slung across the horses, were cut up, fires lighted, and supper eaten, and when two men had been posted as sentinels, the rest wrapped themselves in their burnooses and lay down to sleep. Edgar's reflections were not pleasant, and he sat up for some time talking to Sidi.

"You think that we shall be beaten," the latter said, after they had talked for some time. "There is no reason, brother, why you should take part in a fight that you think will end badly. Why should you not leave us, and go out of one of the gates in the morning?"

"I cannot do that, Sidi. I have, of my own free-will, cast in my lot with your people. It is thanks to them that I have escaped a prison and perhaps death, and I cannot withdraw now because there is danger. To tell you the truth, I am more disgusted at the murder of all the unfortunate shopkeepers than thinking of any personal danger to-morrow. There is nothing brave or patriotic in slaying unarmed men, and the deeds done yesterday are rather those of street ruffians thirsting for plunder than of men trying to shake off subjection to foreigners. Such doings as these bring disgrace upon a cause."

This view of the case was new to Sidi. In the wars that the Arabs carried on with each other, or with the tribes of Morocco, there was no fine distinction between combatants and non-combatants: women as well as men were killed or carried off as slaves, and that there was anything wrong in this had never occurred to him.

"But they are enemies," he ventured to protest.

"They were foreigners, but not enemies," Edgar replied.[Pg 109] "Many of them were settled here long before the French landed, and, like my father, lived peaceably among you. They are not in any way responsible for the action of the French government, or of Bonaparte and his army. Among civilized people, save that after the capture of a town by storm, the soldiers become maddened and behave sometimes like demons, the lives of peaceful people are never menaced. Soldiers fight against soldiers, and not against quiet traders or cultivators of the ground. To me all that has been done to-day is nothing short of a murderous butchery, and to-morrow I would much more willingly join in a charge on the rabble who have done these things than upon the French soldiers, who are for the most part honest fellows and have injured no one since they came into the town, though they may have looted houses which they found deserted by their inhabitants.

"However, as my country is at war with them, and I have an opportunity of fighting them, I shall do so, but I would rather have done it with an Arab force alone out on the desert than in conjunction with these blood-stained ruffians. However, the matter is settled now, and at any rate it will be a satisfaction to fight by the side of yourself and your brave father, who sees as well as I do that defeat is almost certain." So saying he lay down to sleep, but with sore forebodings of what was likely to take place the next day.

When daylight broke it soon became evident that the insurgents had neither a leader nor fixed plans. Some were in favour of attacking at once, while others urged that it would be better for the French to do so. The argument was, that whereas at present the French were all assembled, ranged in order, and ready for an attack, they must be broken up as soon as they issued from the various streets[Pg 110] leading into the square. The sheik, after talking the matter over with Edgar, rode with some of his followers to the spot where the leaders were discussing the matter.

"There is much in what you say," he exclaimed, when one of those who urged delay had spoken; "but if we are to await their attack let us prepare for it. All who have firearms should go on to the roofs of the houses of the streets through which they will march, and fire down into them as they pass along. Those who have other arms should take their places in the lanes, running out of them and break into the column as it comes along, while we Arabs will charge them in front."

Some strongly approved of this advice, others said that the question must be referred to the council at the mosque, and things remained as they were before.

The French had made a move early. Soon after daybreak Captain Sulkouski, one of Napoleon's aides-de-camp, started with two hundred cavalry to make a circuit of the town, and to reconnoitre the position of the insurgents. He rashly charged into the middle of a large party of Arabs, but was killed with many of his men. Two hours later scouts rushed into the cemetery, and announced that the French were in movement along the streets leading towards it, and almost immediately afterwards several batteries, which had been placed during the night on spots commanding the cemetery, opened fire.

There was no hesitation now on the part of the insurgents; they rushed forward in confused masses to meet the enemy. As they did so the leading ranks of the columns opened, and cannon, which were being dragged along by the infantry, poured volleys of grape into the crowded mobs. Many of the Egyptians ran into the houses, and from there kept up a heavy fire. But pressing steadily[Pg 111] forward, the French fought their way into the cemetery, and opening out, poured such heavy volleys into the Egyptians that these speedily ran up the streets leading from it, leaving numbers of dead behind. The Arabs had fallen back before the French entered the square, as the crowded tombstones rendered it impossible for them to act with any effect there, and the sheik's party, with several others, took up their position at some distance up the principal street leading towards the mosque.

As soon as a heavy French column entered this street fighting began in earnest. From roof and window a deadly fire was poured into them, bodies of men armed with sword and dagger rushed out of the narrow lanes and threw themselves on the flanks of the column. Many French soldiers were killed, but the bayonet did its work, and the assailants who had pierced the column fell to a man.

The blood of the French soldiers was now up. The sudden attack upon them, the killing of many of their comrades, and of several distinguished officers who had been caught riding unguardedly through the city, had exasperated them to a pitch of fury. They had been under arms all night, and the sight of many shops gutted, and their late inmates lying dead at their doorway or in the road, filled them with a thirst for vengeance, and they moved forward eagerly.

"Now it is our turn!" one of the Arab sheiks said sternly, then raising his war-cry he led the way down the street, followed by a hundred of his followers. Behind them rode Ben Ouafy, with Sidi and Edgar beside him, and his own band following closely. There was only room for eight men to ride abreast. Although their front ranks were swept away by the fire of the leading ranks of the French column, the Arabs charged with splendid bravery, but when[Pg 112] within twenty paces of the column there was a sudden movement, the ranks opened, and two cannon loaded to the muzzle with grape poured a murderous discharge into them.

The effect was terrible. The greater portion of the band that led the charge was swept away; the others would have turned, but the Beni Ouafy were racing forward. "Charge," the sheik cried, "before they can load again!"

"Forward, forward!" the Arabs' war-cry pealed out loud and shrill from a hundred throats, and the whole then dashed down upon the French column. The leading ranks were cut down, the cannon were for the moment captured, and the Arabs pressed forward with shouts of victory; but the French in front, pressed upon by those behind, could retreat but a short distance. Those in front defended themselves with bayonet and clubbed muskets, those behind poured their fire into the Arabs, who, being raised above their comrades' heads, offered an easy mark.

The road was speedily blocked with fallen men and horses, but the struggle continued until there was a movement from the French column, and pressing their way along, a number of soldiers dragged two more guns to the front. Then the head of the column opened sufficiently for the muzzles to project between those of the first line, and again the storm of grape swept the street. This was too much for the Arabs, and those who survived turned their horses and galloped back. The sheik and his party had just reached the French line, all in front of them having fallen, when the cannon poured their contents down the street. Edgar had caught sight of the guns just before, and uttered a warning shout.

"To the right, sheik, to the right!" while he himself, with a sharp pull at the bridle, caused his horse to wheel[Pg 113] to the left, and thus when the guns were fired, their contents passed between Edgar and his two friends. The sheik gave a cry of dismay as he saw that the greater part of his followers were destroyed, and shouted to Sidi and Edgar to fly for their lives. Riding at a mad gallop they dashed along, but the bullets of the French pursued them vengefully, and half-way down the street Edgar felt a sudden sharp pain in his right arm, and at the same moment his horse gave a sudden spring and then rolled over. He was at the time somewhat in rear of the sheik and Sidi, and they were for the moment unaware of what happened to him. Fortunately the horse did not fall upon him, and in an instant he was upon his feet again.

Looking round he saw that he had fallen close to the open door of a shop with an Italian name over it; he ran into it. The shop had been completely ransacked, and three bodies, those of the proprietor and two lads, lay on the floor. There was no door leading out behind, and he ran up the stairs. The rooms were littered with the remains of the furniture and belongings. The bedding, curtains, and everything that could be of use to the spoilers were gone, but the European clothes, which could not be worn by them, were still about. The only windows looked into the street. There was no apparent means of escape; the only hope was in disguise. Tearing off his Arab garments and thrusting them into a cupboard, he threw on without a moment's delay, trousers, a coat that buttoned up, and a pair of European shoes, thrust a cap on his head, and then ran downstairs again. Fortunately the column, after defeating its assailants, had paused for two or three minutes, while the soldiers broke into the houses from which they had been fired upon and slew all they found in them, and its head was still a hundred yards away when Edgar looked cautiously[Pg 114] out. He had time to throw off his coat and to hastily bandage the wound in his arm, from which the blood had been streaming down; then as he heard the tramp of the advancing column he ran down to the door, and as the troops came up, waved his hand, danced as if for joy, and shouted a welcome in Italian, mingled with a few words of French, pouring at the same time a voluble string of maledictions on the ruffians who had killed his master and his two comrades. A mounted officer riding at the head of the column shouted to him to go in and to remain quiet, saying that there was no fear that he would be molested now. Edgar drew back a little, but remained at the door, sometimes shouting encouragement to the soldiers, sometimes apparently weeping convulsively, and acting as if half out of his mind with relief at his deliverance.

As soon as the column had passed he returned upstairs, bandaged his wound much more carefully than before, put on a shirt, and chose the best garments that he could find. All these had no doubt belonged to the proprietor, and he now went boldly out and followed the French column. These met with very slight resistance on their road towards the Mosque of Gama El Ashar. When they neared this spot they halted until the other columns should reach the point of attack. Before they had left the square General Gonmartin had moved round from Boulak with ten guns and taken post on the height near Fort Dupres, and at mid-day thirty guns from this fort and the citadel opened fire on the town. As it was known to the French that great numbers of the fugitives from the cemetery had fled to the mosque, where already a strong body of armed men were assembled, it was deemed imprudent to attack it until secure that there was no danger of a great mass of the insurgents falling upon them while so engaged.[Pg 115]

Shells fell fast on the mosque, and fires broke out in several parts of the town. Edgar joined a group of several civilians, who, having either been hidden during the massacre or having escaped to the French lines, now came up, deeming that they would be safer near the troops than elsewhere. All had stories of hairbreadth escapes to relate, but, feigning not to be able to follow their narratives, Edgar, after a few words in Italian, joined the troops, who were engaged in eating the food that they had brought with them.

At three o'clock a tremendous roar of fire in the direction of Fort Dupres burst out, as some seven or eight thousand of the insurgents, among whom were a number of Arabs, poured out from the nearest gate to endeavour to carry the battery, while at the same moment a tremendous musketry fire from the minarets and roof of the Mosque of Hassan, and from the houses near the wall, was poured at the French artillerymen, to prevent them from working their guns upon their assailants. Gonmartin, however, had with him three battalions of infantry and 300 cavalry, and with these he charged the advancing crowd. The Arabs fought bravely, but were, for the most part, slain, and the insurgents, unable to stand the heavy volleys, followed by a bayonet charge of the infantry, fled back to the gate from which they had sallied out, 400 of them being taken prisoners and sent to the citadel.

A great number of the fugitives fled to the Mosque of Gama El Ashar, which was now crowded. Their reports of the disaster shook the courage of those already there, and when four columns of French infantry emerged simultaneously from the ends of as many streets, the fire opened upon them from the roof of the mosque was but feeble. Six guns were instantly placed commanding its gate, which was shattered after two or three rounds had been fired, and then,[Pg 116]with a shout, the infantry rushed in and commenced the work of slaughter. This was terrible, no quarter was given, and some 6000 Moslems perished there, while 2000 had been killed in the previous fighting.

Satisfied with this terrible act of vengeance, the French troops were marched back to the square they had left in the morning, Bonaparte being sure that there would be no more rioting after the terrible lesson that had been taught the inhabitants. Late in the evening, indeed, the chief men waited upon him and implored mercy for the town. Several of them had been members of the council who directed the movement, but they represented that they had been compelled to act against their will, and Napoleon, satisfied that there would be no more troubles, pardoned them on condition of their at once issuing a proclamation condemning the rioters, and ordering all to return to their ordinary avocations, and to hand over to the authorities any who should preach mischief.

After the capture of the mosque, Edgar went down to the great square occupied by the French, and gathered from the talk of the officers there the result of the sortie. All agreed that the Arabs had fought bravely, and that few indeed had left the field alive. Edgar made his way out of the town by the Boulak gate, which was still open, and found the two Arabs still at the spot where he had left them when he and Sidi rode off to meet the chief at the Pyramids. They were full of excitement at the battle that had raged all day.

"I have bad news," he said. "I rode with the sheik and his son against the French. My horse was killed, and I received a wound in the arm, but, as you see, I obtained a disguise, and have escaped without further harm. You heard that there was a great fight outside the walls?"[Pg 117]

"Yes, my lord. Many men came running past here, and said that the French had beaten them."

"I greatly fear," Edgar went on, "that the sheik and his son took part in that fight. Many Arabs went out with those who attacked the battery, and I think it almost certain that the sheik and his son were among them. Most of the tribesmen were killed in the fight in which I was wounded. The sheik would have joined his countrymen, knowing that there would be no mercy shown the Arabs taken in the town. I hear that almost every one of those who rode out were killed, and I want you to come with me to search among the dead, for doubtless there are many wounded among them, and one or other may yet be alive. There will be a bright moon, and we shall have no difficulty in recognizing them. It will be necessary only to search among those in white."

The two men were greatly moved at the thought of the fate of their chief, his son, and so many of their followers, and assented at once to his proposal.

"We must wait until it gets quite dark," Edgar said. "Have you any food, for I am faint with hunger and loss of blood?"

After he had finished his meal, the horses were handed over by the Arabs to the care of one of their neighbours, with whom they had made acquaintance. The rough tent was pulled down in order that they might wrap the dark blankets over them to conceal their white clothing.

"You had better leave your pistols behind," Edgar said, "but take your knives; we may come across some ruffians engaged in robbing the dead, and the knives may come in useful. I hope that, as is most likely, the French have sent down parties from the forts to watch the gates, so as to prevent any of the leaders in the trouble from making their escape; but some plunderers may well have come across[Pg 118] from Old Cairo, so it is as well to be armed. Take your lances also, not for fighting, but to make a litter with, should we find either the chief or his son."

The sun had set a short time before they started, but the moon would not rise for another hour, and they were unnoticed, or, at least, unquestioned as they went round towards Fort Dupres. Indeed, they encountered no one on the way. The din of battle had been succeeded by a dead silence, no sound was heard from the city, whose population were awe-stricken by the events of the day, and terrified by the expectation of further acts of vengeance by the French. Those in the suburbs had heard but vague rumours of the fighting in the streets and of the massacre at the mosque, but they had learned from fugitives of the defeat of the great sortie, and knew that the insurrection had been completely crushed. The moon was just rising when Edgar and his companions reached the spot between Fort Dupres and the city walls, where the fight had taken place.

The bodies lay thickly piled here at the spots where the struggle had been fiercest. For a time they found none save those of the men of the city, but after two hours' search they came upon a number of Arabs, whose white garments showed up clearly in the moonlight. Lying among them were many bodies of French cavalrymen, showing that the Bedouins had sold their lives dearly. Body after body was carefully examined, a few were found to be still living, and as the Arabs had, at Edgar's orders, brought water-skins with them, they were able to give some little aid to these. Presently they came to a spot where the bodies were more closely heaped than elsewhere and almost as many French as Arabs lay together.

"Now, search most carefully," he whispered, "this is where the last stand was evidently made."[Pg 119]

The greatest caution was indeed necessary, for the fort lay a couple of hundred yards away, and the French sentries could be plainly made out against the sky-line as they marched backwards and forwards. Presently one of the Arabs uttered a low exclamation. Lying by the side of his dead horse, and surrounded by the bodies of five or six French cavalry-men, lay the sheik. His white dress was dabbled with blood, one side of his face was laid open by a sabre cut, and four or five patches of blood at various points of his dress pointed to the existence of other wounds. Edgar knelt beside him and placed his ear to his heart.

"Thank God, he still lives!" he exclaimed; "give me your water-skin; Hassan, lift his head." Edgar poured a little water between the sheik's lips, sprinkled some on his face, and then, tearing off a strip of his garment, brought together the edges of the wound in the face, from which blood was still slowly oozing, laid a wad of rag along it, and then bound it tightly with the bandage.

"We must see to the other wounds after we have got him away," he said. "Now, Hassan, do you two bind one of those spare blankets to the shaft of the two spears, wind it round them until the sides are not more than three feet apart."

While the men were doing this he continued to allow a few drops of water to trickle between the sheik's lips. When the stretcher was ready it was laid on the ground beside him; he was gently lifted on to it, the cloak strapped to his horse's saddle was placed under his head, and the other spare blanket thrown over him. Then the two Arabs lifted the ends of the spears on to their shoulders, and, led by Edgar, made their way from the scene of conflict. When they had gone half a mile they laid the sheik down.[Pg 120]

"Do you stay here, Ali; pour a little water between his lips occasionally. Hassan and I will go back and look for Sidi."

The sheik was lifted from the blanket, and Hassan, shouldering the litter, they returned at a rapid pace to the spot where they had found the sheik. They had already made a hasty search here before leaving, but without success, and now examined with the greatest care the body of every Arab who had fallen near the spot, for Edgar made sure that, unless he had been previously stricken down, Sidi would have fallen near his father. Again their hunt was unsuccessful. Then they widened their circle until after three hours' search they became convinced that he was not among those who had fallen on the field, that he had either been killed in the city, made prisoner, or escaped altogether. When at last convinced that further search would be useless, they returned to the spot where they had left the sheik.

"He has opened his eyes," Ali said, "and murmured two or three words, but I could not hear what he said."

"There are hopes at any rate that he is not mortally wounded," Edgar said. "Now let us go on again with him; do you two each take one of the spears at his head, I will take my place at his feet; we shall get on faster so."

Bearing down towards the river, they reached, after an hour's fast walking, a grove of palm-trees near a village.

"We will leave him here," Edgar said; "it must be five miles from the town. The French will have enough to do to-day without searching for wounded. Do you two stay with him. If he becomes sensible and wants anything, here is some money, and one of you can get food from the village, but beyond some fresh fruit to make him a cooling drink with, he is not likely to need anything. I shall[Pg 121] return at once and enter the town by the Boulak gate as soon as it is open. I heard in the town that there were three or four hundred prisoners taken, and that they were confined in the citadel, and would be tried in the morning. The first thing to do is to find out if Sidi is among them, in which case I shall do all in my power to save him. Pour a little water over my hands, Ali. Wait a moment," and he took up a double handful of the sandy soil, "now pour it on to this. I must get rid of these blood-stains."

After a vigorous rubbing with the wet sand his hands were, as far as he could see in the moonlight, clean, and with a few last words to the men, he started back for the city. It was with difficulty that he made his way to the spot where the horses had been left. It had been a terrible twenty-four hours, with their excitements and emotions, and he had lost a good deal of blood from the flesh wound in his arm. The gray light was just stealing over the sky when he arrived there, and he threw himself down on a secluded spot a short distance from his old camping-ground, and slept for a couple of hours. Waking, he went to the hut, by the side of which the horses were tethered. He and Sidi had spoken several times to the man who lived there, and he possessed two donkeys which worked for hire in the city.

"You do not recognize me?" he said.

The man shook his head.

"I am one of the young Arabs who were staying in the little tent close by. You see I am in disguise. It was not safe to be in the city yesterday in Arab dress, nor is it to-day."

"Of course I remember you now," the man said. "Where are those to whom the horses belong?"

"They are not likely to come here to-day. A friend of[Pg 122] theirs was wounded in the fight at Fort Dupres, and they have found him and carried him off. I have been with them. Tell me, is there any blood on my face?"

The man shook his head.

"Now I want you to go to one of the shops near the gate and get food for me. It matters not what it is some kabobs, or a pillau, or anything they may have, and a large bowl of milk. I am faint and weary. Here is money."

In a quarter of an hour the man returned, and Edgar, after eating a hearty breakfast and drinking a quart of milk, felt greatly better.

He now entered the town. There were no signs of renewed fighting, and listening to the talk of the officers near the headquarters, he gathered that Bonaparte had granted a pardon to the inhabitants, but that the prisoners taken in the attack on Fort Dupres, among whom were many of those most deeply concerned in the rising, were to be tried at ten o'clock by court-martial, and that probably a great part of them would be shot.

CHAPTER VII.
SAVED.

Hiring a donkey, for he still felt weak, Edgar rode out to the citadel. He found the town gate open, as Napoleon, to show his contempt for the population and his perfect confidence that they would not venture to rise again, had ordered everything to go on as usual. Paying the donkey-boy when within a short distance of the citadel, he sat down on a block of stone a little way off the road, and waited for the hour when the court-martial was to open.[Pg 123] From what he had heard in the square he was afraid that the Arab prisoners would all be among those sentenced to death, as the general opinion was that a stern lesson was needed in their case, as they had, with the exception of those dwelling near Alexandria, proved themselves bitterly hostile to the French.

"I am afraid that I shall have to lie," he said to himself. "I hate that, and I would not do it for myself, but the lie will hurt no one and may save Sidi. Anyhow I won't tell more than I can help."

During the two hours that he sat there he made up his mind as to the story that he should tell. As the hour approached, several French officers of rank rode into the citadel. He saw a few people go in on foot, but all were questioned by the sentry at the gate. A few minutes before ten he went up.

"You cannot pass without an order," the sentry said in French.

"I wish to speak to the officer," Edgar replied in a mixture of French and Italian. "I am a witness. I have to give evidence at the trial of one of the scelerats."

The sentry called a non-commissioned officer, who, after speaking a few words to him; entered the guard-house near the gate, and an officer came out.

"What do you want to come in for?" he asked.

"I have evidence to give, monsieur, for one who is, I believe, among the prisoners. He is, like myself, but a lad; but he saved my life from one of those villains of rioters, and slew him with his own hand, when my employer, Signor Pancherasi, and two other of his assistants were killed by them. I would urge this in his favour."

"Well, it is but fair that you should be heard;" and calling a soldier from the guard-house, he told him to accom[Pg 124]pany Edgar to the spot where the court-martial was to be held, and to inform the officer in charge of the prisoners that the lad desired to give evidence in regard to one of them.

Thanking the officer, Edgar went up with the soldier into the great quadrangle. In one corner were a large number of prisoners, guarded by a line of soldiers with fixed bayonets. Three or four officers were standing on the steps in front of a large open door. One of them, as Edgar passed near, called out to his companion:

"Whom have you got there, my man?"

The soldier led Edgar up to the group, saluted, and stood at attention.

"He has come to give evidence for one of the prisoners, general."

"It must needs be pretty strong evidence then," the officer said, "considering that they were all taken when fighting against us. Well, my lad, who are you?"

"I do not speak French well, monsieur: Italian is my language. My name is Giovanni Baptista. I was in the employ of Signor Pancherasi, who sold goods of our country in the broad street leading up from the square of El-Esbekieh, where your soldiers beat the Arabs yesterday."

"I recognize the young fellow," one of the officers said. "He rushed out, half out of his mind with joy, as I rode past at the head of the column. Well, go on, lad. Tell us what you have got to say."

"Well, monsieur, an Arab boy saved my life when the others were killed. One had fired at me, and the bullet went through my arm, when the Arab, who had some of his people with him, sprang forward, and just as the man was going to rush at me with his scimitar he sprang upon him and stabbed him between the shoulders. I do not[Pg 125] remember much more, for I was frightened; but there was a quarrel between him and his Arabs and the others. I think I fainted. When I came to I was alone with the bodies of my master and comrades, and there I remained in hiding until your troops came along."

"But why should this Arab have interfered in your behalf?"

"A few days before, sir, I was going with a parcel of my master's goods through one of the narrow lanes, when I saw two rough men ill-treating an Arab boy. He seemed to be the son of a sheik, and they were trying to rob him and he resisted, and seeing that he was a boy like myself, I shouted at the top of my voice for aid, and ran in with my knife. Then we fought for a minute, but doubtless it would have gone hard with us, had not two of your soldiers, who heard me shouting, come running up, and the men then took to their heels. The young Arab said that his father would show his gratitude to me for having aided him, but I had not heard of him again until, hearing our cries, he ran in with some other Arabs, and, as I have said, saved me from death."

"Let me look at your wound?" the general said. Edgar took off his coat and showed the blood-stained bandage.

"Well, you can look among the prisoners and see if your friend is here. If he is, when you see him brought in you must come in and repeat your story. By the way, how did you understand what this Arab said about his father?"

"I have been out here some years, monsieur, and can speak a little Arabic."

"Well, as you have lost your master, and are out of employment, if you go down to the intendence and say that General Rombaud sent you, and that you can speak enough French and Arabic to get on with, they will find you some employment where you can be of use."[Pg 126]

"Thank you very much, monsieur," and, bowing, Edgar went off with the soldier to the group of prisoners.

There were in all about a score of Arabs, and these kept in a body together. To his great joy, he recognized Sidi among them. His head was bound up, and he looked weak and exhausted, but, like his companions, and indeed the great proportion of the prisoners, he maintained an air of indifference to his position. Thinking it as well that he should not be recognized, and feeling sure that the guard would permit no communication to take place with any of the prisoners, Edgar turned away and went and sat down on some steps between the prisoners and those on which the officers were standing. In a few minutes they went in by the door behind them.

Five minutes later a sergeant came out, and calling four men from a company drawn up near the door, went across to the group of prisoners and presently returned with six of them. In a few minutes they came out again. Three of the men, in charge of a single soldier, were marched away in the direction of the gate; the other three were taken to a door a short distance away, thrust in, the door was locked after them, and two soldiers placed there as sentries. The barred windows told their tale, and Edgar had no doubt that the three men who had entered were sentenced to death. In the meantime, another party had taken six more prisoners in. So the matter proceeded for upwards of an hour, five minutes at the outside sufficing for each batch. At the end of this time the group of Arabs was reached. Hitherto about half of the men taken had been suffered to depart, but this time the six Arabs were all taken to the fatal door.

Edgar did not recognize any of them, and indeed, he knew that the greater part of the sheik's followers had[Pg 127] fallen in the attack on the French column in the street. Sidi was in the next group, and Edgar rose to his feet, saying to the soldier who still stood by his side, and who had heard the conversation with the general, "That is the lad." The man went with him to the door, told the sentries there that the general's orders were that the witness was to be allowed to enter, and Edgar followed the party into a large room. Six French officers were seated at a table. The president, who was the general who had spoken to him, looked up:

"Is that the lad?" he asked, pointing to Sidi.

"That is he, monsieur."

"As we have heard your testimony, it is not necessary to take it again." Sidi had given a sudden start on hearing Edgar's voice. "This young fellow has testified to us," General Rombaud said to two of the members of the court-martial, who had not been present on the steps when the conversation took place, "that this young Arab saved him from murder at the hands of some of the rabble, by killing the man who was about to slay him, and that he did this in return for a service this young Italian had rendered him in succouring him when attacked, some time before, by two robbers. As he is but a lad, and of course acted under his father's orders, I think we may make him an exception to the rule. You can go free, young sir, but let the narrow escape that you have had be a lesson to you not to venture to mix yourself up in treasonable risings again. You can take him away with you," he added to Edgar.

Sidi moved away from his companions with an unsteady step. He had made up his mind that his fate was sealed, and had been prepared to meet it, and the sudden revulsion of feeling was almost too much for him. He gave his hand silently to Edgar, and as the latter bowed and murmured his thanks to the general, they went out together, one of[Pg 128] the soldiers accompanying them. In spite of his Arab stoicism, the tears were running down Sidi's cheeks as they issued into the open air.

"I am not crying for joy that I am freed, brother," he said, "but with pleasure at seeing you alive. When we got to the end of that street and saw, for the first time, that you were not with us, and, looking back, could see that your horse had fallen, we gave you up for dead, and bitterly did my father reproach himself for having permitted you to share in our attack. He is among the dead, brother; I saw him fall. I had been separated from him by the rush of the French horsemen, but I saw him fighting desperately, until at last struck down. Then, almost mad, I struck wildly. I felt a heavy blow on my head, and should have fallen had not a French soldier seized my arm and dragged me across his saddle in front of him. I was dimly conscious of being handed over to the infantry, and placed with some other prisoners. I sank down, and should have bled to death had not an Arab among them bandaged my head. The fight was nearly over then, and I was brought up here."

"I can give you good news, Sidi. I went last night with the two men whom we had left behind, and searched for some hours among the dead for you and your father, and found him at last. He was insensible, but not dead. We carried him off, and the other two are with him in a grove six miles away, and I have every hope that he will recover. He has five or six wounds, but I do not think that any of them are mortal."

Sidi fairly broke down on hearing the news, and nothing further was said until they had issued from the gate. The officer was still there who had spoken to Edgar on entering.

"So you have saved your friend?" he said pleasantly, as Edgar passed. "He is lucky, for I fancy he will be the[Pg 129] only one of the Arabs who will issue out of here to-day."

"I thank you much, monsieur, for having let me pass," Edgar said gratefully. "I feared so much that I should not be allowed to enter to speak for him."

The officer nodded, and the two lads went out. They had gone but a hundred yards when Sidi said:

"I must sit down for a while, Edgar. I have eaten nothing since yesterday morning, and I have lost much blood, and all this happiness is too much for me. Don't think me very childish."

"I don't think you so at all, Sidi. It has been a fearful time, and I don't wonder that you are upset. Look, there is a quiet spot between those two huts. Do you sit down there; you can't go on as you are. In the first place, your dress is covered with blood; and in the next, you are too weak to walk. I will go into the town. There are plenty of shops close to the gate, and I will buy a burnoose that will cover you, and a change of clothes for you to make afterwards. I will get you some food and a little cordial."

Sidi shook his head.

"Nonsense, man!" Edgar went on. "This is medicine, not wine, and you must take something of the sort or you won't be fit to travel. I shall get some fellah's clothes for myself, a basket of food and other things to take out to your father, and I will hire a couple of donkeys. You are no more fit to walk six miles than you are to fly, and I feel rather shaky myself. I sha'n't be away more than half an hour."

After seeing Sidi seated in the place he had indicated, where he would not be seen by those passing on the road, Edgar at once went in through the gate. The provisions,[Pg 130] and two or three bottles of good wine, were quickly purchased, but it took him some little time getting the clothes, for had he not bargained in the usual way, it would have seemed strange. As it was, the man of whom he purchased them congratulated himself on having made the best bargain that he had done for many a day. He bought two Arab suits, and two such as were worn by peasants, and a brown burnoose for Sidi to put on at once. Then, going out with the provision-basket and the clothes in a bundle, he went to the gate again, chose a couple of donkeys from those standing there for hire, and went along the road for a short distance. Telling the donkey-boy to wait with the animals until his return, he took the basket and the burnoose, which had been made up into a separate parcel, and went to the spot where he had left Sidi, who rose to his feet as he reached him.

"I am better now, and can go on."

"You are not going on until you have made a meal anyhow," Edgar replied; "and I feel hungry myself, for I have been up a good many hours."

Sidi sat down again. The basket was opened, and Edgar produced some bread and some cold kabobs (kabobs being small pieces of meat stuck on a skewer). Sidi eat some bread and fresh fruit, but he shook his head at the meat.

"I shall do better without it," he said. "Meat is for the strong. My wound will heal all the faster without it."

He did, however, drink from a tumbler Edgar had brought with him a small quantity of wine mixed with the water.

"I regard you as my hakim, and take this as medicine because you order it."

"I feel sure that the Prophet himself would not have forbidden it when so used. You look better already, and there is a little colour in your cheek. Now, let us be off.[Pg 131] If your father has recovered consciousness, he must be in great anxiety about you."

"But I want to ask you about yourself?"

"I will tell you when we are mounted. The sooner we are off the better."

He was glad to see that, as they walked towards the donkeys, Sidi stepped out much more firmly than before. He had put on his burnoose as soon as Edgar joined him, and this concealed him almost to his feet when he had mounted.

"We are not pressed for time," Edgar said to the donkey-boy. "Go along gently and quietly."

The donkey started at the easy trot that distinguishes his species in Egypt.

"Now, Edgar," Sidi said, as soon as they were in motion, "here have you been telling me about my father, and I have been telling you about myself, but not one word as yet have you told as to how you escaped, and so saved the lives of both of us. Allah has, assuredly, sent you to be our good genius, to aid us when we are in trouble, and to risk your life for ours."

"Well, never mind about that now, Sidi. I will tell you all about it; but it is a good long story."

So saying, he narrated his adventures in detail, from the time when his horse fell with him to the moment when he entered the room where the court-martial was being held. He made the story a long one, in order to prevent his friend from talking, for he saw when he had spoken how great was his emotion. He made his narrative last until they came within a quarter of a mile of the village near which the sheik was hidden.

"Now we will get off," he said, "and send the donkeys back."[Pg 132]

He paid the amount for which he had bargained for the animals, and bestowed a tip upon the boy that made him open his eyes with delight. They turned off from the road at once, made a detour, and came down upon the clump of trees from the other side. The Arabs had seen them approaching, and welcomed Sidi with exuberant delight. To his first question, "How is my father?" they said, "He is better. He is very weak. He has spoken but once. He looked round, evidently wondering where he was, and we told him how the young Englishman, his friend, had come to us, and how we had searched for hours among the dead, and, at last, finding him, had carried him off. Then he said, 'Did you find my son?' We told him no, and that we had searched so carefully that we felt sure that he was not among the dead, but that you had gone back to the town to try and learn something about him. He shook his head a little, and then closed his eyes. He has not spoken again."

"Doubtless he feels sure, as we could not find you, that you are dead, Sidi. I have no doubt the sight of you will do him a great deal of good. I will go forward and let him know that you are here. Do not show yourself until I call you."

The sheik was lying with his eyes shut. As Edgar approached he opened them, and the lad saw he was recognized.

"Glad am I to see you conscious again, sheik," he said, bending over him.

The sheik feebly returned the pressure of his hand.

"May Allah pour his blessings upon you!" he whispered. "I am glad that I shall lie under the sands of the desert, and not be buried like a dog in a pit with others."

"I hope that you are not going to die, sheik. You are sorely weak from loss of blood, and you are wounded in[Pg 133] five places, but I think not at all that any of them are mortal."

"I care not to live," the sheik murmured. "Half my followers are dead. I mourn not for them; they, like myself, died in doing their duty and in fighting the Franks—but it is my boy, of whom I was so proud. I ought not to have taken him with me. Think you that I could wish to live, and go back to tell his mother that I took him to his death."

"He was not killed, sheik; we assured ourselves of that before we carried you away, and I found that, with twenty other Arabs and two or three hundred of the townsmen, he was taken prisoner to the citadel."

A look of pain passed across the sheik's face.

"Your news is not good; it is bad," he said, with more energy than he had hitherto shown. "It were better had he died in battle than be shot in cold blood. Think you that they will spare any whom they caught in arms against them?"

"My news is good, sheik," Edgar said calmly; "had it been otherwise I would have left you to think that he had died on the field of battle. I have reason to believe that Sidi has been released, and that you will soon see him."

For a moment the sheik's eyes expressed incredulity; then the assured tone and the calm manner of Edgar convinced him that he at least believed that it was true.

"Are you sure, are you quite sure?" he asked, in tones so low that Edgar could scarce hear him.

"I am quite sure—I would not buoy you up with false hopes. Sidi is free. He is not far off now, and will speedily be here, directly he knows that you are strong enough to see him."

For a minute the sheik's eyes closed, his lips moved, but[Pg 134] no sound came from them, but Edgar knew that he was murmuring thanks to Allah for his son's preservation. Then he looked up again.

"I am strong enough," he said; "your news has made a man of me again. Send him here."

Edgar walked away and joined Sidi.

"Be very calm and quiet," he said; "your father is very, very weak. Do not break down. He knows that you are close by, and is prepared to see you. Do not, I beg of you, agitate him; do not let him talk, or talk much yourself; be calm and restful with him."

He turned away and walked to the end of the trees, where he engaged in a short conversation with the two Arabs. Then he turned again, and went near enough to catch a sight of the sheik. Sidi was kneeling by his side, holding his hand to his heart, and a smile of happiness illuminated the drawn face of the wounded man. Satisfied that all was going on well, he joined the men.

"In the basket you will find a small cooking-pot," he said. "Pick up some of the driest sticks that you can find, so as not to make any smoke. Put some kabobs into the pot with as much water as will just cover them; then place it over the fire, and let it stew until the meat is in threads. Strain the broth off. I will give it to him, a sip at a time."

"We need not be afraid of the smoke," one of the men said. "We went down to the village to get bread and dates. A man saw that we were Arabs, and asked us for news of what was going on in Cairo. Some fugitives passed along yesterday evening, and said that the French were killing all the Moslems. We told him that it was not as bad as that, but that many had assuredly been slain. He called down maledictions upon the French, and seeing that he was a true man we said that we had a wounded[Pg 135] comrade with us, and that he was lying in the grove. He told us that he was the owner of it, and that we were welcome to use it, but prayed us not to come to him again; for if the Franks came along in search of fugitives, and happened to search the grove, and found that he had been supplying a wounded man with provisions, it might cost him his life. We told him that he need not fear, for that we would not betray him, but that, at any rate, we would not come to his shop again."

"Then make the fire immediately, Hassan; the sooner the sheik has a little nourishment, the better. If he seems strong enough to bear it, I want to carry him off to the mountains at once. It is quite possible that the French may be searching the villages round for wounded fugitives, and I would fain get him up among the hills. Sidi, too, has an ugly wound in the head, and needs a few days' rest. I think I have everything that they can want for the next two or three days, and you have a good supply of fruit. We must find some place among the rocks sheltered from the sun. When it is dark you must go down to the fountain and fill up your water-skins there."

An hour later Edgar carried the cup of broth to the sheik.

"Sidi, do you lift your father up a little—a very little. I want him to take some of this broth. It is all a question of keeping up your strength now, sheik, and I hope that you will try and drink a little."

"I, too, want to get strong," the sheik said, "I have something to live for now."

He drank a few mouthfuls, and then motioned to his son to lower his head down again.

"'Tis strange," he said, "that we three should be together again when it seemed that none of us would meet on earth."

"It is very pleasant to be together again," Edgar said[Pg 136] heartily, "and it will be more pleasant still when we are able to get about again together."

There had been but few words exchanged between father and son. To be restored to each other was sufficient, and the sheik had not even wondered as to how his son had so unexpectedly arrived. After drinking the broth he closed his eyes, and in a few minutes it was evident, by his quiet breathing, that he was asleep.

Edgar moved quietly away, beckoning to Sidi to follow him, and when he joined him at the edge of the grove, told him of the plan that he proposed.

"Do you think that he is strong enough?" Sidi asked.

"I do not think that it will do him harm, Sidi; indeed I think that if, before he goes to sleep, we lay him on that blanket that we brought him here in, we might carry him without waking him. Of course I should tell him this evening what we thought of doing. It may be that the French will make no search for the wounded. I saw proclamations signed by some of the principal sheiks and ulemas, calling upon the people to be tranquil, and announcing that Bonaparte had consented to forgive the past; but you know that did not prevent their trying those prisoners this morning, and, I doubt not, executing a large number of them. Therefore, although they may leave the lower class alone, they may seize any of their leaders they may find, and if they came upon your father, his wounds would show that he had been engaged in the fighting; and if they took him to the town many of those who saw him there might denounce him as the sheik who led his horsemen against one of their columns. Of course they may not search, but it is as well to be on the safe side, and it is better to run the slight risk that the journey might do him than to chance his being captured here."[Pg 137]

Sidi heartily agreed.

"Now, Sidi, you may as well get rid of those clothes and put on the peasant's suit I bought you. I shall do the same; then should we be caught sight of, at a distance, we should simply be taken for two fellahs who have gone up into the mountains, either to shoot game or for some other purpose, while the white clothes would excite suspicion. I am sorry now that I did not get them for Hassan and Ali, but it is likely enough that I may be able to buy such things in the village. By the way, your father said, when we were riding from the Pyramids to the town, that there were a good many old tombs up in the hills. Of course, for to-night, it would be enough if we take him a short distance up, then to-morrow we can search, and if we can find one of those tombs, it will be a safe place for him to stop in; and being cut in the solid rock, it would be pleasantly cool. There will be no fear whatever of any French soldiers coming along and entering there, and we can live quietly until he is fit to sit a horse. When you have taken off those things that you have on, you had better tear off a number of long strips for bandages. We did what we could roughly when we first carried your father off the field; but we can bandage his wounds carefully now, and yours also must want looking to badly."

When the sheik woke, after two hours' sleep, he drank some broth. His voice was louder and clearer, and it was evident that even the small quantity that he had taken before, and the quiet sleep, had refreshed him greatly.

"Now, sheik," Edgar said, "Hassan and Ali are going to bandage your wounds carefully. They say that they are both accustomed to it, and no doubt they have some experience, for wounds are common enough in your raids and forays."[Pg 138]

Edgar by this time had put on the dark-blue blouse, reaching down below the knee and girt by a belt at the waist, which forms the main article of dress of every Egyptian peasant. On his head was a brown cap of rough wool, of something of the same shape as a fez. These, and a pair of low Turkish shoes, completed his costume, underneath which he wore the European one, the trousers being rolled up above the knees, so as not to show. While the operation of dressing the wounds was going on, he went down into the village, and finding a shop where they sold such things, bought similar suits to his own for the two Arabs. When he returned, the sheik's wounds had been dressed, a blanket rolled up under his head, and he was looking altogether more comfortable. Edgar now told him his plan of carrying him off.

"It will be best," he said, "much the best. Though I have said nothing, I have wondered to-day whether the French would come along, and it has troubled me; besides, I shall gain strength faster up in the hills. Your plan is a good one. I think that I shall sleep well in the blanket. Even if I wake it will not matter; the motion will be easy, and my wounds have been well bandaged, and I have no fear of their breaking out again."

In addition to the severe sabre cut on the face, the sheik had another on the left arm. A third had struck him slantingly on the right side, as his arm was raised to strike; a musket shot had also made a deep groove on the hip. When in the village, Edgar had purchased, among other things, several sticks of kabobs, and when it became dark the two Arabs, now in their peasant dress, went down and filled the water-skins at the village well. The sheik drank off the rest of the broth, and was then carefully lifted and laid down on the blanket, which was still attached to the[Pg 139] spears. The other blanket was then placed under his head, and in half an hour his son, who was watching him, was glad to see that he was again asleep. Some more kabobs were put in the pot to stew, and when ready the broth was poured into a wine-bottle that Edgar had emptied. As soon as the moon was fairly up they started, as before, the two Arabs taking the pole at the sheik's head, Edgar those at his feet, where the weight was comparatively a light one. Sidi would have divided this with him, but Edgar laughed at the idea.

"I shall be well pleased, Sidi, if you can do the walk without needing help; the weight is really nothing. If he had been a big fleshy Englishman it would be a different thing altogether, but you Arabs are simply bone and muscle, and divided between three the weight is not worth talking about."

The blankets had been rolled up and placed across the men's shoulders, the water-skins hung by their straps on either side, and they carried the baskets, on which were also placed the bundles of clothes, between them. No stir or movement showed that the sheik was conscious of being lifted from the ground. After twenty minutes' walking they got beyond the area of cultivated ground, and were able to head directly for the hills, and two hours later they were well up among them, and Edgar and Sidi agreed that there was small chance indeed of any French parties, especially of cavalry, searching such broken and rugged ground. A spot was chosen where the ends of the spears could be laid on two flat stones high enough to keep the bottom of the hammock from touching the ground between them.

Sidi bent over his father, and, listening to his breathing, saw that he was sound asleep. His only share of the burden had been a small, shallow iron pot, in which a little charcoal[Pg 140] fire glowed brightly. A small bag of this, the most common fuel in Egypt, had been bought in the village. The broth was poured into a tin, which was hung a short distance above the fire, so that it would warm slowly. Then Edgar and Sidi, who were both completely worn out, wrapped themselves, one in his burnoose and the other in a blanket, and lay down; Hassan and Ali, who had by turns slept during the day, undertaking to keep watch by the side of the sheik, and to give him the broth as soon as he woke.

Edgar dropped off to sleep instantly; when he awoke the sun had risen. He saw that Sidi was still asleep. The hammock had been lowered to the ground, and Ali was holding the cup to the sheik's lips. Edgar saw at once that he was better, the drawn expression and the ashen shade round his lips had greatly abated, and his eyes were brighter. Living so frugal and active a life, the Arab, like the Red Indian, can bear wounds that would be fatal to a dweller in towns; and as none of the sheik's wounds were in themselves very serious, and it was loss of blood alone that had brought him to death's door, the night's rest, the nourishment that he had taken, and above all, his joy at finding his son living, had already placed him on the path to recovery.

"I am glad to see you looking much better than you did yesterday," Edgar said heartily as he came up. "I hope that you have slept well?"

"I have woke but twice, and each time took some of the broth, and straightway went off to sleep again. I did not feel my move here, and was indeed surprised on my first waking, when Ali told me that I was safe up in the hills. See, I can already lift my right hand. I shall not be your patient long."

"There is no hurry," Edgar replied. "After I have had some breakfast I shall start out to look for one of those[Pg 141] tombs that you told me of. There we shall have shelter from the heat of the sun and from the night-dews. There will be no fear of the French lighting upon us; and indeed I do not think that, now they have Cairo under their feet again, they will trouble more about the matter. They have other things to think about; and although Cairo will be quiet for a long time after this, the French will know that their merciless slaughter of the Mussulmans will excite the deepest feeling of hatred against them, and that it will be even less safe than before for small parties to move about.

"Kleber will no doubt start again with his division for Damietta. Desaix is many days' journey to the south. Probably a force will march to Suez. I heard it said by some French officers that this would probably be the next move, and Napoleon will not care to further weaken the garrison of the city by sending out search parties."

"Is Sidi's wound a bad one?"

"No, it is nothing like so severe as that which you received on the cheek. It was a downright blow, but his turban saved him. It is a pretty deep scalp wound extending down to the ear, and he lost a good deal of blood, but it was anxiety for you and the prospect of death for himself in the morning that caused it to seem more serious than it was. In three or four days he will be nearly himself again."

"And you, did you escape unhurt? We deemed you certainly dead."

"No; my horse was shot, and I at the same moment got a bullet through my arm. Beyond the loss of a little blood it was of no consequence. I ran into a house close by and sheltered there until the French column came out, and then went out in some European clothes I found there, and had no more trouble."

[Pg 142]

CHAPTER VIII.
AN EGYPTIAN TOMB.

While the Arabs were preparing breakfast, Edgar searched for a spot where the sheik could lie in shelter during the mid-day heat; for, hot as it was on the desert sands, the heat was fully as great on the bare rocks of the hills. After some search he found a spot where two ledges of rock ran parallel to each other, with a passage of some six feet between them, on each side of which they rose perpendicularly some twelve feet in height. The fissures ran nearly north and south, and therefore, except for an hour at noon, the bottom was entirely in shade.

It was within half a mile of the spot where they encamped for the night; and returning, the sheik was carried there at once, and was laid on the blanket. The spears were found to be long enough to reach across at the top. The blanket that had formed the hammock being unrolled, it formed a sort of awning that could, when the sun was high, be moved a little one way or the other, so as to keep him in the shade. Learning from the sheik in which direction the tombs that he had spoken of were situated, Edgar started with Hassan, and after half an hour's walking came upon them. They were, for the most part, square-cut holes in the face of the perpendicular rock. Some of them were only flanked by pilasters cut in the stone; others had more ornate designs. All had originally been closed by great stone slabs. These had long since been moved or broken up by treasure-seekers. The plan of most of them was similar—a short passage, terminated by a chamber of from ten to twenty feet square. Vestiges of the paintings that[Pg 143] originally covered the walls could still be seen. Choosing one of the larger tombs, Edgar aided Hassan to remove fragments of stones that projected above the dust and sand, which lay six inches deep over the floor. Well satisfied, he returned to the sheik.

"We have found a good place," he said. "The air was quite cool in there, and the sand will make a much more comfortable bed than this bare rock."

The sheik made no reply, but lay looking at him with an expression that puzzled him, and he was about to turn to Sidi to ask whether his father was worse, when the latter said, "While you have been away my son has been telling me all that you have done for him, and that it was you who saved his life as well as mine. I am weak now, I cannot say what is in my heart, it is too full for words."

"Don't say any thing about it, sheik," Edgar said earnestly. "Did you not adopt me into your tribe? Does not Sidi call me brother? Have you not sheltered me in your tents when I had nowhere else to go? Is it not natural then that I should do all in my power to repay these benefits, and to rescue you and my brother Sidi from the hands of your enemies? I deem myself most fortunate that I have been enabled to do so, and, indeed, ran but little risk in either case. It was a small thing to search for you among the dead, and to have you carried off; while, having found the disguise of a European, there was no risk of my being recognized as having fought against the French when I went to testify in favour of Sidi. Save as to my own name I had need to go but little beyond the truth. I had won Sidi's gratitude by aiding him against two ruffians. He had slain a man who was about to attack me, though that did not take place, as they supposed, at the time of the massacre of the European shopkeepers, but the main facts were true,[Pg 144] and there was no fear that in the telling of them I should get myself into trouble."

The sheik shook his head. "'Tis well to say so, my friend, and I suppose that it is the way with your people to make but little of their good actions. It was not the risk you may have run. Many men are brave, and we who charged that column of Franks, after those in front of us had been swept away by their cannon, have a right to say that we are not cowards; but you see the difference: Sidi and I thought you dead, but beyond resolving to avenge you, we did nothing. The idea that we might disguise ourselves, and, after the Franks had advanced, gone and searched the streets and found whether you were still living, never occurred to us, and I think that no Arab would have thought of it.

"But you had scarcely passed through the first danger of being discovered than you began to think of us. You learnt that many Arabs had been killed when we poured out of the city, and that others had been taken prisoners. Wounded yourself, you lose no moment in finding my two followers. All night you search among the dead for me, and carry me off to a place of safety. Then, without rest, without pause, you return to the city and begin to take measures to rescue Sidi. He was in the citadel, strongly guarded by French troops. There was but one way of succeeding. You thought of that way. You planned it all out. You invented a likely story, which was yet very close to the truth. You went into the midst of the men that you have been fighting against, and you so sustained the character that you had chosen, that none of the French officers suspected for a moment that you were aught but what you seemed, and so, listening to your pleading on his behalf, let him go free. Well did I say, the other day,[Pg 145] that though we might be beaten, I believed that you and my son would escape, for that Allah had clearly sent you to save him from danger, and that he would therefore assuredly preserve you both."

"It is Allah, who is our God as well as yours, who is to be thanked, sheik, that all our lives have been preserved," Edgar said reverently, "and that we are again united when so many have perished."

In spite of the shade of the blanket overhead, Edgar found it tremendously hot in the middle of the day, but as soon as the sun had passed west, he was able to get some hours' comfortable sleep. A short time before sunset they started again and carried the sheik to the cave. The two Arabs did this while Edgar and Sidi loitered behind pulling up the parched-up bushes that grew here and there among the rocks, and making them into faggots. As soon, therefore, as the sheik was laid down the fire was lighted, giving a cheerful air to the dark chamber. Ali and Hassan went down again and brought up the provisions, water, and bundles. The air was cool and pleasant in the tomb, and a hearty meal was made by all but the sheik, who, however, not only drank a cup of broth, but ate some dates with something like an appetite.

"Now, sheik," Edgar said, after he had put some more sticks upon the fire, "we can chat about our future plans. I have been talking with Sidi. It must be a fortnight or three weeks before you are fit to sit a horse again. It is very fortunate, by the way, that you sent your favourite horse, as well as Sidi's and mine, back by two of your followers from the Pyramids when you decided to enter the town; and that we rode other horses in that charge in Cairo. It would have been a loss, indeed, if those noble steeds of ours had been all killed."[Pg 146]

"That was one of my first thoughts when I was able to think," the sheik said. "Next to my wife, my son, and you, I love Zeila, and it would have sorely spoiled my joy that we are reunited, had she fallen in the battle. It was your advice that saved her life also."

"My idea is," Edgar went on, "that either Hassan or Ali shall go back to the town, get one of their horses, and ride to the oasis, where all your spare horses and some of your followers are."

"I have thirty men there," the sheik said. "I thought it as well not to bring all, for had misfortune happened, the women and children would have been left without protectors; but there is surely no occasion for Hassan to go yet. In three days he might be there, and be back in another three, and though I hope to mend quickly, surely I could not mount a horse in a week's time."

"That I quite see, sheik, but as your wife and the women are there also, I thought it well that he should start at once. Two or three of your men may have escaped from that fight. They would be sure to make for the oasis, and will doubtless report that all, save themselves, have been killed. Your wife will be mourning for you and Sidi as dead, and it is for that reason that I would send one of the men at once with the good news."

"How thoughtful you are, lad! No gray-beard could think of things more than you do. I had not once thought that the news might reach her; but, as you say, it may well be that two or three at least of my men may have escaped. Ali shall start to-morrow at daybreak, but when he has given his message to my wife, what next is he to do?"

"I should say, sheik, that he should bid your men be at the Great Pyramid in twenty-one days from this, and that on the following morning you will join them there at daybreak."[Pg 147]

"I may be well enough before that," the sheik said.

"That we cannot say for certain," Edgar said; "'tis best that we should name a date when we may hope that you will be fit to ride long and far again if need be. We know not what are the plans of the French, but 'tis like enough that though they may have granted pardon to the people of the city, Bonaparte will endeavour to strike some heavy blows at the Arabs. He knows how terribly they harassed him on his march here, and that wheresoever his troops may move, they will again swarm round him. He has overawed Cairo, and can safely leave a small garrison there if he marches away. And he may well seek to overawe the Arabs by making expeditions against their oases, which he can now easily do, as his cavalry are all mounted on Egyptian horses, capable of supporting thirst and making long journeys, and he may think that by striking at your camping-places, cutting down your palm-trees, and filling up your wells, he may compel you to promise to cease from all attacks upon his troops."

"He might certainly damage us greatly in that way," the sheik agreed; "but few of his horses are equal to ours. You may be sure that the tribes near Alexandria, who basely sold him horses, did not part with their best, while those the Franks took at Cairo are not accustomed to the desert, save, indeed, those of the Mamelukes, of whom there were few, for most of their horses were killed with their masters. But were they even as well mounted as we are, they might indeed reach our oases and do terrible damage, as for ourselves, we could laugh at them, for they would have to carry far heavier weights. It is not that the French soldiers are heavier than we are, but with their riding-boots, their accoutrements, their valises, and other matters, they would ride from forty to fifty pounds heavier than we should,[Pg 148] and their horses, unaccustomed to such burdens, would soon tire. Would it not be well to bid, say, four men, to come straight hither to act as a guard?"

"I think not, sheik; the fewer of us there are about here the better, and were we discovered, four men or forty would be useless. We might defend the mouth of the tomb for a short time, but even were we to beat off every attack, it would be but a matter of hours before we were forced to surrender for want of water. Hassan can start with Ali to-morrow morning, and bring the second horse back here; it will be very useful for bringing up water and provisions. And now that Hassan has his peasant dress on, he would attract little attention were he noticed riding among the hills. I will tell him to buy two more skins, larger than those we have. The four will then bring up sufficient water to last us and the horse for three days at least, so that he will only have to make an occasional journey down to the village. Indeed, there are several villages within a short distance of each other on the river bank, and by going sometimes to one and sometimes to another for food and water, he will not attract attention at all."

"So be it," the sheik said. His voice now had weakened, and, after drinking some more broth, he composed himself for sleep—an example which was speedily imitated by the others. Sidi gave Ali and Hassan the necessary instructions, and before they started, Edgar took the former apart and had a private conversation with him.

"It is possible, Ali, that the sheik's wife will, when you arrive there, want to start at once to attend him. If she does, do not try to dissuade her, it will be a great comfort to him to have her with him, and will aid his recovery. I know that she is skilful in the dressing of wounds, and will be able to cook things such as he would like, far better than[Pg 149] we could. No one can guide her here but yourself. Of course, when you are once fairly across the river, you will take off that long blue gown, and ride in your Arab dress, and she will ride with you in her own dress, until you get within a short distance of the river; beyond that, of course, you will again put the peasant's dress on; and before you start to-day get such a dress also for her, and let her slip it on over her own.

"It were best that you did not approach the ferry until it is getting dark. You would do well to bring a comrade to take the two horses back; Ayala could not use them. One frequently sees women riding on donkeys, but for a peasant woman to be mounted on a horse would be unusual. Besides, we should not know what to do with them here, and they would have to go down every day for water. If you start at noon to-day from Cairo, you will be there on the afternoon of the third day, and if you start again next morning will be here on the sixth day. I will light a fire a short distance from the front of the cave so as to act as a guide to you when you get into the rough ground. If you are not here that night I shall know that she is not coming. I shall say nothing about it to the sheik or Sidi; it is better that they should not be looking forward to it. If she did not come they might be fearing that some misadventure had happened on the journey. In any case, you understand that you are not to propose it to her, but are to remain altogether silent on the subject unless she herself insists on coming."

Hassan returned with the horse carrying the four water-skins and some provisions, including a supply of coffee, just as darkness set in; he reported that Ali had started before noon. The next six days passed quietly. Hassan went down twice with the horse for water, fresh meat,[Pg 150] fowls, and other provisions, and a supply of grain for the horse, which was stabled in the next tomb to that they occupied. The sheik gained strength, slowly indeed but steadily. At each meal he took a basin of broth prepared either from fresh meat or chicken, and to Edgar's satisfaction his hands remained cool, and there were no signs of fever. On the sixth day he was able to sit up, leaning against the wall of the chamber.

At dusk that evening Edgar strolled out, as he usually did, to enjoy the cool evening air. He told Hassan to accompany him, and they soon plucked up some withered and dead bushes among those growing between the rocks. These were piled some twenty yards on one side of the entrance to the tomb. Then Hassan went into the chamber, picked up a piece of glowing charcoal out of the fire with which to light his pipe, placed it on the bowl, and after taking two or three draws, went out into the air. The piece of charcoal was placed among some dried leaves and twigs and blown until a flame shot up. Then some dried sticks, which had been collected for the purpose, were placed carefully on this, and the fire soon burned up.

"That will do, Hassan," Edgar said. "I don't want a big blaze that can be seen a long distance away. You sit here and feed it carefully, so as to keep up the flame not more than a foot or two in height."

Hassan obeyed the orders. Ali had told him on leaving that he might possibly return with the sheik's wife, but that he was not to mention it to Sidi or the sheik himself. Edgar walked up and down near the fire. An hour later he heard voices below, and gave an exclamation of pleasure, and two or three minutes later Ali and Ayala appeared within the circle of light, the former leading the horse on which she was sitting.[Pg 151]

"How is he?" she exclaimed, as she slipped from the saddle, and hurried forward to meet Edgar.

"He is getting on very well; he is gaining strength, and has had no fever. I will lead you to him. Hassan, you can put out that fire now, but bring some of the brands into the tomb; they will make a cheerful blaze. Perhaps you had better do that before we go in. If the sheik asks why you do it, say it is by my orders, and that I thought it would be more cheerful than the glow of the charcoal.

"He will not be a minute, Ayala, and were you to go in now you would scarce see him or he you."

With the patient obedience of Arab women she stopped at once.

"Ali has told me," she said, turning to him, "how much you have done for us, and how you saved the lives of both my husband and son."

"I was fortunate in being able to do so," he replied, "and that without the slightest risk to myself." Then changing the subject, he went on, "I thought that you would wish to come."

"Certainly I should," she said. "My place is by his side. And is Sidi well also? And you—Ali said that you also were wounded?"

"Mine was a trifling business," he said, "and Sidi's not much worse. We both suffered from loss of blood, which perhaps is a good thing, as we have had no fever, and though our wounds are somewhat sore, we have almost ceased to think of them. There, I can see by the light that the fire is burning up inside. Now we will go in. Keep a little way behind me; it would startle him were you to go in suddenly."

He walked into the tomb.

"Sheik," he said, "here is a friend come to see you."[Pg 152]

"A friend!" the sheik repeated in surprise. "Who is it?"

"She has ridden all the way from the oasis, sheik. I was sure she would come. She is your wife!" and Ayala ran forward and threw herself upon her knees by the side of the sheik. Edgar went out with Hassan, and left them and Sidi together.

Ayala now took the entire charge of the sheik. Edgar went down frequently to one or other of the villages on the river bank, partly for change and exercise, partly to learn what he was doing at Cairo. He heard that, under the direction of French engineers, the greater portion of the population of Cairo were employed in building forts on elevated positions round the town, where the guns would completely dominate the city, that it was said that the Sultan had declared war with France, and that an army from Syria had advanced and had established itself at a fort in the desert half-way between the frontier of Syria and Egypt.

"I made sure," he said, after talking the news over with the shiek and Sidi, "that the Sultan would be driven to declare war against the French. It would have been impossible for him to have allowed the French permanently to establish themselves as masters of his province of Egypt. Even if he himself had been willing to suffer it, the whole Moslem population would have risen against him. No doubt the news of the destruction of the French fleet decided him to take this step. Now that no more reinforcements can reach them here, he may well consider that his army is capable of annihilating them. The Turks are good soldiers— that is to say, they have always shown themselves capable of fighting desperately when well led.

"Unfortunately, that is not likely to be the case. The pashas have no experience in war, while the French have the best generals in Europe. The Turks are badly disciplined,[Pg 153] while the French are veteran soldiers with perfect confidence in themselves and in their leaders. Still, in any case, this will greatly increase Napoleon's difficulties; he will have to send the greater portion of his army to meet the Turks, at the same time will have to keep Egypt in subjection. The British government will be blind if they do not see that the opportunity is a grand one for striking a blow at the French, and I should think that they would ere long send an army out here, though they may not do so unless they see that the Turks alone can do nothing against them."

Later Edgar heard that columns of French cavalry had gone out into the desert and had driven away the bodies of Arabs that had assembled again a few miles off the Nile. They had, however, been unable to gain any advantages over them, as the Arabs had always fallen back upon their approach, and the French, finding pursuit useless, had returned to the city. Once or twice a few Arabs had been killed when the cavalry had been so closely followed by a battery of artillery that the Arabs were unaware that the French had guns with them, and had therefore contented themselves with keeping beyond carbine shot, their first intimation of their presence having been when the cavalry rode rapidly to the right and left, leaving the guns exposed.

Even then their loss had been slight, for the slight undulations of the desert afforded shelter, and riding at full speed along some hollow they were almost out of range before the artillery could limber up after the first discharge of their guns and advance to a position whence they could see their flying foes.

By the end of the three weeks the sheik was strong enough to walk up and down for some time in front of the[Pg 154] tomb, and he declared himself quite able to make the journey. Edgar had some doubt on the subject, but he knew that the Arabs were so thoroughly at home on their horses that they scarcely felt the slightest inconvenience after the longest day's journey, and Zeila's pace was so easy and smooth that he hoped the chief might not suffer from it.

At two o'clock on the morning of the day when the band would be awaiting them at the Pyramids the party started. All, save the sheik, were in their peasant disguises. He was in his Arab dress, disdaining, however great the occasion, to put on the dress of a peasant. He wore, however, a dark burnoose which completely covered his figure. Edgar and Sidi had, the day before, carefully examined the face of the hill, and had found a track by which peasants drove up their goats to pasture among the hills at the time when the shrubs were sufficiently fresh and green for them to browse. The chief mounted the horse with an exclamation of pleasure at finding himself again in the saddle. The two lads led the way a pace or two in front of the horse. Ayala walked by the side of her husband. Hassan and Ali followed behind with the second horse.

The descent required great care. Although Sidi carried a torch, it took them upwards of an hour to get to the foot of the hills. When on the level ground Ayala was assisted to mount Ali's horse, and they went more briskly along. There was, however, no occasion for haste, for the ferry was but four miles away, and the boat would not cross until dawn. Ali, however, had gone down on the previous day and had bargained with the ferryman to be ready, as soon as it was light, to take over a party who had a long journey to make. Dawn was just breaking as they reached the banks of the river. A few moments later the ferryman arrived. He looked surprised at seeing an Arab with four[Pg 155] peasants, but made no remark; he was to be well paid for getting up two hours earlier than usual, and it was no business of his whether an Arab crossed or not. The sheik, his wife, and the two lads first got on board, then Ali and Hassan led the horses and stood by their side as the boat pushed out from the shore. In ten minutes they were across. As soon as they landed, the sheik and Ayala mounted and set off at an amble—a pace between a walk and a trot, the two legs on each side moving together. This pace is in general use among horses in Egypt and Turkey, and is as comfortable and easy as a walk.

The sun had risen half an hour when they neared the Pyramid. As soon as they were seen a party of thirty horsemen dashed out and rode towards them at full gallop, brandishing their spears or guns over their heads, and as they approached uttering shouts of welcome. Sidi and the two Arabs had, like Ayala, taken off their peasant smocks and caps, and had wound their turbans round their heads as soon as they had landed. To them the disguise was very repugnant, for the Arabs looked down with supreme contempt upon the fellah population of Egypt. Edgar had followed their example, not from any dislike to the dress, but because he thought that the sheik would prefer rejoining his followers, with the whole party dressed in Arab costume.

There was no doubting the genuineness of the welcome that the Beni Ouafy gave their chief. Until Ali had arrived with news of their escape, they, like his wife, had deemed that he and his son had fallen, and there was deep emotion in their faces as they circled round and round the little party, discharging their guns, tossing their spears in the air, catching them as they fell, and shouting their welcome. The sheik and those with him fired off their guns as the party[Pg 156]came up, and the sheik, in spite of his efforts to maintain the impassive expression of his face, was evidently much moved. As soon as the demonstration ceased he started again without a word. The others followed his example, and they rode in a body until they reached the Pyramids, when he dismounted. In an instant all were off their horses and gathered round him.

"My brothers," he said, "I thank you for my welcome. It gladdens my heart to be among you again, but I cannot forget that many saddles have been emptied, that many of our women are widows and their children fatherless. I rode away with fifty men. I hear that but ten, and they all wounded, returned to your tents. Two, Ali and Hassan, remained with the horses; the rest met their death with their face to the foe, dying as a Moslem should do in defence of his faith and his country. But the loss to us is a grievous one; half of our fighting strength is gone. You have heard from Ali that had it not been for this brave young friend, whom you regard as one of yourselves, since he is my son's adopted brother, both I and my son would have died. Later I will tell you how he sought for and carried me senseless from among the dead upon the field of battle, and how he ventured into the council of the Franks and by stratagem persuaded them to free my son, who was one of the Arab prisoners.

"It will be a tale to tell your children how this English lad, himself wounded, saved the lives of the sheik of your tribe and his son. But this is no time for telling it to you in full now. See, there is a great dust rising by the river; it is probably the cavalry of the Franks, with perhaps some guns. They are far away yet, but it will not be long before they are here. I have resolved to journey quietly back to our home. I feel that it will be some time ere I shall be[Pg 157] fit to ride fast and far. My wife will, of course, accompany me. I will take Ali and Hassan and two others. We shall travel quietly and slowly, and shall keep well out from the river, so as to run no risk of falling in with any fresh party. The rest of you will ride back to fetch the women and children, with the camels and other animals, and to warn my brother that bodies of French cavalry are moving about, devastating the oases, cutting down palm-trees, and filling up wells. I should advise him, for the sake of the tribe, to hasten to make his submission, which, as he did not take part in the rising in Cairo, he may well be able to do, though they will perhaps send him into that town, and hold him as a hostage for his people. Now bring out the horses."

Zeila was first brought up, and her delight was as great as that of the sheik at the meeting, but there was no time for prolonged endearments. After a few loving words to the horse the sheik mounted. Ayala, who was to ride behind him, was lifted to her seat, Ali and Hassan, with two men the sheik picked out, sprang into their saddles, and the party started north. Then Sidi and Edgar mounted their own steeds and set out with the rest towards the south-west. By this time the French were within a mile of them, and it could be made out that they were a body of some fifteen hundred cavalry, who were, as far as could be seen, unaccompanied by guns.

"'Tis probable that they are going a long distance," Edgar said, "and that the guns would much delay them, for it is hard work indeed dragging them over the sands."

The French had already experienced that they had no chance of overtaking the Arabs, and the cavalry accordingly paid no attention to so small a party, but continued their journey at a trot. After riding for four or five miles they[Pg 158] were left far behind by the tribesmen, but the dust-cloud showed their position.

"They are coming exactly the way that we are," Sidi said, looking back; "it may be that they are bound for my uncle's oasis."

"It would be as well to find that out, Sidi. Do you give me two of your best mounted men and then ride straight on with the others. We will remain here till they approach, and then ride on for another eight or ten miles, still keeping them in sight. They will assuredly camp at the wells of Orab if they are making for the oasis. These are about twenty miles from the Nile, and they will go no further to-day, for it is as much again before they come to another well. When we have with certainty made out that they are making for the wells of Orab, we will follow you at full speed, but do not wait for us, and, save to give your horses a drink, do not draw rein till you reach your people and deliver your father's message. I don't suppose that I shall overtake you before you get there, but I shall not be long after you, and my report may decide him what he had best do."

Sidi at once picked out two men who were, he knew, among the best mounted of the tribe, and told them to remain with Edgar and act under his orders. Then at a much more rapid pace than before he pursued his journey. Edgar and his men dismounted, sitting down on the sands until the French were again within a mile of them, then they cantered on ahead. The French had followed so exactly the line along which the party had ridden that Edgar felt quite convinced that they were making for the wells. However, he kept at the same distance ahead of them until the Arabs told him that they were now within five miles of the water.[Pg 159]

"Then we will go on," he said. "It is certain now that they are going there, and as you say there are no camping grounds within many miles of the wells, I think it is certain that they are bound for the oasis of the Beni Ouafy."

They now rode at full speed to the wells. Here for a quarter of an hour they halted, refilled their water-skins, gave the horses a drink and a handful of dried dates, eat a few themselves, and then started on their long ride. Had not Edgar had perfect confidence in the Arabs' knowledge of the country he would have felt uneasy, as hour after hour they rode across wastes of sand without, so far as he could see, any landmark whatever to guide their course. He remarked this to them. Both smiled.

"You Franks can make your way over the sea when there is nothing whatever to guide you," one of the men said; "it would be strange if we could not do the same over the land that we have traversed many times before."

"At sea they have a compass with a needle that points always to the north, so that they know in what direction they are going."

"We have the sun," one of the Arabs answered; "but even without that we could find our way, and do so even on the darkest night. The horses know the way as well as we do. When they have once journeyed over a track they never forget it, and even did they swerve a little it would not matter, for they can smell water miles away, and would always, if unguided, make for it."

At ten in the evening Edgar rode into the Bedouins' encampment, having passed over eighty miles since leaving the Pyramid. Sidi's party had arrived there half an hour earlier, and he found that his friend was now in the tent of the sheik. Edgar went there at once, and Sidi introduced him to his uncle, who was some years older than his father.[Pg 160]

"I am rejoiced to see you," the sheik said gravely. "I heard how you had before befriended Sidi, and the messenger who arrived here told us how you had saved the lives of my brother and nephew, and I wanted to see your face.

"Truly you are young, indeed, to have done such wonderful deeds, and to have so much wisdom, as well as courage. Sidi tells me that some fifteen hundred of the Frankish cavalry are riding hither."

"I think that there can be no doubt of it," Edgar replied. "Certainly they have gone to the wells of Orab. We left them but a short distance from it. They will camp there to-night. They may, for aught I know, change their direction to-morrow, but in any case it will be three days before they are here. They would not journey more than twenty miles a day."

"They are too strong for us to fight," the sheik said. "I was at the battle near Cairo, though, as we arrived late, and did not know at what point my brother's men were gathered, I did not join them, but when all was over rode off with Mourad and his Mamelukes. I can put but six hundred horsemen in the field at short notice; though, had I a week's time, I could call up another four hundred, who are encamped at some wells far away to the west. But even were they here I could not venture to engage in open fight with fifteen hundred Franks.

"I have given orders that at daybreak the tents shall be struck, and all the women and children, with the baggage and as many bunches of dates as the camels can carry, shall start at once for the wells of Azim, seventy miles away. It is a long journey, and there is no water by the way, so there is no fear of the French following. There are already a hundred of my tents there, for although this oasis is a large one, being nigh eight miles long and two wide, it is not[Pg 161] large enough for the whole of my people. The one at Azim is smaller, but it will support us for a time; and there is an abundance of water for the camels, which number twelve hundred, and the sheep and goats, of which there are about two thousand. A hundred of my men will ride with them as a guard, and to drive the animals.

"With the others I shall, if the Franks do damage here, harass them on their retreat, and by dashing among them at night will do them such harm that they may regret the day that they came hither. Sidi will start in the morning with the women and camels of his father's branch of the tribe. I shall send in the morning two horsemen with a white flag to meet the Franks, and to tell them, in my name, that none of my followers have aught to do with the affair in Cairo, and that I desire to live in peace with them. Upon their return I shall know what to do."

An Arab woman now brought in refreshments, consisting of a pillau and sherbet, after which coffee was handed round, and Sidi and Edgar threw themselves down on heaps of blankets for a few hours' sleep. As soon as day broke, the encampment was a scene of bustle and confusion. The women pulled down the tents, rolled up the blankets composing them, and fastened the poles in bundles. Numbers of men scattered to cut bunches of dates, and of these huge piles were collected. Three hours later the camels were brought up, and men and women alike employed in loading them. This occupied over an hour. As soon as it was completed, the women and children took their places on the top of the burdens, and the camels at once filed off, three abreast.

A party with the sheep, goats, and spare horses had started as soon as it was light. The rest of the escort scattered themselves along on each side of the long column[Pg 162] of camels. Sidi's party left at the same hour. The sheik up to that time had been engaged in superintending the arrangements for shifting camp, and asked Sidi and Edgar to stop behind for an hour or two in order that he might hear a full account of the events at Cairo. When the story was finished they partook of a meal, and then, after saying adieu, mounted and rode off, and in an hour's time overtook the slow-moving cavalcade. Six days' travel took them to their old camping-ground, where the sheik, with his little party, had arrived three days previously.

CHAPTER IX.
SIR SIDNEY SMITH.

The first intimation that Napoleon received that the Sultan had declared war with France, was the news that an army from Syria had advanced and established itself at a fort in the desert half-way between the frontier of that country and Egypt. He had, in the interval, endeavoured to make himself familiar with the country. Forts had been erected all round Cairo on heights dominating the town, so that a comparatively small force could overawe the population. He himself paid two visits to Suez. Desaix had pushed the Mamelukes still farther into Upper Egypt; a division had established the French authority at Damietta and Rosetta, and every arrangement was made by which the main body of the army could move away with a fair hope that Egypt would remain quiet during its absence.

It was now the beginning of December. During the journey down to the coast Edgar had thought seriously[Pg 163] of his position. It seemed to him that, although finally the French would have to evacuate Egypt, a long time might elapse before this took place, and he finally came to the resolution to attempt to escape. He was doing neither himself nor his father any good by remaining. He had already witnessed a great battle by land, and one by sea, and he thought, by returning home and rejoining his father, he would be better employed in acquiring commercial knowledge in a business in London than in remaining in Egypt. Accordingly, on the day after his arrival at the oasis he mounted and rode into Alexandria, and entered his father's place of business for the first time since the French had landed. Muller did not recognize him as he entered, owing to his Arab dress and coloured skin. There were two native clerks present, and Edgar went up to him, and said in a low voice:

"I want to talk with you, Mr. Muller." The latter started slightly on hearing the voice, but only requested him in Arabic to follow him into the inner office, then he closed the door.

"My dear Edgar," he said, "I am delighted to see you. I have been in great uneasiness about you. I had no doubt that you were with that Bedouin chief, but whether he had taken part against the French, or remained quiet, I knew not, and have been for a long time expecting to hear from you."

Edgar gave him a brief sketch of what he had been doing since he had been away, and then said, "I am desirous of making my way to England. Of course it will be impossible to go direct, but if I could get to Italy, I might get a ship home from there."

"That would not be difficult. No large Italian vessels come in here, but small ones do so not infrequently. They generally bring spirits, wines, and other goods that com[Pg 164]mand a ready sale here, and they make a considerable profit on their trading. No doubt you could obtain a passage in one of these."

"And how goes on business, Mr. Muller?" Edgar asked after the question of the passage had been discussed for some time.

"We have been pretty busy ever since the French arrived. Many of the transports and store ships received damage on their voyage. We have had a fair share of the work. Before you go I will draw up a short statement of what we have done, for your father. I am on very good terms with the French general and his staff. I represented to them that your father had, on seeing the approach of their fleet, determined to abandon his business altogether and leave the country, and that having saved a considerable sum during my service with him, I was able to purchase from him the heavy goods that he could not take away with him, and arranged to conduct the business on my own account. I may tell you what perhaps you did not know, that, before leaving, your father executed a deed of partnership with me, by which he gave me a fourth share in the business, and moreover arranged that I was to receive half the profit of it during the French occupation. On his return it was arranged that the business should be conducted under the name of Blagrove, Son, & Muller."

"I am glad to hear it, Mr. Muller. My father indeed mentioned to me, some months before he left, that he intended to take you into partnership, and that possibly he should, after a time, leave me here with you and should fix himself in London and carry on the business of the firm there, so the French invasion has only hastened it on. Of course I have my European clothes here, and though I fancy I have grown a couple of inches in the last five[Pg 165] months, I daresay they will do very well for me. The best plan will be to take the passage for me as a French lad, the son of a trader in Cairo, who, in view of the late events there, his father is sending home."

"I will look at my sailing lists," Mr. Muller said, "and will see if any Italian craft is intending to sail in the next day or two."

He left the room, and returned in two or three minutes.

"There is one bound for Naples. She will sail on Saturday, so there are four days to make your preparations."

"That will do well," Edgar said; "on Friday evening I will be here."

He had, on the previous evening, acquainted the sheik and his son of his intention. Both had expressed deep regret, but acknowledged that his arguments in favour of the plan he proposed were so strong that they could urge nothing against them. On the Friday afternoon the sheik and Sidi both rode down to Alexandria with him. The former returned that evening to his camp, one of his followers taking Edgar's horse, which they promised to keep for him until his return, as he assured them that it would be next to impossible to get a passage for it to England, and that even could he do so it might die during the voyage, and moreover that it would be useless to him in London. Sidi slept at the house, and accompanied him on board on the following morning.

The Italian craft was a brig of about a hundred and fifty tons burden, but as Edgar was the only passenger the accommodation was ample. A few minutes after he stepped on board the crew began to get up the anchor, and as soon as this was done, Mr. Muller and Sidi said good-bye and returned to shore. Edgar had, on coming on board, spoken a few words to the captain, who was glad to find that his[Pg 166] passenger spoke Italian fluently. The wind was very light, and the brig made but little progress, and five days after sailing was still a hundred miles south of the Italian coast. Edgar, however, greatly enjoyed the time. He was in no particular hurry, and the comparatively cool air and the fresh green of the sea was delightful to him after the dry heat and sandy waste of Egypt.

On the sixth day a vessel-of-war was seen in the west. The captain felt no uneasiness; coming from Alexandria, a French vessel would regard him as a friend, while a British ship would certainly not interfere with an Italian trader, for the court of Naples was most friendly, and a portion at least of the British fleet were off the town. The ship-of-war was bringing up the breeze with her, and came along fast, and ere long the captain was able to declare that she was British. As she approached they found that she was the *Tigre*, an eighty-gun ship captured some time before from the French. When she came near she fired a gun across the bows of the brig, which at once lowered her sails. The man-of-war was thrown up into the wind as she approached, and a voice shouted in French, "What ship is that, and where from?"

"He wants to know your name and where from," Edgar translated, and the captain shouted back, "the *Annetta*, bound from Alexandria to Naples."

"Send a boat alongside with your captain," was the order from the *Tigre*.

"Shall I go with you, captain, to translate," Edgar volunteered.

The captain gladly assented, and the boat was at once lowered, and they were rowed to the *Tigre*. On ascending the deck they were taken to the captain. The latter glanced at Edgar and said, "Why, surely you are English?"[Pg 167]

"I am, sir. My father was a merchant at Alexandria. I was away at the time the French arrived, and was left behind, and have been with a party of Arabs ever since."

"Can you speak Arabic?"

"Yes, sir."

"Any other languages?"

"French and Italian, sir. It was for that reason that I came on board with the captain to interpret for him."

"Where are you going now?"

"I was going to Naples first, in order to take a passage home from there."

"Ah! What have they got on board?"

"Little enough, sir. They came across with spirits and wine and other cargo. The man is a small trader and part owner of the ship."

"Tell him if he carries stores again to Alexandria his ship will be seized as a prize by the first ship-of-war that comes across her. By carrying them to Alexandria he is aiding the French. Now about yourself. What are you going home for?"

"To join my father in England."

"What are you going to do there?"

"I believe that I shall go into an office, sir, till my father can return to Egypt again."

"You speak these three languages well."

"Yes, sir; well enough to pass as a native."

"Have you been doing any fighting ashore?"

"Not much fighting, sir,—the Arabs could not stand against the French; but I have seen a good deal. I saw the battle of the Pyramids, the sea fight in Aboukir Bay, and the street fighting in Cairo."

"Well, with your knowledge of languages you ought to be able to do better than go into a London office. You[Pg 168] might be very useful to me, and if you like to go with me to Constantinople, where I am bound, I will give you a midshipman's rating. You may have an opportunity of seeing some more service, and when this affair is over you could, of course, leave the navy if you thought fit and rejoin your father. What do you say? I will give you five minutes to think it over."

It required less time than this for Edgar to take his resolution. He had no fancy whatever for work in a London office, and the prospect of serving on board ship, the chance of seeing Constantinople and other places, and possibly of active service against the French, was vastly more pleasant. Before the end of that time he went up to the captain, touched his hat, and said that he thankfully accepted his offer.

"Very well, then, that is settled," the officer said kindly. "I will give you ten minutes to row back to the brig and return with your clothes."

In ten minutes Edgar was on board again, having explained to the astonished captain that he was going as interpreter on board the British ship. As soon as he stepped on deck again orders were shouted, the sails trimmed, and the *Tigre* proceeded on her way. An officer came up to Edgar.

"What is your name, sir?"

"Edgar Blagrove, sir."

"I remember the name," the officer said. "I put into Alexandria some ten months ago to get some repairs done, and I remember that your father undertook them." He beckoned to a lad of about the same age as Edgar. "Mr. Wilkinson," he said, "you may take this young gentleman, Mr. Blagrove, down to the cockpit and introduce him to your messmates. He is entered on board the ship as a midshipman by Sir Sidney Smith's orders."[Pg 169]

The midshipman took him below without a word. There were two other lads in the cabin.

"Allow me," Edgar's guide said with a theatrical flourish of the hand, "to introduce to you Mr. Blagrove, a fellow midshipman and messmate."

"Really, Wilkinson, one never knows whether you are in earnest or playing the fool," growled one of the others, who was a master's mate some nineteen years old.

"On the present occasion I am in earnest, Mr. Condor," Wilkinson replied.

"Where did he spring from?"

"He has just come on board from that little brig that we made lie to just now."

"I come from Alexandria," Edgar said quietly.

"From Alexandria!" Condor repeated in surprise, for he had not been on deck when the Italian captain had answered the hail.

"I was accidentally left behind when most of the English inhabitants left when the French ships came in sight."

"What did they do to you? Have you been in prison ever since?"

"Fortunately they never laid hands on me. A sheik of one of the Arab tribes was a friend of mine, and I have been staying with him ever since."

"How did you make them understand what you wanted?"

"I can talk Arabic as well as I can English," Edgar replied.

"Still you must have felt it awfully slow stopping at an Arab camp all this time."

"It has not been by any means slow. The tribe harassed the French on their march. We were present at the battle of the Pyramids, though we did not take any active part in it; for when the Mamelukes were defeated the Arabs knew[Pg 170] that alone they had no chance of success. Then we came down to the place where they generally encamp, some twelve miles from Alexandria, and I had the good luck to see Nelson's fleet destroy the French in Aboukir Bay."

"That was luck!" Wilkinson said warmly. "I would have given anything to have been in that fight."

"You are taking late to the sea," the midshipman who had not yet spoken remarked.

"I have no intention of taking to the sea for good," Edgar replied. "My father has one of the largest businesses in Alexandria, and as soon as the French leave Egypt I shall go back there. Sir Sidney Smith asked me to come, as I talk French and Italian as well as Arabic, and he thought that I should be useful to him as an interpreter, and said he would rate me as a midshipman. I was very glad to accept, as I should have nothing particular to do if I had gone home, and I thought that it would be far more pleasant to have two or three years of active service."

"Have you been in England?" Wilkinson asked.

"Yes, I was there nearly three years, and only returned a few months before the French landed."

"Well, it seems a rum start," Condor said, "but I suppose Sir Sidney knows what he is doing."

"I should imagine he did," Edgar said quietly. "Possibly, if you like to question him he will be good enough to explain the matter to your satisfaction."

"Look here, youngster!" Condor growled. "You have come in here as a midshipman, and let me tell you that whether a fellow is an interpreter or not we don't allow cheek here."

"But you allow rudeness, eh?" Edgar said quietly. "I am new to ship's manners, but at school, anyhow, a fellow was just as likely to get thrashed for rudeness as he was for cheek."[Pg 171]

"Come, Condor," Wilkinson said, as the master's mate sprang to his feet, "you won't do yourself any good by quarrelling with a fellow who has just come on board. He has certainly said nothing offensive to you. Moreover, it is quite possible that the captain may want to ask him questions about Egypt, and if he had any marks on the face you may be pretty sure you would get such a wigging that you would never want another, and possibly you might never have a chance of getting one."

"Very well," Condor said, sitting down again, "you are safe for a day or two; but mind, the first time I get an opportunity I will give you the soundest thrashing that you ever had."

"I am sorry that it must be postponed," Edgar said quietly, "but I daresay it will keep."

"Come on deck, Blagrove," Wilkinson said, putting his arm into that of Edgar. "He is an ill-tempered brute," he went on as soon as they had left the cockpit. "He only passed his examination a week before we sailed, and we all heartily wish that he had failed. He is a regular bully, and as none of us are older than I am he has pretty well his own way, for he is a strong chap, and, as I heard from a fellow who sailed with him, knows how to use his fists, and none of us would have any chance with him. It is a great nuisance, for we should all be very pleasant together if it were not for him. However, I don't expect he will dare touch you, for the captain may, at any time, want you to put questions to craft he may overhaul, and Condor would certainly get it hot if he found out that he had been interfering with you."

Edgar smiled.

"I can assure you that I do not want the captain's assistance in the matter. Boxing is a branch of my educa[Pg 172]tion which has not been neglected, and I fancy that Mr. Condor will not find that he has it all his own way."

"Well, if you could lick him we should all regard you as a benefactor, Blagrove; but I am afraid you will find him a great deal too strong and heavy for you."

"Well, we shall see, as he says, on the first opportunity. I don't think that I am at all a quarrelsome chap, but I am certainly not going to put up with being bullied by a fellow like that."

At this moment the boatswain came up. "Mr. Blagrove," he said, "I have the first lieutenant's orders to take you to the tailor to be measured for your uniform—an undress suit, he said. The tailor can manage that, but you will have to get the rest of your kit later on."

"You will find me on deck, Blagrove," Wilkinson said, as Edgar followed the boatswain, who led the way to the lower deck, where, by the light of a couple of lanterns, two or three tailors were at work.

"Hall, the first lieutenant's orders are that you are to measure this young gentleman for a midshipman's undress uniform, and you are to put everything else by and push it forward."

"Very well," the man replied. "It makes no odds to me what I does first. I doubt whether the first lieutenant will be pleased to-morrow; he tore his trousers yesterday, and sent them down to me to be mended."

"Well, one of your hands can finish that," the boatswain said. "Anyhow, you have got to do this suit, or you will hear of it."

Edgar was measured for his uniform by the head tailor, who was a cockney who had been carried off by the press-gang. It was soon found that he was of no use as a sailor, but as he was by trade a tailor he was given a rating below,[Pg 173] and it was not long before he gave such satisfaction that he was made chief of the little party employed on that work.

Returning on deck Edgar rejoined Wilkinson, and was introduced by him to several other midshipmen, who were all predisposed to like him, as Wilkinson had informed them of his little encounter with Condor, and of his readiness to fight the bully of the mess. This was considered, however, a sign of pluck rather than wisdom, and one of them expressed the general sentiment when he said, "You see he has been brought up among these Egyptian chaps, who have no idea whatever of fighting. He may have licked some of them easily, and that may have made him think he can fight; he will find the difference when he stands up against a fellow like Condor."

The first lieutenant presently sent for Edgar to come to the quarter-deck.

"I quite understand, Mr. Blagrove, that although you are given a midshipman's rating, it is really as an interpreter that Sir Sidney Smith has engaged you. Would you wish to perform midshipman's duties also? I have asked him what are his wishes in the matter, and he left it entirely with you, saying that the very nominal pay of a midshipman was really no remuneration for the services of a gentleman capable of interpreting in three or four languages, but that as the rules of the service made no provision for the engagement of an interpreter, except under special circumstances, and as you said that you did not think it likely you should make the sea your profession, you might not care to undertake midshipman's duties in addition to those of interpreter."

"Thank you, sir; but I should certainly wish to learn my duties as midshipman, and to take my share in all work. My duties as interpreter must be generally very light, and I should find the time hang heavily on my hands if I[Pg 174] had nothing else to do. I hope, therefore, sir, that you will put me to work, and have me taught my duty just as if I had joined in the regular way."

"Very well, Mr. Blagrove, I think that you are right. I will put you in the starboard watch. I am sure that Mr. Bonnor, the third lieutenant, will be glad to keep a special eye on you. Do you understand anything about handling a boat?"

"Yes, sir. I have been accustomed to sailing, rowing, and steering as long as I can remember."

"That is something gained at any rate. Do you know the names of the various ropes and sheets?"

"I do in a vessel of ordinary size, sir. I was so often on board craft that were in my father's hands for repair that I learned a good deal about them, and at any rate can trust myself to go aloft."

"Well, Mr. Wilkinson is in your watch, and as I put you in his charge to start with, I will tell him to act as your instructor in these matters. Please ask him to step here.

"Mr. Wilkinson," he went on, as the midshipman came up, "I shall be obliged if you will do what you can to assist Mr. Blagrove in learning his duties. He has been knocking about among boats and merchant craft since his childhood, and already knows a good deal about them; but naturally there is much to learn in a ship like this. You will, of course, keep your watches as usual at night, but I shall request Mr. Bonnor to release you from all other duties for the present, in order that you may assist Mr. Blagrove in learning the names and uses of all the ropes, and the ordinary routine of his duty. He will, of course, attend the master's class in navigation. There will be no occasion for him to go through the whole routine of a freshly-joined lad in other respects; but he must learn[Pg 175]cutlass and musketry drill from the master-at-arms, and to splice and make ordinary knots from the boatswain's mate. Thank you, that will do for the present."

Lieutenant Bonnor came up to Wilkinson a few minutes later, and told him that he was to consider himself relieved from all general duties at present.

"I hope you won't find this a nuisance, Wilkinson," Edgar said.

"Not at all," the other laughed; "quite the contrary. It gets one off of all sorts of disagreeable routine work, and as you know something about it to begin with, I have no doubt that you will soon pick up your work. A lot of the things that one has to learn when one first joins are not of much use afterwards, and may not have to be done once a year. However, I can lend you books, and if you really want to pick up all the words of command you can study them when you have nothing else to do; and I can tell you there are plenty of times when one is rather glad to have something to amuse one; when one is running with a light wind aft, like this, for instance, we may go on for days without having to touch a sail. Well, we will begin at once. We won't go aloft till you have got your togs; a fellow going aloft in landsmen's clothes always looks rather a duffer. Now, let us see what you know about things."

As the names of the halliards, sheets, and tacks are the same in any square-rigged vessel, Edgar answered all questions readily, and it was only the precise position assigned to each on deck that he had to learn, so that, even on the darkest night, he could at once lay hands on them without hesitation; and in the course of a couple of days he knew these as well as his instructor. On the third morning he put on his midshipman's clothes for the first time.

"You are a great deal stronger fellow than I should have[Pg 176] taken you for," Wilkinson said, as he watched him dressing. "You have a tremendous lot of muscle on the shoulders and arms, and on the back too."

"I took a lot of exercise when I was at school in England," Edgar replied, "and I have been accustomed to riding ever since I was a boy, and for the last five months have almost lived in the saddle. I have done a good deal of rowing too, for I have had the use of a boat as long as I can remember. Of course, I have done a lot of bathing and swimming— you see, the water is so warm that one can stay in it for a long time, and one can bathe all the year round. I cannot even remember being taught to swim, I suppose it came naturally to me. I am sure that my father would never have let me go out in boats as I used to do if he had not known that I was as much at home in the water as out of it."

"Now we will go aloft," Wilkinson said.

Edgar ran up almost as quickly as his companion. He had not only been accustomed to ships in the port of Alexandria, but on the voyage to England and back he had spent much of his time aloft, the captains being friends of his father, and allowing him to do as he liked, as soon as they saw that he was perfectly capable of taking care of himself.

"This is not the first time that you have been aloft, sir," one of the top-men said, as he followed Wilkinson's example, instead of going up through the lubber's hole.

"It is the first time that I have ever gone up the mast of a man-of-war," Edgar replied; "but everything is so big and solid here, that it seems easy after being accustomed to smaller craft. It is a wonderful spread of sail, Wilkinson, after having been on board nothing bigger than a brig. I used to help reef the sails on my way back from Eng[Pg 177]land; but these tremendous sails seem altogether too big to handle."

"So they would be without plenty of hands, but you see we have a great many more men in proportion here than there are on board a merchant craft. Will you go up higher?"

"Certainly." And they went up until nothing but the bare pole, with the pennant floating from its summit, rose above them. "You don't feel giddy at all, Blagrove?"

"Not a bit. If she were rolling heavily perhaps I might be, but she is going on so steadily that I don't feel it at all."

"Then I will begin by giving you a lesson as to what your duties would be if the order were given to send down the upper spars and yards. It is a pleasure teaching a fellow who is so anxious to learn as you are, and who knows enough to understand what you say."

For two hours he sat there explaining to Edgar exactly where his position would be during this operation, and the orders that he would have to give.

"When we get down below," he said, when he had finished, "I will give you all the orders, and you can jot them down, and learn them by heart. The great point, you see, is to fire them off exactly at the right moment. A little too soon or a little too late makes all the difference. It is generally a race between the top-men of the different masts, and there is nothing that the men think more of than smartness in getting down all the upper gear. When you have got all the words of command by heart perfectly, you shall come with me the first time the order is given to send down the spars and yards, so as to see exactly where the orders come in. It is a thing that we very often practise. In fact, as a rule, it is done every evening when we are cruising, or in harbour, or at Spithead,[Pg 178] or that sort of thing. When it is a race between the different ships of a squadron, it is pretty bad for the top-men who are the last to get their spars down. But, you see, as we are on a passage I don't suppose we shall send down spars till we get to Constantinople."

"What are we going there for?"

"As far as I can understand, the captain is going on a sort of diplomatic mission. His brother is our ambassador there, and he is appointed to act with him in some sort of diplomatic way, I suppose, to arrange what troops the Sultan is going to send against the French, and what we are to do to help him, and what subvention is to be paid him, and all that sort of thing. I expect you will be pretty busy while we are there. Do you understand Turkish?"

"Yes, it is very like Arabic. All the officials and upper classes in Egypt are Turks, and one hears more Turkish than Arabic, except among the Bedouin tribes."

While they were talking they were leisurely descending the shrouds side by side. As soon as they gained the deck, the captain's steward came up to Edgar, and said that Sir Sidney Smith would be glad to see him and Mr. Wilkinson to dinner that evening. The captain had abstained from inviting him until he should have got his uniform, thinking that he would find it uncomfortable sitting down in civilian dress. The fact that he was going to dine late in no way interfered with Edgar's enjoyment of his mid-day meal. During the two days he had been on board, he had got on friendly terms with all his messmates excepting Condor, who studiously abstained from noticing him in any way. The younger midshipmen he bullied unmercifully, and had a general dictatorial way with the others that made Edgar frequently long for the opportunity of giving him a lesson.[Pg 179]

He had no doubt that Condor had determined to postpone the occasion until they had left the Pireus, at which point they were to call, as his service might be required there to interpret. Once away from the island, he would not be likely to be called upon to translate until they arrived at Constantinople.

It was a pleasant dinner in Sir Sidney Smith's cabin. There were present the first and third lieutenants, the captain of the marines, the doctor, Wilkinson, and Edgar. Sir Sidney Smith was a delightful host; he possessed a remarkable charm of manner, was most thoughtful and kind to all his subordinates, and, though strict in all matters of discipline, treated his officers as gentlemen and on terms of equality in his own cabin. He had already accomplished many dashing exploits in the Baltic and elsewhere, and was beloved both by the sailors and officers. It was a time when life in the navy was very rough, when the lash was unsparingly used for the smallest offences, and when too many ships were made floating hells by the tyranny of their commanders.

"I should have asked you to dinner on the day that you came on board, Mr. Blagrove," Sir Sidney said kindly, as the two midshipmen entered, "but I thought that you might prefer my not doing so until you got your uniform. It has been some privation for myself, for I am anxious to hear from you some details as to what has been doing in Egypt, of which, of course, we know next to nothing at home."

During dinner no questions were asked, but after the cloth had been removed and the decanters were placed upon the table, he said:

"Now, Mr. Blagrove, we shall be glad if you will give us details of how you came to be left behind, of your personal[Pg 180] adventures, and what you yourself witnessed, and your opinion of the situation in Egypt. This is desirable, not only as a matter of general information, but because it will be really useful to me to understand the situation fully, for the purposes of my mission."

Edgar began his story, but was interrupted almost at the outset by Sir Sidney asking him how he came to be so intimate with these Bedouins. He was therefore obliged to relate how he had rescued the sheik's son from an attack by two of the lowest class of Europeans in Alexandria. Edgar told the story modestly, making as little as possible of his share in it.

"And were these fellows armed, Mr. Blagrove?"

"They had their knives, but they had not time to use them. These fellows have no idea of boxing, and a straight hit is a mystery to them. The thing was all over in less than a minute."

"Then, I suppose, you can box?" Sir Sidney said, with a smile.

"I was taught it in England, sir. My father thought that it would be useful, for the population of Alexandria is a rough one."

Sir Sidney said no more, and Edgar told his story without further interruption, and then answered many questions as to the proceedings of the French, the rising in Cairo—of which Sir Sidney now heard for the first time, and the prospect of a general insurrection.

"I don't think that there is much chance of that, sir. The defeat of the Mamelukes led them to believe that the French were invincible. The destruction of their fleet showed that this was not the case, and led to the rising at Cairo, but their easy defeat there, and the terrible slaughter inflicted upon them, will certainly cow them for a long time,[Pg 181] and as long as the whole French army remains there, I don't think there will be much further trouble, but if a portion were to march away, no doubt they might muster up courage to attack those that remained. Mourad Bey, with a considerable force of Mamelukes, still keeps the field, and the Arab tribes would certainly join him if they saw a chance of defeating the invaders."

"And the two men you had that trouble with, have you ever come across them again, Mr. Blagrove?" the first lieutenant asked.

"We came across them in Cairo, sir," Edgar replied reluctantly. "I was with my friend, the sheik's son. They did not recognize me, being in my Arab dress, but they knew him at once and pounced upon him, and were dragging him into a house. Of course, I took his part and there was a fight."

"And what was the result, Mr. Blagrove?"

"The result was that they were both killed," Edgar said quietly. "They attacked us with knives, and we had to use ours. My friend killed one of them and I killed the other. It was unfortunate, but it was their lives or ours, and if we hadn't done it then, the thing would have happened again, and next time we might have been stabbed before we had a chance of defending ourselves."

"I can quite understand that, Mr. Blagrove," Sir Sidney said kindly, while the others smiled at the matter-of-fact way in which Edgar related what must have been a very dangerous business.

"I see that, whatever else we may have to teach you, it will not be how to use your weapons. Indeed, it seems to me that you are getting on very fast. I saw you go up the shrouds to-day, and I can see that you will very soon be as much at home there as any of my midshipmen. And now,[Pg 182] gentlemen, we have had rather a long sitting, for it is nearly ten o'clock; but I am sure that you must have been as interested as I have been myself, in the information Mr. Blagrove has been good enough to give us."

"By Jove, Blagrove," Wilkinson said when they had left the cabin, "if you had told me all this before I should not have felt so doubtful about your fight with Condor. So you can really use your fists well?"

"I learnt for over two years from some of the best light-weights in London," Edgar replied, "and unless he has had wonderfully good teachers I ought to have no trouble about the matter."

Two days later the *Tigre* left the Pireus. To Sir Sidney Smith's disappointment, he had not found Lord Nelson there, as he had expected to do, and he was the more disappointed inasmuch as he had missed Lord St. Vincent, who was commander-in-chief in the Mediterranean, at Gibraltar.

CHAPTER X.
A SEA-FIGHT.

Finding that the last news from Lord Nelson was that he was sailing to join the fleet blockading Toulon, Sir Sidney Smith remained but a couple of days at the Pireus, and then continued his voyage to Constantinople. They had had no intercourse with any of the natives, and Edgar's services had consequently not been called into requisition.

In the afternoon Condor came up to Edgar, who was talking with some of the other midshipmen, and said:[Pg 183]

"Now, Mr. Blagrove, if you really meant what you said, I think this is a good opportunity to settle our affair. Your valuable services are not likely to be required for a few days, and if you don't wish to back out you had better come with me below."

"With pleasure," Edgar said quietly. "I have had some difficulty in waiting, and have several times been on the verge of stopping your pleasant habit of bullying youngsters."

"Well, you need not say any more," Condor said savagely; "let us see what you can do."

Wilkinson and two or three others who were off duty went down at once with Edgar, and as the news spread among the others, every midshipman who could possibly get away unnoticed, stole off also, and joined them on the lower deck. Half a dozen lanterns were lighted and hung up from the beams. A few of the sailors, seeing so many midshipmen going down there, guessed that there was a fight coming off, and descending the hatchway forward, stole noiselessly aft to watch it.

Wilkinson had said nothing to the others of what he had heard in the cabin. The general belief was that although Edgar, no doubt, would make a plucky fight of it, he had no chance whatever with an opponent nearly three years his senior, two or three stone heavier, and with a reputation for being able to use his fists well.

The opponents stripped to the waist and faced each other. Wilkinson acted as Edgar's second; none of the older ones would act for Condor, but a lad of fifteen, who dared not refuse his request, did so.

The combat is best described in the language in which one of the tars who witnessed it related it to his comrades.

"I never seed such a thing in all my born days," he said.[Pg 184] "It did not look a fair thing, for it was like a man against a boy. Condor is about three inches taller than the young 'un, and much more strongly built. The young 'un stripped well, and looked a wonderfully wiry young chap; there was a determined look about his face, and I guessed that he was game to the backbone; but his chance did not seem worth speaking of. Well, they stood up. The young one moved about quick on his pins for a moment, and then, it was so quick that you could scarce see how it was done, he gave a sort of bound, and hit out with his right, and the next moment Condor was on his back.

"I never saw such a clean, knock-down blow in all my life. The mids, they all cheered, and it was plain enough to see which way their 'pinions went. Condor was not down a moment; up he jumped again, looking as savage as a bull, but somewhat dazed. He meant mischief this time, and went with a rush at the young 'un; but lor, the latter just jumped out of his way, and hit him such a smack in the eye that it staggered him altogether. But he did not lose his legs this time, and made another rush. It was the same thing over and over again. The young 'un did just what he liked with him, and after five minutes he knocked him silly, his eyes were beginning to close, he was just bleeding like a pig at the nose; but it was a cut on the mouth that finished him, and knocked him out of time altogether, and the young 'un had never been as much as touched once.

"You should have heard how the middies cheered. As to the young 'un, he seemed to take it as a matter of course, and said, 'There is nothing in it. Condor fought pluckily enough, but he knows next to nothing of boxing, while, though I say it myself, I am a first-rate boxer. I ought to be, having been taught by the best masters in London for a couple of years.'

[Pg 185]"They had to chuck some water on Condor's face to get him round, for the force with which he struck the deck stunned him. When he was helped to his feet, the young 'un went up to him and held out his hand. 'I hope there will be no more ill-feeling between us, Condor,' he said. 'You have made a bad mistake, and have had to pay for it. Only I say this, that as long as I am on board there shall be no more bullying in the cockpit. We are all gentlemen, I hope. As long as we are on duty, of course, we obey the orders of our superiors, and, as our senior officer, we should all obey you; but when off duty we are equals. And if anyone attempts to bully anyone else, he has got me to reckon with.

"'There is no reason why we should not have a pleasant time when we are below, and I will do my best to see that we do have it. You are the senior of the mess, and as such have to keep order; but beyond that you have no right to interfere. Now let us shake hands and say no more about it.'

"Condor shook hands without saying a word, and then slipped away. I have seen many a fight since I first took to the sea, but never such a fight as this before. It were just a massacre of the innercents, and I don't think a fellow was ever more thoroughly sucked in than Master Condor when he undertook the job."

Condor had to go on the sick-list half an hour after the fight was over. His eyes were almost closed, his face was enormously swollen, and he had lost three teeth—the effect of the blow that had brought the conflict to a close.

"Did you know how it was going to be, Wilkinson?" one of the other seniors said as they went up on the deck again.

"I guessed pretty well, from what Blagrove was telling[Pg 186] Sir Sidney when he dined with him, that Condor would meet his match, but I did not think that it was going to be a hollow thing like that."

"What do you mean, sir, by skulking below?" the second lieutenant angrily asked one of the midshipmen of his watch as he returned on deck.

"I just slipped below for a few minutes, sir," the lad said.

"Well, you had better be careful, or you will find yourself at the mast-head," the lieutenant said sharply.

"I fancy there has been a fight," the first lieutenant said as Mr. Knight passed him, grumbling to himself. "I noticed just now that there were only two midshipmen on deck. Do you see, they are coming up the hatchway, one by one, looking as innocent as a cat that has been at the cream-jug. They seem to be pretty nearly all here now, but I don't see any signs in any of their faces that they have been in trouble.

"Well, well, midshipmen are only boys, and boys will quarrel. I expect we both had our share of it before we got our epaulettes."

The other laughed. "I suppose so," he said; "and after all it does them no harm, and it is much better, if two boys do quarrel, that they should fight it out and have done with it, instead of always wrangling."

"I thought it might have been Blagrove," the first lieutenant said. "A new hand generally has a fight before he has been on board a fortnight. After that he finds his level. However, it is not him, for there he is, looking as cool as a cucumber. It must have been some sort of meeting to discuss some fancied grievance. I daresay we shall hear something about it sooner or later."

Half an hour afterwards the doctor came on deck. There[Pg 187] was a smile on his face as he went up to the first lieutenant.

"One of your officers is on the sick list, Mr. Canes."

"What is the matter with him?"

"I should say that it would come under the head of contusions."

The lieutenant laughed.

"Bad contusions?"

"Rather more serious than is usual in these cases. Face greatly swelled, eyes closed, very great enlargement of the nose, lips puffed and badly cut, three front teeth missing."

"By Jove, that is severe punishment! Who is it?"

"Master's mate Condor."

"Why, who has he been fighting with?"

The doctor laughed. "I could hardly believe it when I heard. I waylaid young Jocelyn, who was executing a war-dance of delight, and questioned him. It is your last acquisition, Blagrove."

"Impossible, Doctor! There is the lad himself, without the slightest sign of having been engaged in a fight. I have been looking at them all rather closely, for they nearly all disappeared about half an hour ago, and one knows what that generally means. Mr. Knight was very angry about it, so when they came back again I glanced at them; and as none of them were marked in any way, or showed any signs of their having been engaged in a bout of fisticuffs, I came to the conclusion that there had been no fight. And you mean to say that Blagrove punished Condor in that fashion without receiving a mark himself? Condor is a powerful fellow, and must be nearly three years older than the lad. It seems well-nigh impossible!"

"I was astonished myself, but, if you remember, he told us the other evening at the captain's table that he had[Pg 188] earned the good-will of those Arabs by rescuing the sheik's son from an attack by two European ruffians. He certainly told it in a very modest tone; but that a lad could thrash two men armed with knives seemed to me to border on romancing. Young Jocelyn said that the fight did not last more than five minutes, and that Blagrove did not receive a scratch. His delight was excessive, and I fancy Condor is rather a bully. You see there is nobody else in the mess anywhere near his weight and age, and he took advantage of it accordingly. The boy said that after it was over and they shook hands, Blagrove told Condor that there should be no bullying in the mess in future.

"I asked what the affair was about. Jocelyn did not know, but said that he heard that something had happened when Blagrove first came on board, and that they all knew that there was going to be a fight, but he thinks that it was put off until they left the Pireus for some reason or other."

"That young fellow must be a marvellously good boxer to be able to punish a fellow so superior in age and weight without showing a mark himself. The lesson is certainly likely to do Condor good. I have heard from Mr. Bonnor, who was in the same ship with him on his last commission, that the fellow had a bad name as a bully, but that, unlike most fellows of that sort, he had pluck, and could fight, which makes Blagrove's victory all the more surprising. However, of course we shall take no notice of it. I have merely your official report that Mr. Condor is on the sick-list suffering from severe contusions. I suppose it will be some days before he can show up?"

"I should say that it will be a week before he is fit to come on deck. As to the loss of his teeth, it will be a serious disfigurement until he gets home again and can be fitted with some fresh ones. Well, at any rate this will give[Pg 189] Blagrove a good standing among the others. It is always awkward for a lad who joins a good bit later than usual."

It was not only among the midshipmen that the defeat of Condor established Edgar as the most popular member of the mess. During the voyage out, Condor had already rendered himself obnoxious to the men by the roughness of his tone when speaking to them, and by his domineering manner whenever the officer of the watch was engaged elsewhere, and the report of the manner in which he had been punished excited great delight among them, and rendered Edgar a most popular personage. They had noticed his behaviour the first time that he had gone aloft, and had agreed that the new middy was a good sort and no greenhorn.

"He will make a first-rate officer," one old tar said. "You mark my words if he don't. New hand as he is, you will see that he will show up well on the first opportunity."

The fight, too, raised rather than lowered Condor in their opinion. The men who had seen it all agreed that, although he had not a shadow of chance from the first, he had fought with unflinching pluck, and struggled on most gamely until knocked out of time. Consequently, when he returned to duty he was treated with the same respect as before, and with none of the covert grins that he had expected to notice among them.

The young fellow was not a fool, and while in the sickbay had thought matters over a good deal. It was of course mortifying to have been thrashed by an antagonist he despised, but he was conscious that he had brought the punishment upon himself. Hitherto he had not, since he first joined the service, met with his match among those of his own age and standing, and had come to think himself an exceptional sort of fellow; but the discovery that he was[Pg 190] but a child in the hands of a really good boxer, while it humiliated him, was extremely useful. A lesson of this kind is sure to have an effect, good or bad. Among some it sours the temper, produces an active hatred of the person who gave it, and renders a lad savage and morose. On the other hand, among more generous natures it has an opposite effect. Thinking matters over, a lad will feel that he has been going in the wrong direction, that he has been puffed up with an exaggerated idea of his own powers, and he will determine to get into a better groove, and to break himself of his faults.

Condor belonged to the latter class. As he lay in bed he saw clearly that he had made a great mistake, that his successes had been won simply because those he licked were less skilled or strong than himself, and that, in point of fact, instead of being, as he believed, a good boxer, he knew next to nothing about it.

Edgar had, after the first day, gone in regularly to have a chat with him. He had been somewhat doubtful as to how his advances would be received, but had determined to do his best to become friends with Condor, whom he felt, rather remorsefully, he had punished terribly severely.

"I hope, Condor," he said the first time he entered, "that you will believe that I have come in because I am really sorry that you have been hurt so much, and not from any idea of triumphing over you. It was only natural that I should have got the best of it. I knew beforehand that I was sure to do so. I learned boxing for over two years from some of the best light-weight fighters in London. I worked very hard, and at the end of that time, except that I was of course their inferior in strength, I could hold my own very fairly with them. That was more than a year ago, and since then I have gained a lot in height, in length of[Pg 191]reach, and in strength, so you really need not feel mortified that you were so easily beaten, because I consider that if you had been twice as strong as you are, and four or five years older, it would have come to the same thing. A man who can box only in what you may call a rough-and-ready way has practically no chance whatever with a really scientific pugilist, which I may say I am. I hope you bear me no malice, and that we shall be friends in future."

"I hope so too, Blagrove. I feel that I deserve what I have got, and it will be a lesson that I shall not forget. You have taken me down a great many pegs in my own estimation, and I shall try and make a fresh start when I am about again."

"I am very glad to hear it," Edgar said warmly. "I am sure it must be very much more pleasant to be liked by everyone than to be disliked; and one is just as easy as the other."

"I don't know that I ever thought of it before," Condor said, "but I suppose it must be. I will try the experiment when I get up. I shall feel very small among the others."

"I don't see why you should. You did all that you could, and no one could have done better who had not been taught as I have, and I am sure that no one will think the least degree the worse of you because you had no chance with me. Why, I thrashed a couple of ruffians in Alexandria, armed with knives, in a quarter of the time that it took me to beat you."

"At any rate I shall know better in future," Condor said, with a poor attempt to smile with his swollen lips. "I have learned not to judge from appearances. Who would have thought that a fellow brought up in Egypt would have been able to fight like a professional pugilist. You said that you had been a couple of years at school in England, but that[Pg 192] didn't go for much. We have all been at school in England, and yet not many of us know much of boxing. How was it that you came to learn?"

"Well, you see that there is a very rough population in Alexandria—Greek, Maltese, and Italian, in fact the scum of the Mediterranean—and my father, who is a very sensible man, thought that the knowledge of how to use my fists well might be of much greater value to me than anything else I could learn in England, so he asked my uncle, with whom I lived when I was at school, to get me the best masters in boxing that he could find. I got to be very fond of it, and worked very hard. I had three lessons a week all the time I was at school, and the last year changed my master three times, and so got all their favourite hits. Of course I used to get knocked about, for some boxers can't help hitting hard, and to the end I used to get punished pretty heavily, because though I might hit them as often as they hit me, they were able to hit much harder than I was, but I fancy now that they would find it pretty hard work to knock me out of time. My father used to say that being really a good boxer kept a man or a boy out of trouble. A man who knows that he can fight well can afford to be good-tempered and put up with things that another man wouldn't, and if he is driven to use his fists gets off without being knocked about; and besides, as soon as it is known that he can fight, others don't care about quarrelling with him. I know that it was so with me. I had a fight or two at first, but I very quickly improved, and after that I never had a quarrel for the rest of the nearly three years I was at school."

"One thing is certain, Blagrove, you are not likely to have another quarrel as long as you remain on board the *Tigre*. You will come and see me again, won't you?"

"Certainly I will. I can see that it hurts you to talk[Pg 193] now, but you will soon get over that, and then we can have some good chats."

During the voyage up to the Dardanelles, the *Tigre* encountered changeable weather; the sails had often to be shifted. When he was on watch, Edgar always went aloft with his friend Wilkinson and took his place beside him, listened to the orders that he gave, and watched him at work. In a few days he was able to act independently and to do his duty regularly, and to aid in tying down a reef when a sudden squall came on.

They caught sight of many islands as they passed through the Aegean. Edgar was disappointed with the Dardanelles, but delighted with his first view of Constantinople. It was on the day that they cast anchor that Condor for the first time put in an appearance at mess. His face had resumed its normal appearance, save that there were greenish-yellow patches under the eyes. Wilkinson, who was by a week or two the senior midshipman, and had occupied the president's chair with reluctance, at once left it. They had not expected him until the next day, or he would not have taken it. Edgar had that morning particularly asked the others as a personal favour to give Condor a hearty welcome on his return.

"I think you will find him a much more pleasant fellow than he was before," he said. "At any rate he has been punished heavily, and I think that you ought to welcome him heartily."

Wilkinson and two or three of the older midshipmen had gone in several times to see Condor, and had been pleased at the friendly way in which he had spoken of Blagrove. There had, however, been little talk between them, for Condor had not seemed disposed for conversation. Condor walked to his accustomed seat at the head of the table.[Pg 194]

"I hope things will go on better than they have done," he said gruffly. "All I can say is, it sha'n't be my fault if they don't;" and without more words he proceeded to cut up the salt meat placed in front of him. For a short time the conversation was constrained, and it was evident that those who spoke were talking for the sake of talking; but this soon wore off, and by the end of the meal even the youngest mids were talking and laughing with a feeling that somehow a change had come over the place. A quarter of an hour after the meal had ended, a boat was lowered.

"Mr. Wilkinson, you will take charge," the first officer said. "Mr. Blagrove, you will accompany the captain on shore."

A few minutes later they reached the landing-place. A number of men at once crowded round to proffer their services, and the captain said:

"Choose one of them for a guide, Mr. Blagrove. Ask him to take us to our embassy."

Edgar at once chose a quiet-looking Turk, and, to the latter's surprise, addressed him in his own language. The others fell back disappointed, and the guide soon conducted them to the embassy.

"I shall not want you here, Blagrove. I shall be engaged for at least a couple of hours. You can either stroll about and have a look round or go back to the boat as you please. It is now two o'clock; call again here for me at four."

Cairo had prepared Edgar for Constantinople, and indeed he thought the former city more picturesque in the variety of costume than the latter. The views from the hill of Pera, whether looking up the Golden Horn, across it at Stamboul, over to Scutari and the shores of the Sea of Marmora, or up the Bosphorus, were beautiful beyond[Pg 195] anything that he had ever seen, and leaving the exploration of the city for another day, he sat down under the shade of some cypress trees close to a Turkish cemetery and entered into a conversation with the guardian of the tombs, who pointed out the various mosques and places of interest to him. At the end of two hours he repaired to the embassy. Presently a dragoman came down and asked him if his name was Blagrove, and on his replying in the affirmative, said that Sir Sidney Smith had ordered him to say that he could return in the boat to the ship, for that he would dine ashore, and the boat was to be at the wharf at ten o'clock.

Sir Sidney Smith remained two months at Constantinople. His duty, in conjunction with his brother, Mr. Seymour Smith, was to engage the Sultan in an active alliance with England, and to concert, as a naval officer, the best plan to be pursued to render that alliance effective. The former portion of the commission had already been carried almost to a successful termination by his brother, and the treaty was signed on the first week of January, 1799. The details of the latter were arrived at in the course of several meetings between Sir Sidney Smith and the Turkish pasha and admiral. To these latter meetings Edgar always accompanied his chief as interpreter, Sir Sidney preferring his services to those of the dragoman of the embassy, as he was better able to understand and explain the naval points discussed.

The Porte, indeed, was able to do but little towards aiding in the naval operations. Two bomb ships and seventeen gun-boats were all the vessels that they were able to produce, but it was some time before they would agree to place these entirely under Sir Sidney Smith's command. Ahmed Pasha, or, as he was generally called, Djezzar Pasha—Djezzar meaning the butcher, from the cruel and brutal[Pg 196] nature of the man—the Governor of Syria, was in Constantinople at the time, and was present at these meetings. He was aware that Napoleon was marching against him; and although usually he paid but little attention to the Porte, or recognized any orders received from it, he had now hurried there to represent the situation and ask for assistance.

Bonaparte lost no time after hearing that Djezzar had sent forward a force to occupy the fort of El-A'rich in the desert, between Syria and Egypt, and on the 8th of February set out with 12,428 men for the conquest of Syria. Djezzar, who had returned to his pachalik, having early news of the movement, despatched a force, consisting principally of cavalry, to support the garrison of El-A'rich, and they were joined there by Ibrahim Bey with a force of Mamelukes. The march of the French was painful, and they suffered greatly from thirst. However, they defeated the Turk and Mameluke cavalry with heavy loss, and El-A'rich at once surrendered. The garrison were allowed to depart on undertaking not to serve again, and four days later the army entered Palestine, and believed that their fatigues and sufferings were at an end.

Two days later, however, a cold rain set in, and the troops, who had been suffering greatly from heat, felt the change painfully. On the 3rd of March they arrived in front of Jaffa. A Turk was sent in to summon the garrison to surrender. The commandant simply ordered his head to be struck off and sent no reply. The fire of the field artillery in a few hours effected breaches at several points. The French, in spite of opposition, burst into the town, which was given up to sack, and a large number of the inhabitants, as well as the soldiers, were massacred. Between 3000 and 4000 prisoners were taken, among these doubtless were[Pg 197] some of those who had been allowed to march away from El-A'rich. The difficulties in the way of provisioning the army were great. Many were ill from the effects of the change of climate, and the position was becoming serious.

To feed 3000 or 4000 prisoners added greatly to the difficulties, and Napoleon took a step which has been a foul blot on his reputation. They were marched into a vast square formed of French troops; as soon as all had entered the fatal square the troops opened fire upon them, and the whole were massacred. The terrible slaughter occupied a considerable time; and when their cartridge-boxes were emptied, the French soldiers had to complete the massacre with their bayonets. Of the whole of these victims one only, a mere youth, asked for mercy; the rest met their fate with heroic calmness and resolution. Napoleon's excuse for this hideous massacre was that the soldiers had broken the engagement they took at

El A'rich, but this applied to only a very small proportion of the garrison, and the massacre was wholly indefensible, for if unable to feed his prisoners, they should have been allowed to depart unarmed to seek subsistence for themselves.

The effects of this horrible massacre recoiled upon those who perpetrated it. The great number of dead bodies speedily tainted the air, and the maladies from which the troops suffered became vastly more serious, and the plague broke out among them and carried off a considerable number. Kleber's division made a reconnaissance towards Jerusalem, but the people of Nablous and the mountaineers assailed them with so terrible a fire, as they endeavoured to make their way up the narrow valleys, that they were forced to retire and join the main body of the army. When the French marched from Jaffa there were still many of their[Pg 198] men stricken with the plague in hospital. Napoleon has been accused of having had these poisoned.

The statement has been repeated over and over again, and has been as often vehemently denied, among others by Bonaparte himself. It still remains, and always will remain, doubtful. There can be no doubt that the transport of plague-stricken men would have been a source of danger to the whole army; and as very few of those once attacked by the plague ever recovered, but few would have benefited by the operation, while the condition of the great majority would have been rendered still more hopeless and painful by the journey. Upon the other hand, had they been left behind they would assuredly have been massacred by the inhabitants, who had suffered so terribly at the hands of the French. Rather than be so left, the unfortunate men would assuredly have vastly preferred some painless form of death at the hands of their friends. The probabilities are that all the sick, whose final recovery was considered by the surgeons as within the limits of probability, were taken on, and that those whose cases were absolutely hopeless were not allowed to fall alive into the hands of their foes.

Napoleon's position was an extremely difficult one. He had shown much solicitude for the wounded. When the whole army were panic-stricken at the outbreak, he had himself visited the hospitals, been present at operations, talked encouragingly to the sick, and had done all in his power to relieve their condition. But he could keep the army no longer in the tainted air of Jaffa. He could not take men at the point of death away with him to communicate the malady to those who had so far escaped, nor could he leave them to be murdered in their beds by the infuriated population. It is uncertain really what course was taken;[Pg 199] but it must be assumed that Napoleon, who was always anxious to win the affection and regard of his troops, would, putting all other matters aside, not have perpetrated any act that would have been condemned by the soldiers of his army.

CHAPTER XI.
ACRE.

At last all was satisfactorily arranged. By the terms of the convention, Sir Sidney Smith was appointed to the command, not only of the Turkish fleet, but of the Turkish army in Syria, a most important point, as the Porte had no confidence whatever in Djezzar, who, like many others of the pashas of the outlying possessions of Turkey, almost openly defied the authority of the sovereign. Djezzar was already at Acre, and some Turkish gun-boats, under Hassan Bey, had also been despatched thither towards the end of February. The welcome order was issued for the *Tigre* to sail on the 1st of March. Her destination was Alexandria, which, as forming part of the Sultan's possessions, came under the terms of the convention; under the terms of which it had been agreed that two British men-of-war and three frigates should be stationed in Eastern waters to give such aid as was possible to Djezzar, both in active operations, and by capturing store-ships destined for the use of the French army.

The *Theseus*, of 84 guns, commanded by Captain Miller, was already at Acre; and her captain and Colonel Phelypeaux were giving great assistance to the pasha in putting the place into a better state of defence, while his presence[Pg 200] there animated the pasha and his troops to determine upon a stout defence.

It was with deep satisfaction that the officers and men of the *Tigre* received the orders to prepare for sailing at once. They had now been nearly two months in Constantinople; the novelty of the scene had worn off, and all were impatient for active service. Things had been going on pleasantly among the midshipmen. Condor had shown by his behaviour that either he sincerely regretted the conduct that had made him so unpopular, or that the lesson that he had received had been so severe that he would not risk any repetition of it. At any rate there was peace and comfort in the cockpit.

Just at first, two or three of the younger middies were disposed to take advantage of the altered state of things, but Wilkinson, Edgar, and the other two seniors supported Condor, and told them that if the latter did not keep them in order, they would do so themselves, after which threat matters went on quietly. The change from salt provisions to fresh meat, with an abundance of fruit and vegetables, had been very pleasant, and added to the good temper and harmony that prevailed. Edgar had not felt time hang heavily on his hands, for he was constantly on shore with Sir Sidney Smith, who found his services as interpreter of great value. Had it been an ordinary case, the other midshipmen of older standing would have felt somewhat jealous, but they knew that he went as interpreter rather than as midshipman, and as some of them had leave to go ashore every day, they could amuse themselves according to their liking, while he was kept hard at work translating documents, examining the state of stores, or attending prolonged meetings between his commander and the Turkish naval officials. They had therefore no reason for envying him his post.[Pg 201]

He himself was glad of an occasional holiday at the rare intervals when Sir Sidney had no business on land, and made excursions to his brother up the Bosphorus, or to towns on the Sea of Marmora, when Edgar was able to join parties who, hiring horses at the landing-place, took long rides over the country, starting sometimes from Pera, and sometimes from Scutari on the other side of the water. He was certainly not less glad than his comrades when the order came to prepare for sailing. The wind was favourable, the voyage was a speedy one, and the *Tigre* arrived off Alexandria on the 7th of March. Here they remained for some days. News had already been received by sea from Jaffa of the capture of El-A'rich, and of the approach of the French army to Jaffa.

This had caused no uneasiness, as the town, having a garrison of 8000 men, was believed to be able to resist any assault. When, however, on the fifth day after the arrival of the *Tigre* off Alexandria, a small Turkish vessel brought the news that Jaffa had been captured, and some 3000 of the garrison killed in cold blood, besides a large number of the inhabitants, Sir Sidney decided to start instantly, in order to aid in the defence of the important stronghold of Acre, which would certainly be the next object of assault by the French. Committing to the captain of the *Lion* the charge of continuing the blockade with the gun-boats under his command, sail was at once hoisted, and the *Tigre* started for Acre.

On her way she picked up the *Theseus*, which was out cruising, and the two men-of-war arrived off Acre on the 15th of March, and, to the satisfaction of all, found that Napoleon had not yet appeared before the town; Sir Sidney Smith, owing to the terms of the convention, at once assumed the command of the operations. The arrival of the men-of-[Pg 202]war excited great enthusiasm among the garrison and inhabitants, who, now, for the first time, believed in the possibility of beating off the French, and of being spared the horrors that had befallen Jaffa.

On the following morning the French were seen marching along between the lower slopes of Mount Carmel and the sea, and the men-of-war boats, running in close to the shore, opened fire upon them, and compelled them hastily to change their course and to ascend the hill until beyond the range of the guns.

As no attempt had been made to return the fire by the artillery, Sir Sidney Smith was convinced the French must be unprovided with a siege train. Having learned from people who had escaped by boat from Jaffa, that only field-pieces had there been employed to batter the wall, he ordered a constant watch to be kept for any ships seen approaching, as Bonaparte would hardly have hoped to take so strong a place as Acre without heavy guns, and had doubtless arranged for a battering-train to be sent from Alexandria by sea. This would probably be ordered to make either for Jaffa, or for Caiffa, a small port a few miles south of Acre. The *Theseus* was at once sent down to Jaffa, to prevent any landing of guns or stores being effected there, while the *Tigre's* boats were placed at intervals between Caiffa and Acre.

The next day a corvette and nine gun-boats were seen rounding the promontory of Mount Carmel. The signal was made for the recall of the boats, and the *Tigre* at once got under sail and started in pursuit, picking up her boats as they came alongside. Bonaparte had been ignorant that there were any British vessels on the coast, or he would hardly have sent the boats from Alexandria without a stronger escort, and the corvette and gun-boats no sooner[Pg 203] caught sight of the *Tigre* than they made out to sea. The chase lasted for some hours, and one by one seven of the gun-boats were picked up, surrendering in each case as soon as the *Tigre's* guns opened upon them. The corvette and the other two gun-boats succeeded in making their escape, but their commander, believing it hopeless to attempt to carry out his mission in the face of a British man-of-war, sailed direct to France.

The capture was a most valuable one, for the possession of the gun-boats enabled a blockade of the coast to be carried on much more effectually than could otherwise have been done, and on board were found, as expected, the guns and battering-train intended for the siege of Acre. The *Tigre* returned with her prizes to the port, and the crew were at once employed in transporting the captured guns and ammunition on shore, when they were conveyed by the Turkish troops to the batteries, which were before very deficient in guns, and the capture added, therefore, much to the strength of the defences.

Edgar's services as an interpreter were again called into requisition. Mr. Canes was sent on shore with a party of sailors to assist the Turks in moving the guns to their new positions, and half an hour before landing he sent for Edgar and told him that he had arranged with Sir Sidney Smith that he was to accompany him.

"A good deal of the hard work will have to be done by the Turks, and it will save much trouble if you are with me to translate my orders to them, or rather to their officers. Sir Sidney is of opinion that there will be a great deal more for you to do on shore than on board. He will, of course, be much on shore himself, and I am carrying a note to the pasha, requesting him to assign a suitable house for him to take up his abode there and which he will make his head[Pg 204]quarters. Lieutenant Beatty will be posted there with twenty marines, furnishing a guard, and for other purposes. A room is to be assigned to you. You will then be handy whenever the captain is on shore, and at other times will assist me or other officers with working parties. Of course two or three natives will be engaged as servants. One of them will be a cook, and Lieutenant Beatty and you will establish a small mess together. You will, of course, have shore allowances. I think that you may consider yourself fortunate, for you will have an opportunity for seeing all that goes on, while the others will of course only come ashore by turns."

"Thank you, sir," Edgar said, much pleased. "I shall like it very much."

The Turkish soldiers worked well, tugging at ropes, while the sailors used levers to get the guns up steep places. Edgar was kept busy translating the first lieutenant's orders to the Turkish officers, and for the first three days had hardly time to snatch a meal until the sailors returned at nightfall to the ship. He got on very well with the lieutenant of the marines, who was a pleasant young fellow. On the day after they landed they heard heavy firing, and going up to the highest point of the rocky promontory on which Acre stood, could make out that a number of gun-boats were cannonading Caiffa. The place appeared to make no reply to the fire, and at last two gun-boats, believing that there could be but few French troops there, sailed up the harbour.

Lambert, the French officer in command, had, however, a howitzer and a small gun, and eighty French troops, but he gave orders that these should not reply to the fire of the gun-boats, and that not a musket should be discharged until he gave the word. The two small gun-boats came on con[Pg 205]fidently, until, when at a distance of only a hundred yards from the shore, where they intended to land and set fire to the French storehouses and to do as much damage as possible, a heavy fire was suddenly poured in. The two guns, loaded to the muzzle with grape, swept their decks, and the heavy volley of musketry did much damage. Lieutenant Beatty, who had brought a telescope on shore with him, exclaimed:

"By Jove! those two little gun-boats have caught it hot. See, there is one of them putting about, but the other seems to be drifting towards the shore."

This was indeed the fact; she was slightly in advance of the other, and was the principal target of the fire. The midshipman who commanded her, and most of her crew, were killed, and before the few survivors could recover themselves from the surprise into which they had been thrown by the unexpected attack, the vessel had grounded. The heavy fire of musketry continued, the guns again poured in their fire, and as escape was impossible, the few men who remained alive at once hauled down their flag and surrendered. The capture was a valuable one to the French. The gun-boat carried a 32-pounder, and as Napoleon's heaviest guns were but 10-pounders, the cannon was invaluable.

As soon as its capture was known, some artillery horses were sent to the port and transported it to the batteries, at which the French were already hard at work. For the first day or two it was almost useless, for, with the exception of a few shot taken with it, they had none that would fit it; but as soon as the besieged began to fire they obtained an ample supply of cannon balls, which were eagerly collected by the soldiers, a small reward being paid for every shot that was brought in. In a short time, however, the French were in a better position for carrying on[Pg 206] the siege with vigour, for as it became necessary to retain the *Tigre* and *Theseus* to assist in the defence of the town, French vessels were able to land artillery at Jaffa and other points, and they had ere long an ample supply for their batteries.

"There is no doubt," Lieutenant Beatty said, "that that gun-boat has been captured, and from her not attempting to go round and sail out as her companion did, I am afraid that the crew must have been almost annihilated by the enemy's fire. It was a very risky thing to send those two small craft in alone, even though the place had not replied to their fire, for even if the French had no guns, they might have had many hundreds of men in the town, against whom the crew of those two boats could have done nothing whatever. However, the loss is not serious except in the matter of the crew. I don't suppose she carried more than one gun."

"But even that is important," Edgar said, "for I know they have pretty heavy guns on board those boats, and in the hands of the French it would give us some trouble."

"We shall have hot work of it presently, Blagrove. The walls are absolutely rotten, and it would be absurd to call them fortifications; and if the French open fire at close quarters, they will make a breach in no time. If Phelypeaux's plans had been carried out, the place would have been in a position to make a serious defence; but I hear that he and Captain Miller of the *Theseus* have been trying in vain to get the Turks to carry out their plans.

"Djezzar was always saying that what they wanted should be done, but it went no further than that; and what little has been accomplished has been done by the men of the *Theseus*; and I believe that the dragging of the guns we captured to their places was the first job on which the Turkish soldiers[Pg 207] really worked; but, of course, Sir Sidney had a good deal more influence than Miller had, as he is commander-in-chief of the Turkish army, and if Djezzar did not give him the help he asked for, he would have the power to take the matter altogether out of his hands. His troops have no love for him, for, as his nickname shows, he is as cruel as he is ambitious.

"There can be no doubt that he intended to throw off the authority of the Sultan altogether. The position of the guns show that. I hear that when the *Theseus* arrived there was not a single gun mounted on the face of the town on the land side, every one being planted on the walls to seaward. However, I believe he is personally plucky, but as this place is nothing like so strong as Jaffa was, he must see that, as a garrison of 8000 there could not resist the enemy, the 3000 men under him would not have a shadow of a chance were it not for our help. Even we could do nothing if it were not that the position of the town enables us to cover the land approaches."

The position of Acre, the ancient Ptolemais, was indeed very favourable for its protection by a fleet. It stood on a projecting promontory almost square in shape; three sides were entirely washed by the sea; the north-eastern side had no natural protection, but at an angle of the wall a tower, which was the strongest point of the defences, covered it to some extent. Near the tower, and with its garden abutting against the wall, stood the pasha's palace. The masonry of the greater part of the wall was old and crumbling. From the sea to the north of the town vessels anchored there could cover the approaches to the northern side by their fire, while these could similarly be swept by ships anchored in the Bay of Acre on the south side of the fortress.

The water here, however, was too shallow for the men-[Pg 208]of-war to anchor in. The *Tigre*, therefore, was moored more than a mile from the shore; next to her was the *Alliance* sloop. Three of the gun-boats captured from the French, and two Turkish gun-boats, lay nearer to the shore, and the fire of all these vessels swept the ground across which it was already evident that the French main attack would be directed. This was also covered by the fire of the *Theseus* and three of the captured French gun-boats. The French had, on their arrival, promptly seized a village within half a mile of the wall, and pushed forward their trenches with vigour, establishing four or five batteries, which at once opened fire.

Napoleon calculated that he should be master of the town in three days at the utmost, and this no doubt would have been the case had he only Turkish resistance to overcome. As soon as the *Tigre* returned from her short cruise, Sir Sidney Smith took up his residence on shore. He brought with him Condor and Wilkinson, to act as his aides-de-camp, and fifty sailors were established in an adjoining house in readiness for any emergency. Here the mess was now established, although Lieutenant Beatty and Edgar continued to sleep in Sir Sidney Smith's house, the one to be near his men, the other in readiness to attend upon his commander at any moment night or day.

As far as possible the midshipmen's mess adhered to regular hours for their meals, but Sir Sidney Smith took his at any time when he could snatch them. One or other of the midshipmen came ashore each day with a boat's crew, so that at any moment orders could be sent to the *Tigre* or the *Theseus*. Except at the evening meal, when the fire generally slackened, it was seldom that more than two of the midshipmen's mess sat down together, being constantly employed either in carrying messages or orders,[Pg 209] or in keeping a watch at threatened points, in order that Sir Sidney should at once be made acquainted with any movements of the enemy.

The French had lost no time, for on the 25th their batteries opened fire against this tower, and, after four hours' firing, a breach, considered by the French to be practicable, had been effected.

The Turkish guns had returned the fire, aided by two mortars worked by British sailors, but the Turks believed that their walls were strong enough to stand a prolonged[Pg 210] siege, and as the French fire was heavy against the tower, those near it had betaken themselves to safer positions. Sir Sidney Smith was on board the *Tigre*. Djezzar seldom stirred from his palace. He had no capable officer under him, and no one was in the slightest degree aware of the serious damage the French battery was inflicting upon the tower, and there was no thought that an attack could be made upon the town for a considerable time. Edgar had been engaged all the morning with Sir Sidney, and when the latter went on board ship he went into the next house, where he found the others at dinner.

After that was over he proposed a stroll down to the corner against which the French fire was directed. Wilkinson and Beatty agreed to accompany him, but Condor, who had been all day at work seeing guns placed in position, said that he did not care about going out again. On reaching the wall facing the French position they found that there was little doing. A few of the guns were being worked, throwing their shot into the garden between the French batteries and the town. Along the rest of the line the Turks were squatting under the parapet, smoking and talking.

"What are the French firing at?" Edgar asked a Turkish officer.

"They are firing at the tower. They will do no harm. Some of the shots came in at the loopholes; so, as the soldiers there could do no good by staying, they have come out."

"That seems rather a careless way of doing business," Edgar remarked as he translated what the officer said, to his companions. "Well, at any rate we may as well go and see what the effect of their fire is. Their battery is not a heavy one, but as it is not more than four or five hun[Pg 211]dred yards from the tower it may really be doing some damage."

As they neared the tower at the angle of the wall they found that the ramparts there had been entirely deserted by the Turks.

"This is a rum way of defending a town," Wilkinson remarked. "If this is the way the Turks are going to behave, the sooner we are all on board ship the better."

The French fire was brisk, the thuds of the balls, as they struck the tower, occurring five or six times a minute. The three officers entered the tower. Two or three holes appeared in the wall of the floor by which they entered it.

"The masonry must be very rotten," Beatty said, "or they would not have knocked holes in it as soon as this."

They descended the stairs into the story below, and uttered a simultaneous exclamation of alarm. A yawning hole some eight feet wide appeared.

"This is serious, Wilkinson. Let us take a look down below."

"Look out!" Wilkinson shouted as a ball passed just over their heads and struck the wall behind them. "Stand back here a moment."

He ran forward and looked down.

"By Jove!" he exclaimed, "there is a breach down to the bottom of the tower level with the lower storey ground, and a heap of rubbish at the foot outside. I don't think it is high enough yet for anyone to get up to the opening, but it will soon be practicable if it is not now. Look! look! I can see a large body of French among the trees there. They are about to advance to storm the breach. Run, Blagrove, and wake up the Turks. We will go back and fetch up the marines and blue-jackets. The enemy may be in the place in five minutes."[Pg 212]

Leaving the tower, Edgar ran along the wall.

"Take your men to the tower at once!" he shouted to the first Turkish officer he saw. "The French are crossing the ditch."

Instead, however, of obeying him the officer and his men ran to one of the steps leading up to the wall, and commenced shouting, "The French are in the town!"

Edgar saw that he had told the news too suddenly, and that it was hopeless for him to try to stop the flood, therefore ran along the wall until he reached the stairs leading down to the open space in front of

Djezzar's palace. As he had been frequently there before, he made his way straight to the apartments where Djezzar transacted business.

"The French have breached the tower, pasha," he said, "and their storming party was about to cross the ditch when I came away. There are no troops there to defend the breach, and those on the wall are flying. Unless you yourself go out and rally the men to the defence the town is lost."

Djezzar was thunderstruck at the news. He had showed himself brave in battle, but with the fate of Jaffa in his mind he now lost heart altogether.

"It is too late!" he said, and catching up his sword he ran out of the palace, and directed his flight towards the landing-place.

Edgar ran towards the breach again, and on the way came upon his two companions running along, with the marines and blue-jackets after them. Fortune, however, had done more for the town than its defenders. Led by an officer with sixteen sappers, and followed by twenty-five grenadiers, the French party prepared to mount to the assault. Their orders were to mount the breach and hold it, and the moment this was done the main body of the storming party were at once to follow. But they met with[Pg 213] an unexpected obstacle. Instead of finding, as they had expected, merely a shallow ditch, they found themselves at the edge of a counterscarp, the wall being fifteen feet in depth, with a regular moat filled with water between them and the foot of the breach.

They had brought with them only two or three short ladders, which were intended to be used, if necessary, to aid them in clambering up the heap of rubbish to the breach. The French had no idea of the existence of the counterscarp. The ladders that they had brought were too short to enable them to descend it, and the officer in command hesitated as to what course to adopt. The mysterious silence maintained by the enemy was disquieting. That the Turks had all fled and the tower was undefended did not occur to the officer in command, and he feared that they must have placed mines in the breach, and were for the present abstaining from showing themselves or firing a shot, in hopes of tempting him to make an assault. Before he could decide what was best to be done there was a loud tramp of feet inside the tower, and then the British sailors and marines showed themselves suddenly at the openings on each floor, and at once opened a heavy fire.

Many of the French fell at once, and seeing that there was nothing to be done, the officer gave the order for the rest to retreat, which they did hastily. Djezzar was furious when he heard what had happened, and questioned Edgar; and, on hearing that the tower had been altogether deserted, as well as the adjacent portion of the wall, he ordered the instant execution of six of the officers and a number of the men for this gross neglect of their duty. He was exasperated that he himself should have shared in the panic that had seized them when informed that the French were assaulting the breach, and that no resistance had been offered by[Pg 214] his men; and Edgar congratulated himself that he was not one of his officers. When the old pasha, however, recovered from the state of fury into which he had fallen, he complimented the three British officers highly on the quickness that they had shown, which had, as he rightly said, saved the town, for, had the French found themselves still unobserved, they would assuredly have managed to get down the counterscarp, and to establish themselves in the tower in force before any suspicion of what was going on took place.

The French, whose operations were hidden by the gardens, at once proceeded to drive a gallery in order to blow up the counterscarp, upon which their guns could not be brought to bear, and on the 29th the mine was sprung. It did some damage, but it had not been driven quite far enough. Led by an officer of the staff named Mailly, the French rushed forward as soon as the mine exploded. They clambered down over the breach that had been made on the counterscarp, crossed the fosse by three ladders they had brought with them, and reached the foot of the breach. There was, however, too great a distance between the pile of rubbish at the foot of the wall and the great hole above it for them to enter without fixing their ladders.

As they were in the act of doing this the Turks, who had at their first appearance again been seized with a panic, but had been brought back by a number of their officers, who adjured them to stand, saying that it was better to die fighting the infidel than to be shot by Djezzar, opened a heavy fire. Mailly was killed, several of the grenadiers and sappers fell round him, and the rest retired, meeting, as they climbed the counterscarp, two battalions who had joined them as soon as the breach was reported practicable; but[Pg 215] upon hearing from the grenadiers that this was not the case they fell back again after losing their commanding officer and many men from the Turkish fire.

This success greatly encouraged the Turks, who had heard from those who had escaped from Jaffa that no obstacles were sufficient to daunt the French, and from this time Sir Sidney Smith began to entertain hope that the town could be held, of which, owing to the supineness of Djezzar and his troops, he had hitherto been very doubtful. The French at once recommenced mining. In eight days they completely blew up the counterscarp, and on the twelfth carried their gallery under the ditch with the intention of blowing up the whole tower.

By this time the besieged were aware that the French were at work mining. Colonel Phelypeaux had, during the interval since the last attempt, worked indefatigably. The breach had been filled up with combustible materials, a number of shells had been placed on the platform of the tower, with fuses attached in readiness to hurl down into the midst of a storming party, heaps of great stones had been piled there for the same purpose, and the Turkish soldiers, seeing the readiness and alacrity with which the British worked, had gained confidence. The faint sound of mining under the tower brought about a consultation between Sir Sidney Smith, Captain Wilmot, Colonel Phelypeaux, and the pasha. The engineer officer pointed out to the pasha that it was impossible to say what the result of the firing of the mine might be, as it would depend upon the quantity of powder employed.

"If a large quantity is used," he said, "it may entirely blow down the tower and a considerable quantity of the walls adjoining it, and leave so large a breach that the French would be able to pour in in such force that your[Pg 216] troops, who might well be panic-stricken at the explosion, would not be able to make any effective opposition."

"But what can we do to prevent it?" the pasha asked.

"Nothing can be directly done," Sir Sidney said; "but if we make a sally in force we might drive the French back, discover the mine, and carry out the greater part of the powder, and place a small portion under the ditch, and, exploding it, allow the water to run in; or, if the men carry with them a number of fascines, we might establish a work fifty yards from the foot of the wall. This would put a stop to their mining. An enemy attacking it would, as he advanced, be swept by the guns of the two men-of-war and the gun-boats, and the garrison would further be covered by the fire from the tower and walls. I propose that we should sally out in three columns. The central column, which will be composed of the marines and sailors of our ships, will make straight for the mouth of the mine and force its way in; the other two columns will attack the enemy's trenches on right and left."

"The plan seems to me to be a good one," the pasha said; "it shall be done as you propose."

On the night of the 15th of April two columns of men were gathered at midnight in the street leading to the water-gate, a short distance to the right of the tower, the third column close to a gate some little distance to its left. Lieutenant Beatty was, with his party of marines, to join the landing force, but to their disappointment neither Condor nor the midshipmen were to take part in the sortie, as the little party of seamen were to be held in reserve. Sir Sidney Smith himself intended to take his place on the tower, whence he could watch the operations. Wilkinson and Edgar were to act as his aides-de-camp, the latter to carry messages to the Turkish officers commanding the two[Pg 217] columns, while Wilkinson was to perform the same office to the central column.

"You and Mr. Condor may probably have opportunities of distinguishing yourselves later on," he said; "the other midshipmen may have their turn to-night."

CHAPTER XII.
A DESPERATE SIEGE.

Just as day began to break, the gates were opened, and the columns moved out one after the other. The order that the strictest silence was to be observed was obeyed by the sailors and marines; but the Turks, who were wrought up to a pitch of enthusiasm, made so great a noise that the moment they issued from the gate shots were fired by the advanced pickets, and a few seconds later the roll of drums in the French lines broke out, and it was clear that the whole camp was alarmed. Sir Sidney Smith uttered an exclamation of anger. As concealment was useless, he then sent the two midshipmen to order all the batteries to open fire upon the French trenches, and as the first gun boomed out the ships and gun-boats on both flanks also opened fire, and the trenches by which the French must advance from the village were swept by a storm of shot. The French batteries joined in the din, while the infantry in the advanced trenches opened a heavy musketry fire.

"By Jove, the Turks mean fighting this time!" Wilkinson said, when he and Edgar had both returned from carrying their orders. "Look at them, they are going at the French trenches in gallant style."

The dark masses could be plainly made out in the gray[Pg 218] light that was now stealing over the sky. Undaunted by the heavy fire of the French, the Turks rushed at the earthworks, scaled them, and engaged in a desperate hand-to-hand fight with their defenders. But the chief attention of the little group on the tower, where Captain Wilmot and Colonel Phelypeaux had also stationed themselves, was riveted upon the fight going on in front of them. Already the French were thronging down from their trenches, and the blue-jackets and marines were engaged in a fierce fight. Knight, second of the *Tigre*, received two balls in his left arm as he advanced, but upon arriving at the top of the shaft of the mine he and the pioneers at once leapt down into it.

One ran forward to see if it was charged, and brought back news that it was not. Lieutenant Knight and the little party of sailors worked desperately to pull down the props that supported the roof of the gallery, but they had little time allowed them for doing so. Had it not been that the noise made by the Turks had given the alarm so long before they reached the spot the work might have been completed. As it was, they had performed but a small portion of it when an officer ran in to say that they must at once come up, as the party could no longer keep back the swarming throng of the enemy. Colonel Douglas, who was in command, cheered on his hardly-pressed men, who had found the resistance of the French so desperate that they had been unable to drive them out from their advanced trench.

Lieutenant Knight, exhausted by the loss of blood, and his efforts to aid the pioneers, had to be assisted from the gallery and carried off by the seamen. Major Oldfield, who commanded the marines of *Theseus*, was killed, with two of his men. Mr. Janverin, midshipman of the *Tigre*, and eleven[Pg 219] men were wounded. Beatty, and Forbes, a midshipman of the *Theseus*, were both slightly wounded, as were five marines of that ship, and a seaman and two marines of the *Alliance*. As soon as the party began to draw off, a heavy fire was opened on the French by the Turkish troops on the wall. The batteries opened with renewed vigour, while the bugles sounded to order the retreat of the two Turkish corps. All gained the gates unmolested. The Turks were in high spirits. According to their custom at the time, they had cut off the heads of their fallen foes and brought in sixty of these trophies.

The French loss had been considerably greater, for from the desperate nature of the fighting the Turks had been unable to decapitate the greater part of their fallen foes. In addition to the heads they also brought in a great number of muskets and some intrenching tools. The last were an extremely valuable prize, as the garrison had been much hampered in their work by the small number of available picks and shovels. Although, so far as the main object of the sortie, it had been a failure, the result was, upon the whole, a satisfactory one. The Turks had met the French in fair fight, and had held their own against them, and they were so pleased that during the rest of the siege they never once wavered. The attack, too, showed the French that their enemy was not to be despised, and compelled them to take much greater precautions than before, and to maintain, at all times, a strong force in their advanced trenches.

On the 25th a tremendous explosion was heard, and the troops from all quarters rushed towards the tower to repel the expected assault. Had the mine been carried a few feet farther, the whole tower would have been destroyed, but the French miners had come across a vault[Pg 220] which projected a little distance beyond the tower above it, and believing that its wall was that of the tower itself, they had placed the charge against it. Although therefore a partial failure, the effect was tremendous. A portion of the outer wall of the tower was blown down, some two hundred Turks, who formed its garrison, and some pieces of cannon, were buried in the ruins. A small party of French rushed forward before the smoke had cleared away and established themselves in the lower stories. The Turks, however, rallied very quickly from the shock, and opened so tremendous a fire from the walls, aided by the cross-fire from the ships, that no reinforcements could reach the party in the tower, and the next morning early they evacuated the place, which was rendered untenable by the fire of the Turks in the story above them.

So soon as they had left the building the enemy concentrated their batteries upon it. At the sound of the explosion Sir Sidney Smith, with the sailors and marines of his guard, at once rushed through the streets to the tower.

"Bravo, the Turks!" Wilkinson exclaimed, as he and Edgar ran along by the side of the sailors. "Listen to their musketry fire! It is clear that they are standing their ground anyhow, and that there is no panic this time."

Sir Sidney was greatly relieved when, on his arrival at the tower, he found that, although shaken and shattered, it still stood an obstacle to an entry into the town. He went along the wall, warmly praising the Turkish officers and men for their courage.

"That is a weight off my mind, colonel," he said to Phelypeaux. "I have been scarcely able to close an eye for the last week. That mine has been a perfect nightmare to me. There was no saying when it was going to explode, and although the Turks have worked hard at that[Pg 221] countermine we set them to dig, I had little hope that you would be in time, as you had to take it right under the foundations of the tower. I think that we must congratulate ourselves heartily that it has been no worse."

"I think so, indeed, Sir Sidney. The Turks have certainly behaved admirably to-day. I thought they would when they once got over their idea that the French were invincible. They have always proved themselves splendid soldiers when well led, and I have no doubt the example of your men, and their carelessness of danger, have animated them with a determination to show that they too can fight."

From the time of their entering Palestine the French had been amply supplied with provisions of all sorts by the natives. As soon as he crossed the frontier from Egypt, Bonaparte had sent proclamations broadcast among the people. A large proportion of the inhabitants of the hill country were Christians, and the assurances that he came to free them from the domination of the Turks, just as he had freed Egypt, was received with enthusiasm by the simple and ignorant people, who knew very little of what was passing in the world around them. The consequence was, that as he marched north from Jaffa, deputations met him, comprising most of the leading men. These received presents, and promises that they should never again fall under the dominion of the Turks; while they, on their part, promised to supply cattle, corn, wine, and wood to the utmost extent of their resources. These promises they faithfully kept, and also did good service in aiding the transport of stores landed at Jaffa.

Sir Sidney now endeavoured to counteract the effect of Napoleon's proclamations, and by means of native emissaries landed by the ship's boats at various points along the[Pg 222] coast, sent out a large quantity of addresses of his own, telling them that Napoleon was, it was true, at war with the Sultan, but that this was no question of religion, and that he was but endeavouring to pass through Syria, in order to make his way to Europe, his retreat by sea having been cut off; and that he would be perfectly ready at any time to make terms with the Sultan, and would leave them, without a moment's thought, to the vengeance of the Turks, against whom they were now helping him. He added, that Djezzar Pasha, being convinced that they had been deceived by Bonaparte, and were acting in ignorance of the true state of things, promised solemnly that all who, now that the truth was told to them, withdrew their aid from the French, should be pardoned for the course that they had hitherto taken.

These papers soon bore fruit. The English were known to be favourable to the Syrian Christians, and the assurances of Sir Sidney Smith had great weight, and there was soon a sensible decrease in the amount of provisions and supplies brought into the French camp.

The breach widened under the heavy fire kept up continuously upon it by the French batteries, and as it was evident that other assaults would be made at that spot, the engineers began to throw out a ravelin, or advanced work, from the foot of the walls on each side of the breach, so as to take any assaulting party in flank. On the 1st of May the French, thinking that the breach must now be practicable, advanced for the fourth time.

A heavy gale had blown all day, the ships of war and gun-boats were rolling heavily at their anchorage, and it was doubtless thought that they would be unable to use their guns. In the afternoon, therefore, a body of men ran forward with six scaling-ladders; crossing the moat as before, they planted their ladders and attempted to mount the[Pg 223] breach. They were, however, assailed by so heavy a fire of musketry from the Turks that the leading party were literally swept away. In spite of the heavy weather, the ships joined their fire to that of the batteries, and a storm of shot and shell was rained upon the trenches, and the 2000 men who had been seen to advance in readiness for the assault, finding it impossible to issue from their shelter, retired to their camp. The marines of the two men-of-war had manned the new works, and their fire contributed much to the repulse of the French.

Sir Sidney Smith, in his despatches home, expressed his regret at the heavy loss of life encountered by the French in their desperate attempts to perform the impossible feat of entering by a breach that could only be reached by scaling-ladders. The point of attack had certainly been badly chosen, for, while the masonry of the upper chamber tower was very rotten, that of the lower part was excellent; whereas the walls themselves were, in most places, badly built, and could have been demolished in a very short time by the heavy guns the French now had in their batteries. Thirty of these had been landed at Jaffa, and brought up to the front.

In addition to the sortie of the 16th April, Sir Sidney Smith kept the besiegers constantly on the alert by landing parties from the ships' boats on the flanks of their lines of trenches. The attacks were sometimes pushed home, the earthworks were overthrown, the fascines carried off for use in the redoubts, guns spiked, and intrenching tools captured, and these attacks greatly added to the labour imposed upon the besiegers, who were compelled not only to keep strong bodies in the advanced trenches but to defend the whole line of attack against flank surprises by their enterprising foes.[Pg 224]

The Turks vied with the British in activity, making frequent night attacks on the trenches, and generally succeeding in carrying off a number of fascines, which were greatly needed, and were of special utility in the construction of the ravelin. The day after the repulse of the fourth attack the garrison suffered a heavy loss in the death of Colonel Phelypeaux, who died of fever brought on by want of rest and exposure to the sun. On the same day another, and almost as serious a loss, was sustained, for Captain Wilmot was killed by a musket shot while in the act of mounting a gun in the breach.

The midshipmen had, two days before, lost one of their comrades named Morris, who, with three seamen, was killed in one of the sorties, eight other blue-jackets of the *Tigre* being wounded at the same time. On the night of the 2nd of May the enemy made two desperate attempts to capture the English ravelins, but the marines in charge, aided by the fire from the walls and ships, held their ground, and repulsed the French with much loss. Every day the fighting increased in fury. Between the

1st and 9th the French made no less than five attacks upon the breach; these were all beaten off with very heavy loss; while the defenders, on their part, made frequent sorties to compel the assailants to stand on the defensive, and to interfere with their attempts to carry the approaches up to the foot of the walls.

The fire of the vessels was still maintained, but the besiegers had so raised and strengthened the earthworks protecting their traverses and trenches that they were now able to go backwards and forwards to the front with but little danger from the ships' fire.

Edgar had now lost the companionship both of Condor and Wilkinson. These had both gone back to their ship, for the death of Morris and the wounding of Forbes and[Pg 225] Lieutenant Knight had left the ship short of officers. Condor acted as junior lieutenant until the latter was fit for service again, and both he and Wilkinson took part in the boat attacks and the sorties from the town. Edgar was therefore now in command of the blue-jackets on shore, who were held always in readiness to run to the aid of the garrison at any spot where there might be sudden danger.

It was believed that the French were again mining in several places, and although Colonel Douglas, who had succeeded Phelypeaux in command of the engineering operations, set parties at work to drive countermines, the work progressed slowly, and it was difficult to ascertain the precise direction in which the enemy were driving their galleries. Edgar still acted as interpreter to Sir Sidney Smith, and was the bearer of his orders to the Turkish officers. He was very glad that it was but seldom that he was called upon to accompany his chief in his visits to the tower, for the stench here from the unburied bodies of the French and of the Turks overwhelmed by the explosion was overpowering. Numbers of the Turks stationed here were attacked by mortal illness, others became delirious, and it was necessary to change the force holding it at very frequent intervals.

On the evening of the 7th of May there was immense satisfaction in the town, as a number of sail were seen on the horizon. It was certain that this was the force under Hassan Bey, which had been originally intended for Egypt, but had been diverted from its course by Sir Sidney Smith's orders. Its arrival had been anxiously looked for during the last month, but it had been detained by calms and other causes at Rhodes, and it was only a portion of the force that now, on the fifty-first day of the siege, made its appearance.[Pg 226]

From the enemy's camp on the hills the fleet was made out as soon as from the town, and the effect was in a very short time apparent by the fire of the enemy's batteries being redoubled, and it was apparent that Bonaparte had determined to make a great effort to capture the town before the arrival of the reinforcements; and in a short time a great column was seen advancing to the attack.

Two of the *Tigre's* 68-pounders, mounted on native craft lying in the little port near the water-gate, opened upon them with shells, while two guns, manned by British sailors, one on the castle of the lighthouse, the other on one of the ravelins, poured grape into them. But the column moved on. The tremendous cannonade from their batteries overpowered that from the guns on the walls, and they suffered but little from the fire from the ravelins, as they had, the night before, constructed two breastworks from the end of their trenches to the breach, the materials used being sandbags and the bodies of their own slain.

In spite of the efforts of the defenders the French effected a lodgment in the tower. Its upper story had now been entirely destroyed by the enemy's fire, and the fragments had so increased the heap at the foot of the breach that the assailants were able to mount without the use of ladders. This was the most critical moment in the siege.

Hassan's troops were already in their boats, and were rowing to shore.

"Run down to the landing-place, Mr. Blagrove," Sir Sidney said, "take my gig, and row out to meet the boats, and order them to come round to the port here, instead of landing at the other end of the town. There is not a moment to be lost; the Turks are losing heart."

Edgar had just brought up the little party of sailors, and[Pg 227] leaving them to the leading of the petty officer with them, ran down at the top of his speed to the landing-place. The gig's crew were standing near the boat, listening anxiously to the terrible din of the conflict.

"Jump in, men, and row for your lives!" Edgar exclaimed; "every minute is of consequence. The French will be in the town in five minutes. I want to meet the boats, coxswain."

The sailors, who had already guessed that his errand was urgent by the speed at which Edgar dashed down to the boat, stretched themselves to their oars and rowed as if racing, and met the Turkish boats a quarter of a mile from the shore.

"I am sent by the commander-in-chief, Sir Sidney Smith, to order you to row round to the mole and land there. Order the men to row their hardest. Every moment is of consequence. The French are on the point of entering the town."

At once the flotilla of boats changed its course, the soldiers cheered, filled with the excitement of the moment, and the sailors tugged at their oars; and, headed by the gig, in ten minutes the boats reached the landing-place by the mole, and as the troops leaped out, Edgar, burning with impatience and anxiety, led them to the breach. It was still held. Some of the Turks, as the French entered the tower, had been seized with a panic and fled, but a few remained at their post. While some hurled down stones from above on to the column ascending the breach, others met them hand to hand at the top of the heap. Here Sir Sidney Smith himself took his place with three or four of his officers and the handful of blue-jackets.

The combat was a desperate one. The swords of the officers, the cutlasses of the sailors, the pikes of the Turks,[Pg 228] clashed against the bayonets of the French. Soon an important ally arrived. The news had speedily reached Djezzar that Sir Sidney and his officers were themselves defending the breach. The old pasha had hitherto taken no personal part in the conflict, but had, as was the Turkish custom, remained seated on his divan every day, receiving reports from his officers, giving audience to the soldiers who brought in the heads of enemies, and rewarding them for their valour. Now, however, he leapt to his feet, seized his sabre, and ran to the breach, shouting to the soldiers to follow him. On his arrival at the scene of conflict he rushed forward and pulled Sir Sidney and his officers forcibly back from the front line.

"You must not throw away your lives," he said; "if my English friends are killed, all is lost."

Fortunately, the shouts of the pasha, as he ran, caused a number of soldiers to follow him, and these now threw themselves into the fray, and maintained the defence until Edgar ran up with the soldiers who had just landed.

The reinforcements, as they arrived, were greeted with enthusiastic shouts from the inhabitants, numbers of whom, men and women, had assembled at the landing-place on hearing of the approach of the boats. The garrison, reanimated by the succour, ran also to the breach, and the combat was now so stoutly maintained that Sir Sidney was able to retire with the pasha, to whom he proposed that one of the newly-arrived regiments, a thousand strong, armed with bayonets and disciplined in the European method, should make a sally, take the enemy in flank, or compel them to draw off.

The pasha at once assented, a gate was opened, and the Turks rushed out. Their orders were to carry the enemy's nearest trench, and to shift the gabions and fascines to the[Pg 229] outward side, and to maintain themselves there. The new arrivals, however, were not yet inured to fighting, and as the French batteries opened upon them, and the soldiers, leaping on to the parapets, poured volley after volley into their midst, they faltered, and presently turned and fled back to the gate, their retreat being protected by heavy discharges of grape from the 68-pounders in the port. The sortie, however, had its effect. The French had suffered heavily from the flanking fire as soon as they had shown themselves on the parapet, and the assaulting column, knowing from the din of battle that a serious sortie had been made, fell back from the breach, their retreat being hastened by the discharge of a number of hand-grenades by a midshipman of the *Theseus*on the top of the tower.

But the assault was not yet over. Napoleon, with several of his generals and a group of aides-de-camp, had been watching the fight from an eminence known as Richard Cœur de Lion's Mount, and had been compelled to shift their position several times by shells thrown among them from the ships. Their movements were clearly visible with a field-glass. Bonaparte was seen to wave his hand violently, and an aide-de-camp galloped off at the top of his speed. Edgar, who was standing near Sir Sidney Smith, was watching them through a telescope, and had informed Sir Sidney of what he had seen.

"Doubtless he is ordering up reinforcements. We shall have more fighting yet."

He then held a consultation with the pasha, who proposed that this time they should carry out a favourite Turkish method of defence—allow the enemy to enter the town, and then fall upon them. The steps were removed from the walls near the tower, so that the French, when they issued from the top of the ruined building, would be[Pg 230] obliged to follow along the wall, and to descend by those leading into the pasha's garden. Here two hundred Albanians, the survivors of a corps a thousand strong who had greatly distinguished themselves in the sorties, were stationed, while all the garrison that could be spared from other points, together with the newly-arrived troops, were close at hand. The Turks were withdrawn from the breach and tower, and the attack was confidently awaited.

It came just before sunset, when a massive column advanced to the breach. No resistance was offered. They soon appeared at the top of the ruin, which was now no higher than the wall itself, and moved along the rampart. When they came to the steps leading into the pasha's garden, a portion of them descended, while the main body moved farther on, and made their way by other steps down into the town. Then suddenly the silence that had reigned was broken by an outburst of wild shouts and volleys of musketry, while from the head of every street leading into the open space into which the French had descended, the Turkish troops burst out. In the pasha's garden the Albanians threw themselves, sabre in one hand and dagger in the other, upon the party there, scarce one of whom succeeded in escaping, General Rombaud, who commanded, being among the slain, and General Lazeley being carried off wounded.

The din of battle at the main scene of conflict was heightened by the babel of shouts and screams that rose throughout the town. No word whatever of the intention to allow the French to enter the place had been spoken, for it was known that the French had emissaries in the place, who would in some way contrive to inform them of what was going on there, and the success of the plan would have been imperilled had the intentions of the de[Pg 231]fenders been made known to the French. The latter fought with their usual determination and valour, but were unable to withstand the fury with which they were attacked from all sides, and step by step were driven back to the breach. Thus, after twenty-four hours of fighting, the position of the parties remained unaltered.

Bonaparte, in person, had taken part in the assault, and when the troops entered the town had taken up his place at the top of the tower. Kleber, who commanded the assault, had fought with his accustomed bravery at the head of his troops, and for a time, animated by his voice and example, his soldiers had resisted the fiercest efforts of the Turks. But even his efforts could not for long maintain the unequal conflict. As the troops fell back along the walls towards the breach, the guns from elevated positions mowed them down, many of the shot striking the group round Bonaparte himself. He remained still and immovable, until almost dragged away, seeming to be petrified by this terrible disaster, when he deemed that, after all his sacrifices and losses, success was at last within his grasp.

During the siege he had lost five thousand men. The hospitals were crowded with sick. The tribesmen had ceased to send in provisions. Even should he succeed in taking the town after another assault, his force would be so far reduced as to be incapable of further action. Its strength had already fallen from sixteen thousand to eight thousand men. Ten of his generals had been killed. Of his eight aides-de-camp, four had been killed and two severely wounded.

The next evening the Turkish regiment that had made a sortie on the night of their landing, but had been unable to face the tremendous fire poured upon them, begged that they might be allowed to go out again in order to retrieve themselves.[Pg 232]

Permission was given, and their colonel was told to make himself master of the nearest line of the enemies' trenches, and to hold them as directed on the occasion of his previous sortie. The work was gallantly done. Unheeding the enemy's fire the Turks dashed forward with loud shouts, leapt into the trenches, and bayonetted their defenders; but instead of setting to work to move the materials of the parapet across to the other side, carried away by their enthusiasm they rushed forward, and burst their way into the second parallel. So furiously did they fight that Kleber's division, which was again advancing to make a final attempt to carry the breach, had to be diverted from its object to resist the impetuous Turks. For three hours the conflict raged, and although the assailants were greatly outnumbered they held their ground nobly. Large numbers fell upon both sides, but at last the Turks were forced to fall back again into the town.

The desperate valour with which they had just fought hand to hand without any advantage of position showed the French troops how hopeless was the task before them; and Kleber's grenadiers, who had been victors in unnumbered battles, now positively refused to attempt the ascent of the fatal breach again.

Receiving news the next day that three French frigates had just arrived off Caesarea, Sir Sidney determined to go in pursuit of them, but the pasha was so unwilling that the whole force of British should depart that he sent off the *Theseus* with two Turkish frigates that had accompanied the vessels bringing the troops.

The voyage was an unfortunate one. Captain Miller, as the supply of shot and shell on board the men-of-war was almost exhausted, had for some time kept his men, when not otherwise engaged at work, collecting French shell[Pg 233] which had fallen, without bursting, in the town. A number of these he had fitted with fresh fuses, and a party of sailors were engaged in preparing the others for service, when from some unknown cause one of them exploded, and this was instantly followed by the bursting of seventy others. The men had been at work on the fore part of the poop, near Captain Miller's cabin, and he and twenty-five men were at once killed and the vessel set on fire in five places. Mr. England, the first lieutenant, at once set the crew to work, and by great exertions succeeded in extinguishing the flames. He then continued the voyage, and drove the three French frigates to sea.

The loss of Captain Miller, who had been indefatigable in his exertions during the siege, was a great blow to Sir Sidney Smith. He appointed Lieutenant Canes, who had been in charge of the *Tigre* during his absence on shore, to the command of the *Theseus*, and transferred Lieutenant England to the place of first lieutenant of the *Tigre*.

It was generally felt that after the tremendous loss he suffered in the last of the eleven assaults made by the French that Napoleon could no longer continue the siege. Not only had the numerical loss been enormous in proportion to the strength of the army, but it had fallen upon his best troops. The artillery had suffered terribly, the grenadiers had been almost annihilated, and as the assaults had always been headed by picked regiments, the backbone of the army was gone. It was soon ascertained indeed that Napoleon was sending great convoys of sick, wounded, and stores down the coast, and on the 20th the siege was raised, and the French marched away.

[Pg 234]

CHAPTER XIII.
AN INDEPENDENT COMMAND.

The departure of the French had been hastened by the rapidly-increasing discontent and insubordination among the troops. During the later days of the siege Sir Sidney Smith had issued great numbers of printed copies of a letter from the Sultan authorizing him to offer a safe passage to France to the French army if it would surrender. This offer was a tempting one indeed to the soldiers. They had suffered hardships of all kinds since they had disembarked at Alexandria. They had been parched with thirst, half-choked with blinding dust, and had seen their comrades fall in numbers smitten by sunstroke. They counted but little the losses they had suffered in the battles in Egypt—that was in the ordinary way of the business of a soldier; but the dread of assassination whenever they ventured out from their lines, whether in camp or on the march, had weighed heavily upon them. Then had come the plague that had more than decimated them at Jaffa, and now they were reduced to well-nigh half their strength by the manner in which they had been sent time after time against the breach in the wall of an insignificant town, which would have been of no use to them if taken, as they could have been shelled out of it by the British men-of-war and gun-boats.

Sir Sidney Smith had passed through the terrible siege without a scratch, although freely exposing himself, and two attempts at assassination by the French emissaries in the town had also failed. The *Tigre* sailed at once to place herself between Jaffa and Damietta, and so cut off the retreat[Pg 235] of the French army by sea. Not anticipating that this would be the case, Napoleon, on his arrival at Jaffa, embarked the twenty-three guns he had brought with him, on board ship, together with all the sick and wounded who were unequal to the desert march.

So great was the haste, that the vessels were despatched short of hands, and without provisions or water. As soon as the *Tigre* was made out the vessels all steered for her, confiding in the well-known humanity of the British to their prisoners. They were not mistaken. Sir Sidney had abundance of supplies and water put on board them, and he convoyed them to Damietta, where they received from their countrymen the surgical and medical aid that was beyond his power to afford them. Edgar was not on board the *Tigre* when she fell in with the convoy of wounded. Sir Sidney had, early on the morning after the departure of the French, informed him that he should, in his despatches, report most favourably of the assistance that he had rendered him both as interpreter and aide-de-camp during the siege.

"For the present," he went on, "I shall have no great need for an interpreter, as I shall probably have little to do for some time beyond cruising backwards and forwards on the coast of Egypt to prevent ships from France entering the ports with stores and ammunition, therefore I shall be able to give you employment which I think that you will like. One of the gun-boats captured from the French is a fast sailer. Hassan Bey tells me that when he was at Rhodes he heard great complaints of the piracy that was being carried on among the islands. The Turkish troops in most of these were withdrawn by him to swell his force as he sailed south, and there are now no vessels of war in those waters. The French flag has been driven from the sea, while our work has been too serious to admit of our paying any[Pg 236] attention to the Aegean, although, as I knew before I left London, the complaints of merchants and ship-owners of the capture of merchantmen trading with Constantinople and other eastern ports were numerous. At the present moment I can well spare one of the gun-boats; the others will go down to watch the Egyptian coast. I shall therefore commission the *Foudre*, and re-name her the *Tigress*. I shall appoint Mr. Wilkinson to the command. Mr. Condor would, of course, have had it, but he has been transferred as third lieutenant to the *Theseus*, and as Wilkinson is senior midshipman, he will have her. I shall appoint you his second in command. She carries eight guns, and has room for two more, which I shall place on board from those on the walls. Her own guns are fourteen-pounders, and with two eighteens she will be heavily armed. Her complement was fifty-two men. I will give you forty from the *Tigre*, and will draw fifteen from the *Theseus*, and five from the *Alliance*. You will need a stronger crew with two extra guns; besides, you may want to send landing-parties on shore, or to cut out piratical craft, and ought therefore to be strong-handed."

"Thank you very much, sir. I shall be very glad to be employed on such service."

"Please send Mr. Wilkinson to me, Mr. Blagrove. I have his instructions written out for him."

"Sir Sidney Smith wants you, Wilkinson," Edgar said as he went into the next house.

"What is up?"

"There is a report that you have been making love to a Turkish girl; you will get it hot."

"Bosh!" Wilkinson said, laughing, as he put on his cap. "I have not spoken to a feminine of any kind since we left England."

In a quarter of an hour he returned.[Pg 237]

"Hurrah, Blagrove! this is glorious. I am all the more pleased that you are going with me. How lucky Condor being promoted to the *Theseus*, or of course he would have had it. Then Knight, being still unfit for duty from the effects of the wounds he received in the sortie, and our first lieutenant being new to the ship, the third lieutenant cannot be spared. Sir Sidney spoke very kindly. He said that it was a heavy responsibility for so young an officer, but that he trusted I should prove equal to it, and that I must remember that prudence was just as necessary as courage and dash. He gave me a good deal of advice, which I shall think over and try to act on when I sober down a bit. Now we are both relieved from other duty, so we will pack up our kit.

"Sir Sidney is going on board the *Tigre* in five minutes, and he said that we could go on board with him, and we had better do so, as there was no time to be lost. Mason, one of the gunner's mates, is to go with us. We are to have sixty blue-jackets and five marines for sentries, and so on. He thinks that we can't do better than take the Turk who has been cooking for him, and our cook here. They are both very good fellows. One will be our steward and cook, and the other cook for the men. The boatswain's mate and the purser are to go with us to the brig, and see what is required in the way of stores. Everything has to be got on board by to-night, as Sir Sidney sails early to-morrow morning, so there is no time to be wasted."

While he was talking the two midshipmen were throwing their spare clothes into the kit-bags, in which they had brought them ashore. One of the sailors slung them across his shoulder and followed them down to the landing-place. The bags were stowed under the thwarts forward, and the lads waited until their commander came down.[Pg 238]

"Remember, Mr. Wilkinson," the latter said as he took his seat in the boat, "you and Mr. Blagrove must be here at seven o'clock this evening, for I am landing at that hour to pay a final adieu to the pasha, and he asked me to bring you both with me. I mention it now, as it might slip my memory. The men you had on shore all gave you satisfaction, didn't they?"

"Yes, sir, they were all willing and ready for work at any hour, day or night."

"Then you may as well have them as a body. Some twenty of them have been killed, wounded, or laid up by fever, but with the men now on board they will make the crew up to its full strength."

The gig was now on her way, and the shore party of sailors and marines were gathering round the cutter that had been sent to take them on board. Before leaving the quarters that they had occupied, the midshipmen had made hasty arrangements with the two Turks, who had gladly accepted their offer. They had been told that one or other of the midshipmen would be sure to be on shore some time during the day. Therefore they were to hold themselves in readiness to embark at once. On arriving on board, the lieutenant was requested by Sir Sidney to tell off five marines to form part of the complement of the gun-boat. Ten minutes after their arrival the two midshipmen started with two petty officers to inspect the stores of the gun-boat.

"She is a very pretty craft, Blagrove!" Wilkinson said with delight as he regarded with pride his new command.

"Yes. I doubt whether we should have ever taken her if she had not been so deep in the water with the guns and stores she had on board. The French certainly know how to build ships; there is no question about that. I doubt[Pg 239] whether we have such a good-looking gun-boat in the service. Anyhow I have not seen one."

The petty officer who commanded the gun-boat saluted as Wilkinson came up to the side and announced that he had come to take command of the boat.

"Am I to remain on board, Mr. Wilkinson?"

"Yes, Mr. Philpot. I am to have two petty officers, and Sir Sidney said that as you knew all about the brig you would be very useful to me. All the men are to remain here. Now we must overhaul the stores. What have you got on board?"

"We have a very short supply of powder and ball, not above ten rounds for each gun, and there is hardly any small-arm ammunition. There are twelve barrels of salt junk, eight of flour; there is a cask of rum that was broached last week, half a cask of sugar, and some bags of coffee. I have not sounded the water-tank, but I don't think that there is much in there."

A thorough examination was now made. An exact inventory of the provisions was taken, and the amount of water on board was ascertained, the boatswain's stores were gone over, and were found to be well supplied with rope, sail-cloth, and other necessaries. A calculation was then made as to the amount that would be required for the future strength of the crew for a three months' cruise. The boat was then rowed back to the *Tigre*. As soon as they arrived there, and reported to the first lieutenant what was required, a signal was made to the gun-boat to send one of her boats ashore at once with water-casks, and to fill up the tanks. A party was set to work to hoist up the barrels of stores, according to the list handed in by Wilkinson, while Edgar was sent on shore with forty men, with an order to the Turkish commander of artillery, to hand over[Pg 240] to him two 18-pounders and as much ammunition for them and the 14-pounder guns as could be provided.

Mason, the gunner's mate, who was to sail in the *Tigress*, accompanied him to aid him to get the guns down to the boat. The Turkish officer at once handed over the guns, but was able to supply but little ammunition, for which, now that the French had retreated, there was no longer any use at Acre. However, he told off twenty men to aid the sailors in getting the guns and ammunition down, and in two hours the whole had been placed on board the boats, bringing them down very low in the water. When the last party were on their way down, Edgar hurried to his old quarters and had a consultation with the two Turks, who were ordered to purchase a supply of wine, meat, and such other stores as they could find for the cabin use, and were told to have everything at the landing-place, and to be in readiness to go on board themselves, by four o'clock in the afternoon.

Had the order been given two days before, there would have been little for the Turks to have purchased; but the town was already full of natives from the hills, many chiefs having come down to assure the pasha of their fidelity, and to inform him that bands of their horsemen were hanging on the rear of the retreating French. Great numbers of the villagers had come in to inspect the scene of the desperate struggle that had for upwards of two months gone on unceasingly. Many were anxious to obtain employment in the work of burying the dead and clearing away the ruins. Almost all brought in something to sell—sheep, goats, and chickens, eggs and vegetables. Of the latter Edgar had ordered that a large supply should be brought for the use of the crew; for although native boats from the north had, while the siege went on, often arrived with fresh provisions,[Pg 241] the supply had been insufficient for the demand, and many of the sailors were suffering alike from the want of fresh food and from their hard work, and most of all from the horrible effluvia from the unburied bodies that bestrewed the ground over which the fighting had taken place.

As the heavily-laden boats rowed out to the brig they were overtaken by the water-boats, which were now making their third trip; they reported to Edgar that what they now carried would completely fill up the tanks. Wilkinson was on board, having come off with the boats with the stores from the *Tigre*. It had been a hard morning's work, but both were well satisfied with it; and as they sat down to a lunch composed of a loaf of bread and a bottle of wine Edgar had brought off with him, they chatted over the future prospect in high glee.

"This is not so spacious as the room you have been occupying for the last two months," Wilkinson said, "but it beats the cockpit hollow."

"Yes, it is a very snug little cabin, and the French skipper evidently knew how to make himself comfortable. It is lucky that everyone has been so busy since we took her that no one has thought of stripping it. There are his telescope, a big roll of charts, and two brace of pistols, all in their places. I know the French officers were all permitted to take their clothes away with them; so no doubt the lockers are empty."

This, however, on examination, proved not to be the case, for in them were found three or four dozen of wine, two dozen of brandy, a good supply of chocolate, coffee, and other cabin stores.

"I see, Mr. Philpot," Wilkinson said when they went on deck, "you have husbanded the captain's stores most carefully."[Pg 242]

"Yes, sir; no orders were given to me about them, and I knew that I might be relieved any day. I think I have had three bottles of brandy. I used to take a tot every night, thinking that there could be no harm in that."

"No harm at all," Wilkinson said. "I suppose properly, under ordinary circumstances, the stores should have been handed over at once to the *Tigre*; but as no orders were given about it, I think you were perfectly right in taking toll, though I don't know that it would have been justified by the regulations. However, certainly I shall risk it myself."

"Of course, sir, as commander of the ship, it is a different thing altogether. I was only put here to look after the men working the guns."

For some hours the crew were hard at work lowering down the stores into the hold, packing the ammunition in the magazine, hoisting up the two eighteen-pounders and their carriages, and getting them into position. At half-past three a boat was sent ashore, and returned with the two Turks and a quantity of provisions. The carcases of three sheep were handed over to the crew, with the greater portion of the vegetables, one sheep being kept for the use of the cabin and the petty officers, together with a supply of vegetables sufficient for some days. A good supply of fruit had been brought, which was also divided. As soon as the deck was cleared, all hands were set to wash it down.

"They need not scrub until to-morrow morning, Mr. Philpot," Wilkinson said. "The men have had a hard day's work; they can clean her properly the first thing to-morrow. Have you taken a look at the rigging?"

"Yes, sir, everything is in first-rate condition."

"No doubt she was thoroughly fitted out before she[Pg 243] sailed. She certainly looks like it," Wilkinson replied as he glanced at the coils of ropes. "We shall get up anchor at daybreak. I want to be under sail before the *Tigre*. It would not look smart for a line-of-battle ship to be under weigh before a brig."

At half-past six, Wilkinson and Edgar, both in full uniform—for the latter had provided himself with a full kit, having bought the outfit of one of the midshipmen of the *Theseus* who had been killed, and who happened to be about his own height and size—took their places in a boat and rowed ashore. In a few minutes Sir Sidney Smith arrived.

"Nearly ready for sea, Mr. Wilkinson?"

"Yes, sir, we shall be ready to sail to-morrow morning. Everything may not be quite ship-shape yet, but a few hours' work on the way will get everything in order."

"Very good work!" Sir Sidney said approvingly. "I hardly thought that you would have got your guns on board to-day."

"The commandant gave us a complement of Turks to help to carry them down, sir, which made short work of it."

"I expect that you will be having a more lively time of it than I shall. I may pick up a few store-ships, but blockading is always dull work. However, I hope before very long they will be sending a force out from England to finish with the French in Egypt. You must remember that you can't be too careful with those Greek and Moslem pirates; one is as bad as the other, and from what I hear they generally work two or three together, and though their craft may be small they carry a number of men; therefore, boat expeditions against them should always be strong-handed. You must bear in mind that although a command like this is a fine opportunity for a young officer to distinguish[Pg 244] himself, upon the other hand, if he meets with a misfortune it tells against him. If I had not seen you and Mr. Blagrove both frequently under a heavy fire I should scarcely have ventured to appoint you to such a charge; but I know that you are both cool and steady, and being so short of officers as we are, and feeling that it is of urgent importance to do something to put a stop to the alarming increase of piracy, I consider myself justified in making these appointments."

By this time they had reached the pasha's palace. The latter evidently considered the visit to be a ceremonious one, and a guard of honour was drawn up in the court-yard who saluted as they passed in. For a time the pasha and Sir Sidney exchanged compliments in the usual oriental style, Edgar translating their speeches.

"Without you and your brave sailors the town would have fallen on the first day the French opened fire," the pasha said. "My men were thoroughly dispirited by the events of Jaffa, and to tell you the truth, I myself absolutely despaired of resistance, and should have left before the French arrived had not your ships come into the bay. If Jaffa, which was very much stronger than this place, and with a garrison of 8000 men in good heart, fell at the first assault, what could be done here, where the defences needed but a few shot to fall in ruins, and the garrison were panic-stricken and believed the enemy to be absolutely invincible?"

"No troops could have fought better than yours towards the end of the siege, pasha. The way in which they threw themselves sabre in hand upon the French bayonets was splendid, and my own sailors could have fought no better than they did when the French entered the town."

"Yes, yes, they did well then, but at the beginning their[Pg 245] hearts were water, and a hundred French grenadiers could have taken the place. I hope you will return here soon."

"I fancy that there is little chance of that, pasha, unless it be that I hear that those three French frigates the *Theseus* chased a few days ago are on the coast again, in which case I may run across and try to catch them. Certainly there is no fear of the French coming here again; the news of what has taken place here will cause such excitement among the Egyptians that Bonaparte will have as much as he can do to maintain his hold on the province. I shall take care to do justice to yourself and your soldiers in sending my report of the siege to the Sultan, my sovereign's ally, and in whose service I hold rank."

The old pasha smiled. "At any rate, Sir Sidney Smith, I shall take care that the Sultan shall not send you hither to capture Acre instead of defending it. I have had a lesson that my troops are not so formidable as I had deemed, and he shall have no further reason for complaint against me. And now, young gentlemen," he went on, turning to the midshipmen, "I hear that you are going to sail in one of the gun-boats captured by your commander, to endeavour to punish some of the pirates that are doing so much mischief, not only to the trade among the islands, but to vessels trading from our ports and others with Stamboul.

You, young sir, have rendered me, as well as Sir Sidney Smith, great service throughout this siege by interpreting between us and thus enabling me to understand his wishes, instead of being obliged to learn them through those who might have reported their substance to the French. Likewise you have daily carried his orders to my officers, and often through heavy fire. Had you been an officer of mine I should have known how to recognize your services. I could have given you much promotion, and, for such is[Pg 246] the custom in our army, have presented you with so many purses. As you are not, I have no power to give you promotion, and Sir Sidney Smith tells me that as a British officer you could not receive gifts in money even from a foreign monarch. He has said, however, that, as a personal present, and as a token of my regard for the services that you have rendered me, he considers that you could accept such a present in the form of a jewel as I might think it right to offer you."

He took a box of Turkish make that stood on the table beside him.

"This," he said, "is an aigrette which I myself have worn in battle; and no more appropriate present could be made to one whom I have seen standing unflinchingly in a fire that might well have appalled veterans."

Then he turned to Wilkinson. "You, sir, have throughout the siege been on service on shore here, and during the first part of the siege commanded the little body of sailors who checked the first attempt of the enemy to capture the tower. I saw you fighting bravely during that terrible struggle in the breach when it so nearly fell into the hands of the French. I therefore present you with a ring of honour similar to those that I have requested Sir Sidney Smith to have the kindness to give in my name to the officers who distinguished themselves most greatly in the defence of my town."

Edgar translated the pasha's speech, and then opened the box presented to himself. It contained a superb aigrette, mounted upon a brooch-like ornament by which it was fastened to a turban. This ornament, which was some four inches in diameter, was composed entirely of precious stones, with an emerald of great size in the centre. He looked at Sir Sidney Smith.[Pg 247]

"It is too valuable altogether," he said.

"You can take it," his commander said with a smile; "he showed it to me this morning."

Edgar then expressed his thanks in suitable terms to the pasha, and also those of Wilkinson, whose ring contained a diamond of great beauty; then at a sign from Sir Sidney they left the room, leaving him to conclude his interview with the pasha alone. In a quarter of an hour he joined them outside the palace.

"I congratulate you on your presents," he said. "Yours, Blagrove, is undoubtedly very valuable, and had you intended to remain permanently in the service I do not know that I could have allowed you to accept it. As it is, I see no harm in it. I may tell you that the pasha asked me if I thought that you would remain in his service. He says your knowledge of several languages would be of much value to him, and that he should like to have one about him on whose courage, as well as fidelity, he could rely. I told him that I knew that you had other plans, and that you would probably leave the navy as soon as the French evacuated Egypt, and were, I knew, anxious to return to your parents in England. I have no doubt, Mr. Blagrove, that he would have been willing to give you terms you could hardly have hoped for elsewhere; but the pasha is an old man, you would have been an object of jealousy to his officers and officials, and he is at times guilty of cruelties at which I know you would revolt, and your position therefore would have been a precarious one, and your enemies might not improbably endeavour to remove so formidable a rival in their master's favour by assassination, so I thought that for your own interest it is better that I should take upon myself to decline the offer."

"Thank you, sir. I should not have liked to enter his[Pg 248] service at all. It would be an idle life as well as an unpleasant one, and, besides, I know that my father wishes me to take his place in Alexandria."

"Djezzar has behaved very handsomely," Sir Sidney said. "He obtained from me a list of all the officers of the three ships and of the petty officers who have specially distinguished themselves. He has given me jewels to hand to all the officers in his name, and also purses of money for the petty officers. He is, you know, immensely rich. The old fellow was really grieved that he could not offer anything to me; he said as much, but I at once pointed out that, putting everything else aside, it would be an unheard-of thing for the commander-in-chief of the Sultan's army to receive a present from one, however high in rank, who was under his orders. He just now insisted, however, that we should exchange rings, and as he had absolutely tears in his eyes when he spoke, I could not refuse, though mine was but a signet-ring with my crest, and his a diamond worth, I should say, a thousand pounds if it is worth a penny."

They had by this time reached the landing-place.

"Now, lads, we part here for the present; I hope that you will have a prosperous cruise, and do credit to my choice. You understand, Mr. Wilkinson, that you will remain on your station among the islands until you receive other orders from me."

After seeing Sir Sidney off, the two midshipmen took their places in their boat, and were rowed off to the *Tigress*.

"That was an unexpected piece of luck, Blagrove," Wilkinson said when they had started. "I thought, perhaps, that he might make you a present, for you have seen him every day, and besides interpreting, have carried orders to his officers under a heavy fire, and done all sorts of things,[Pg 249] but except that I landed several times to take part in the sorties, and was lucky enough to be on shore at that fight at the breach and when the French got in, I did no active work. I had no hopes of getting anything beyond perhaps a mention in the chief's despatches."

"I feel quite ashamed at having so much more valuable a present, Wilkinson."

"Oh! I am sure that no one could begrudge it to you," Wilkinson replied. "You don't get any special pay for being an interpreter, and it gives you a tremendous lot of work; besides, going about as you do with Sir Sidney, you were constantly under fire. Besides, the pasha saw a great deal more of you than he did of anyone else, except the chief himself. I congratulate you upon it heartily; if you ever want to turn it into money it will be quite a small fortune. Luckily my father is in a position to make me a good allowance, so I have no intention of ever parting with this ring, it will be a remembrance of the siege, and the sort of thing to wear on grand occasions."

They found that during their absence the men had worked hard, and that, except for a final scrub, the brig was now ship-shape and in good order. At four o'clock in the morning the crew were again on deck It was still dark, but the men set to with a will to scrub the decks, for, as they said, if they passed near the *Tigre* they should not like the decks to look like those of a trader in ballast. An hour's hard work and they had finished, just as the look-out reported that the *Tigre's* men were going aloft to loosen sails. It was light now, and in a very few minutes the canvas was spread and the anchor catted. The *Tigre*, with her great sail spread, was not yet under way, and the brig, as she laid her course west, passed a hundred yards under her stern. The *Tigress* ran up her ensign, for the[Pg 250] sun was just showing, and dipped it in salute. The midshipmen waved their hands to their comrades on board, and saluted more formally Sir Sidney, who stood at the bulwarks watching the craft as she passed, and who returned the salute with a cheery shout of "Well done, *Tigress!*"

Then she went on her course, after the exchange of a cheer between the crews clustered by the bulwarks of the *Tigress* and in the tops of the man-of-war.

"Now we are fairly off," Edgar said, "what do your written instructions say?"

"I am to go to Rhodes, there to make inquiries of the port authorities as to any outrages that have been lately reported, and to be guided by what I hear. In fact, the matter is left entirely in my hands, after we once get there. I don't know how we had better divide the watches. It would hardly be the thing for me, as skipper, to take a watch, and yet that would be the most satisfactory way of arranging it. I could take the gunner and you the boatswain. In fact, I think it would be ridiculous to work it in any other way."

"Just as you like, Wilkinson, but I have no doubt that the boatswain would do just as well or better than I should."

"No, I will take a watch, at any rate until we see how the petty officers get on. It is ticklish navigation among these islands, and I certainly should not feel comfortable if neither you nor I were on deck. There is the *Tigre* fairly under way, steering south by west. We are walking along, ain't we? This breeze just suits her, and she is a very different craft now to what she was when we overhauled her, laden down pretty nearly to her covering-board. I don't think, in a breeze like this, that the *Tigre* would be able to catch us, although, of course, if the wind strengthened much her weight would tell. However, there is no doubt at all that[Pg 251] this craft is fast. I hope ere long we shall try our speed against one of these pirates. I expect that off the wind with those big lateen sails of theirs they are very fast, but on the wind they would have no chance with us. When we get away from Rhodes we will disguise her a bit, put a yellow streak to her, and give her the look of a trader. They are much more likely to find us than we are to find them."

"Where are we to send our prizes, that is, if we take any?"

"If they are small craft we are to burn them, but if we take any that would be likely to be of use to the chief in the blockade we are to sell them. Any prisoners we take we are to hand over to the pasha at Smyrna if they are Moslems; if they are Greeks, the fewer prisoners we take the better. It would be infinitely more merciful to shoot them down in fair fight than to hand them over to the tender mercies of the Turks, but Sir Sidney said that he would largely leave the matter to my discretion. I would rather that he had given me positive orders in writing on the subject, for it is an awkward thing for a midshipman to have a thing like this left to his discretion, especially as at other times superior officers don't seem to think that midshipmen possess any discretion whatever."

CHAPTER XIV.
A PIRATE HOLD.

On arriving at Rhodes, Wilkinson and Edgar rowed ashore as soon as the anchor was dropped, and called upon the Turkish governor. They were received with[Pg 252] much honour, and the governor was delighted to hear the news, which they were the first to bring, that the French had abandoned the siege of Acre and were retreating in all haste to Egypt. He gave orders for a salute to be fired at once in honour of this great success, and then asked Wilkinson what he could do for him, assuring him that he would put all the resources of the island at his disposal. Edgar, as interpreter, assured the governor that they had no occasion to avail themselves largely of the offer, but that, in consequence of the amount of ammunition expended in the siege they were short of both powder, ball, and musketry ammunition, and would be very much obliged for as large a supply as he could spare them. He gave orders at once for the issue to him of as much as they required. Edgar then went on:

"The object of our coming here, sir, is to endeavour to check the piracy that is now being carried on among the islands. Numerous complaints have reached Sir Sidney Smith from Turkish, British, and Greek merchants; ships are constantly missing, and there is no doubt that they have been captured and scuttled, and their crews massacred."

"Your ship is a small one for such a purpose," the governor said, for from the divan on which he was sitting he commanded a view of the port.

"I hope that she is large enough," Edgar replied; "she is heavily armed for her size, and she is a fast sailer. Sir Sidney Smith had no larger vessel at his disposal, as he needs the two men-of-war and the small frigate for watching the Egyptian coast, and, indeed, had he been able to send a larger craft, it would not have been so well suited for the purpose, for the pirates would hardly have ventured to attack her. We shall, after we have put out to sea, dis[Pg 253]guise the brig and rig her as a merchantman in order to tempt them out. We shall not do it until we are well away, for the pirates may have friends here who might send them information. We shall head for the south, and shall give out that we are to rejoin our commander off Alexandria, as we have only come round here to give you news of the retreat of the French. We shall be glad if you will furnish us with two men having a thorough knowledge of the islands, and of the spots where the piratical craft are most likely to harbour. They must be trusty men who will not open their lips here as to our designs."

"I can find you two such men," the governor said. "They both used to be captains of craft that traded among the islands, but now own several vessels; some of these have disappeared, and they are continually coming up here and pestering us with their complaints, though I have told them again and again that I can do nothing in the matter; I know that they would very gladly go with you in order to aid in the punishment of the pirates."

Such indeed turned out to be the case. Edgar had a long talk with them, and learned from them the spots where it was supposed that the pirates had their rendezvous, as many vessels whose course had lain near them had disappeared. He asked them to go into the town and gather what further information they could from men whose craft had been chased but had succeeded in getting away, and told them to be at the landing-place after dark so that their passage to the ship would be unnoticed, for they agreed with him that undoubtedly many of the pirates had agents at Rhodes and other important ports, and that intelligence was carried by small, quick-sailing craft, to the pirates, of vessels likely to be valuable prizes. An abundant supply of ammunition was taken off to the brig in the course of[Pg 254] the afternoon, and the supply of fresh provisions replenished.

The two young officers dined with the governor, who had a large party in their honour, including many of the military authorities. The next morning they started at six, and held their course south until they were sure that the brig could no longer be seen even from the highest point on the island, and at four bells in the afternoon changed their course, and, sailing between Scarpanto and Carso, headed north and passed before nightfall between Slazida and Placa. The crew had been busy painting a broad yellow line round the brig, in slackening the rigging, and giving the vessel the appearance of a slovenly merchant brig. They had learned from the Turks that although undoubtedly acts of piracy took place in the Western Archipelago, these were comparatively isolated acts committed upon small vessels becalmed near one or other of the islands, the attacks being made in boats, but that it was among the numerous islands lying off the coast of Asia Minor between Nicaria and Samos on the north, and Serrest and Piscopia on the south, that piracy was most frequent.

As a rule, they said, vessels coming down from the Dardanelles kept well west of Mitylene and Chios, rounded Naxos and Syra and bore south to Santorin before shaping their course east, if bound for Syria, so as to avoid the dangerous neighbourhood. To begin with, they advised that the course should be laid so as to pass a short distance east of Astropalaia. This, they said, had long been one of the headquarters of piracy. It had, before the war began, been several times attacked by Turkish or European ships of war, the craft found there burnt, and the coast villages destroyed; but since then it was believed that it had again become the headquarters of pirates from some of the other[Pg 255] islands, as its position was a favourable one for attack, lying in the direct lines of traffic between both Constantinople and Greece and the eastern trades with Rhodes, Cyprus, Syria, or Egypt.

The night was fine, with a gentle breeze. A sharp look-out was kept for two groups of tiny islands that were scarce more than rocks, that had to be passed before nearing Astropalaia. The breeze died away at daybreak, and left the vessel becalmed at a distance of some six miles from the island.

"We could not be better placed," one of the Turks said. "You see the group of islands at the mouth of that bay; they are called the Pirate Rocks, and in the old days every one of those rocks was the stronghold of a pirate ship. Thirty years ago four Turkish frigates caught eighteen piratical craft lying at anchor behind their shelter, and destroyed every one of them, but it was not long before others took their places."

"If there were a good wind blowing, Edgar, I should like nothing better than to sail right in there," Wilkinson said, "but in this light breeze those fellows would run away from us with their big sails and their sweeps."

"If there are any of them in there now," one of the Turks remarked as Wilkinson closely surveyed the islets through his glass, "most likely they have made you out before this. I only hope there will not be too many of them."

"The more the merrier!" Wilkinson laughed as Edgar translated this. "With ten guns and sixty blue-jackets we ought to be able to beat off any number of the scoundrels. Ask him how many guns these fellows generally mount?"

The Turk shook his head.

"They are of all sizes; some are only row-boats, without[Pg 256] guns at all, and carrying perhaps not more than a dozen men. Two will row, and the rest lie down in the bottom. They will have some fruit, perhaps, piled up in the stern, and as they row up to a small craft at anchor or becalmed, there are no suspicions of their real character until they get close alongside. Then they leap up, and carry the vessel before the crew have time to arm themselves. If she is very small and useless to them, they will take out everything of value, fasten the prisoners down below, and scuttle her; if she is larger, they will tow her into some little bay and take out the cargo in boats at their leisure, cut the throats of the prisoners, alter the appearance of the ship so that she cannot be recognized, engage a dozen more hands, and set up on a larger scale.

"Some of the craft are used as fishing-boats when times are quiet and there are ships of war about, while the larger ones may go into trade. Some of the smaller craft will carry a couple of guns, the larger ones eight or ten, but these are generally much smaller than yours, though sometimes they are armed with cannon taken from prizes; but, as a rule, they do not trust at all to their guns. They do not wish to draw attention by their sound to what is going on, and they either attack at night and carry their prey by boarding, or, if it be in the day, the crew are sent below, the guns hidden, and they have so peaceful an aspect that it is only when they change their course suddenly, when within a few hundred yards, that any alarm is excited, and they are alongside before a trader can load his guns, and, as they are crowded with men, carry her before any serious resistance can be offered."

At Rhodes they had taken on board a dozen bucket-loads of earth. The night before, some of these had been emptied into a large tub, which was then filled up with water and[Pg 257] stirred briskly, after which the sailors had gone aloft and wetted the sails with muddy water, rendering their appearance dingy in the extreme. Here and there white patches had been left, which gave the sails the appearance of being old and recently mended, and with the yards set at different angles and slackened rigging, the *Tigress* would not have been recognized as the smart craft that had, twenty-four hours before, sailed from Rhodes. The sailors were all in high glee. After the hard work they had had at Acre they looked upon this as a holiday, and entered with the greatest zest into the work of disguising the ship.

"Now, lads, you must sit down," Wilkinson said, "and only five or six heads must be shown above the bulwarks. They doubtless have some good glasses taken from the ships they have captured, and if they saw that we had an unusually strong crew they might smell a rat."

It was now a dead calm, the sails hung idly down, and the brig lay almost motionless on a waveless sea.

"I am pretty sure that I can make out the upper spars of two or three craft behind that long, low islet, Wilkinson," Edgar said after, for the twentieth time, gazing long and earnestly through his telescope.

"I fancied so two or three times, Edgar, but I am by no means sure that it is not fancy. I felt more sure of it at first than I do now, for there is a slight mist rising from the water. If they don't come out to us by the afternoon we will go in and have a look at them. We have got half a dozen sweeps on board, and with those and the boats we could work her in in a couple of hours."

"I hope we sha'n't have to do that," Edgar replied. "They would guess what we were at once, and would be scattering in all directions. We might pick up one or two, the rest would get off and carry news of us to all the islands round."[Pg 258]

"Perhaps you are right," Wilkinson agreed. "It would certainly be unfortunate to begin by giving them a scare."

"Besides," Edgar went on, "if the calm holds till night, they may come out and try to take us by surprise."

The day passed very slowly. The heat was great, and the men picked out spots on the deck where the sails threw a shade, and dosed off to sleep. They had, long before, made every preparation; the cutlasses had been ground, the boarding-pikes sharpened, and the pistols loaded and primed. Piles of shot lay by the side of the guns, and it needed only to fetch up the powder cartridges from the magazine to be ready for action. The marines had cleaned and loaded all the muskets, and placed them in the racks. At two o'clock, after dinner had been eaten, Wilkinson said to the boatswain:

"The starboard-watch can sling their hammocks and turn in if they like. If these fellows mean to come out and attack us, they will hardly do it before it becomes dark; perhaps not until two or three o'clock in the morning, and as we shall have to be watchful, there is no occasion for both watches to stay on deck now. The port watch shall go off from two bells till eight; as they take the first watch they will be all the brighter for a snooze beforehand."

"I wish the beggars would come out and have done with it," he went on to Edgar, as the boatswain turned away and blew his whistle. "I think I may as well go down, as it is your watch on deck. Have me roused when they change at two bells if I don't wake of my own accord."

Contrary to their usual custom in a calm, the earnest desire of all on board was that it should continue, for should a breeze spring up they would be forced to sail away, and the pirates might not pursue them. As soon as it got dark, Wilkinson told the boatswain that it would be as well that[Pg 259] a song should be started occasionally, but that not more than five or six men were to join in chorus. If, as they came out, they heard a dead silence they might think it unnatural, and it was quite possible that a boat would come on ahead of them to try and make out what they really were. In the intervals between the songs silence reigned, and all on deck listened intently.

About nine o'clock Edgar exclaimed: "I can hear oars!"

"So can I," Wilkinson replied, after listening for a minute. "I don't think that they are sweeps. No, it is a boat rowed by either two or four men— four, I think."

In a minute or two they were satisfied that it was but a boat. The order was given for another song, after which three or four men were to talk and the rest to sit down below the bulwarks and to keep silence. The two Turks took their places near the officers. From the speed at which the boat was approaching it was certain that she was not deeply laden, and there was no fear, therefore, of a surprise being attempted. She passed within twenty yards of the tafrail, and they could make out that she was an ordinary fisherman's boat. There was a pile of nets in the stern, and four men were standing up rowing.

"I wish we could get a little wind!" one of them called out.

"We wish so, too," one of the Turks answered. "We have been lying becalmed all day."

"Bound for Constantinople, I suppose?" came from the boat.

"No, for Smyrna. We are bringing a cargo from Ancona, and shall load up at Smyrna with fruit."

With a Turkish good-night the men rowed on, and the singer forward at once began another song. For a quarter of an hour they could hear the sound of the oars growing fainter and fainter, then it ceased.[Pg 260]

"They have rowed straight on till they think they are out of hearing," Wilkinson said. "Now they will make a circuit and go back to their friends with the news. There is no doubt we are in luck if we get a brush with them the first night after our arrival on our cruising ground."

About three o'clock in the morning a confused sound could be heard. In two or three minutes every man was at his post.

"There are only two, or at most three of them," Edgar said, in a tone of disappointment, "and I doubt whether they are not big rowing-boats. The strokes are too quick for either sweeps or for boats towing. What a beastly nuisance! I suppose when these fellows took back the report, that though we were a good-sized brig we did not seem to have many hands, they thought that it was not worth while to tow out a big craft when row-boats would do. They think that with twelve or fifteen hands in each boat, and the advantage of surprise, they would be able to overpower us at once."

"The surprise will be the other way," Wilkinson said angrily. "We shall send them all three to the bottom at the first broadside."

"I don't think I should do that, Wilkinson; for, if you do, there is an end of our chance of capturing any of their larger craft."

"Of course I see that; that is the annoying part of the business. What do you propose, then?"

"I should say that the best plan would be, not to hail them until they get close on board, then for a man forward to give a sudden shout, as if he had been asleep on his watch and had only just heard them. Then they will come tumbling on board, thinking that the ship is already theirs. We might divide our men, and keep them half forward and[Pg 261] half aft. The moment they all get on board, rush down upon them. Tell off six men, with orders to jump down into their boats as soon as they can, and to push them off, so as to cut off their retreat. The boats will be very useful to us, for we can tow the brig in with them. The people in there will think that she has been captured, and we shall get right in the middle of them before they find out that they have caught a tartar."

"By Jove, that is a first-rate idea!"

To their surprise, the men were at once called away from their guns and divided into two parties. Edgar and the boatswain commanded that gathered forward, Wilkinson and the gunner that aft. Nine men were told off for the capture of the boats, for, as Edgar pointed out, when the pirates found that they were caught in a trap, a good many of them might leap overboard and try to get into the boats, and it might need fully three men to keep them off.

"Now, lads, you understand," Wilkinson said, as the parties were about to take up their places, "you must crouch down and keep yourselves perfectly quiet until the word is given; it is important to get them all on board. When they see no one on deck they will think that the one or two men who might be on the watch have run below. You can use your pistols freely when the fighting once begins. When the fellows find that they are trapped, they are likely enough to fight hard, and I don't want to lose any men. Keep your cutlasses in readiness, but trust principally to your boarding-pikes."

The boats were but four or five hundred yards away when the crew of the *Tigress* took up their position. A minute later one of the men in the bow shouted suddenly:[Pg 262]

"There are boats coming!—quick, on deck!—pirates! pirates!"

Then four or five men down in the forecastle also shouted, ran up on deck, and then, with cries of alarm, ran below again, and then, but quietly this time, joined their comrades, who were crouching as closely together as possible forward of the bitts. There was a roar of voices from the boats. They could hear the oars plied desperately; then closely following this came three bumps against the side of the brig, and, clambering up the chains, the pirates poured tumultuously upon the deck, breaking into a shout of triumph as they met with no resistance. There was a pause of astonishment as the guns were seen; then their leader shouted that these could be but dummies, intended to run out and frighten people in the daytime.

"Down below, men!" one shouted; "finish with them first; it will be time to talk afterwards."

One of the Turks, who spoke a little French, crouching by the side of Wilkinson, translated his words. Some of the pirates rushed towards the forecastle, others aft to the cabins, where they would find the officers. Then some figures crawled out from below the tarpaulins that were loosely thrown over the guns, looked over the rail, and then sprang down into the boats, which were entirely deserted. As they did so there was a shout from Wilkinson; it was answered by Edgar, and then five-and-twenty seamen sprang up from each end of the vessel, and with a tremendous cheer flung themselves upon the pirates. Taken completely by surprise, and somewhat outnumbered, many of these were cut down or run through by the pikes before anything like serious resistance could be offered; then, headed by their leaders, they fought with the desperation of cornered animals.[Pg 263]

All of them carried pistols as well as yataghans. Some few of them ran to the side, and with yells of fury leaped overboard to recapture the boats. Pistols cracked on both sides, cutlass and yataghan clashed together; but the British shouts rose high over the yells of the pirates. In three minutes the fighting was virtually over, the greater portion of the pirates lay dead on the deck; a few had jumped overboard, and the rest, throwing down their arms, fell on their knees and cried for mercy.

"That will do, men—that will do!" Wilkinson shouted; "scoundrels as they are, we cannot kill them in cold blood. Get some lengths of rope, boatswain, and tie them hand and foot."

The men who had leapt into the water and swam towards the boats did not attempt to climb in when they saw three sailors in each, standing with cutlass and pistol ready to oppose them, and they swam back towards the brig. A rope was thrown to them, and they were permitted to climb up one by one, being bound and laid by their comrades as they gained the deck. None of the sailors had been killed, though several had received ugly gashes.

"Now, boatswain, put the starboard watch into the boats; lower the two ship's boats also—we will get as many oars to work as possible till daylight."

Each of the captured boats rowed six oars, and thirty men were soon at work towing the vessel towards the bay. The port watch then set to work to clear the deck. The dead were all thrown overboard; the others were unbound, made to strip off their jackets, then bound again and carried down to the hold, the hatchway being closed on them. They found that most of the survivors were Greeks, the Turks having to a man fallen fighting.

"These mixed crews are worst of all," one of the Turks[Pg 264] said. "The Turkish pirates are bad enough, and so are the Greeks—there is little to choose between them; but it is only the worst desperadoes who will consort together. You did wrong to spare a man."

"We could not kill them when they threw down their arms," Wilkinson said. "We will hand them over to your authorities, either at Smyrna or at Rhodes. They will make short work of them, I fancy."

As soon as the first gleam of dawn appeared in the sky the boats were called alongside. Those of the *Tigress* were hoisted up, and the men in the others were given the jackets of the prisoners, some having turbans and some the Greek headgear. These garments had also been stripped from the dead before the bodies were thrown overboard, and were laid in a heap in readiness for those on deck to put on when they approached the bay. When it became daylight they were not more than a mile and a half from the islands. The men in the boats had been warned not to row too regularly; and those on board had already put on their disguises. As they passed between two of the islets exclamations of satisfaction burst from Wilkinson and Edgar, for six vessels were anchored behind the largest of these. The brig's head was turned towards them, and as they approached shouts of welcome and exultation could be heard from their crews.

The craft were of various sizes, two of them were not above thirty tons burden, and each carried two light guns, the others were from fifty to a hundred and fifty tons, and carried from six to twelve guns. The *Tigress* was within about four hundred yards of the line when the helm was put down, as if to take her in between two of the largest craft. Then Wilkinson, who, with Edgar, were both in the Turkish disguises, waved his hand for the men in the[Pg 265] boats to come alongside. As they did so there was a shout of surprise from the crew of the nearest vessel, for there was no mistaking the sailors' white trousers for the baggy integuments of the Turks. At the same moment the port-holes opened, the guns were run out, and before the last man had gained the deck, the ten guns poured in their broadsides.

By Wilkinson's orders three on each side were trained on the craft nearest to them, the remaining two on each broadside being aimed at the vessels next to these. The guns had all been double-shotted, and at the same moment the broadsides were fired the ensign was run up to the peak. A wild hubbub of shouts of astonishment, fury, and alarm rose from the pirate ships, and were re-echoed by numbers of men belonging to their crews, clustered on the shore, to see the prize brought in. Some ran to their guns and began to load them, others jumped into their boats or sprang overboard and swam towards the shore. As fast as the guns on board the *Tigress* could be loaded the fire was kept up, the forward ones sweeping the deck of the craft nearest to them with grape, while the others sent round-shot into those farther away.

It was but for a short time that the pirates thought of fighting; their light guns were no match for the heavy metal of those on board the brig, and in a quarter of an hour after the first shot was fired the largest of their craft had been sunk, and the other five were entirely deserted. The boats were manned, the brig's head was first pulled round until her broadside bore on the shore, then the anchor was dropped, and the guns on the port side opened with grape upon the pirates on shore, and at five or six houses that were perched high on the rock. Leaving the boatswain in charge, Wilkinson and Edgar both took their[Pg 266] places in the boats and rowed from ship to ship. All were found empty, and as they agreed that only two of the largest were worth taking away, the other three were burned.

When they were fairly on fire the boats returned to the brig. Not a pirate was to be seen on the island, though they were sure that although numbers of them had been killed, there must still be fully two hundred of them there, but they must either have hidden among rocks or made their way down to the seaward face. As several boatloads might have rowed away to other islets, it was decided to take a landing party of five-and-thirty men on shore, for as their operations would be covered by the guns of the brig, there was little probability of the pirates attempting to attack them. As soon as they landed, the sailors, led by the two midshipmen, climbed rapidly up the hill, and without a shot being fired approached the houses on the top. From these a heavy musketry fire suddenly broke out. The men would have rushed forward at once, but Wilkinson called out to them to throw themselves down behind shelter, and as they did so a shell flew overhead, struck the largest of the houses and exploded.

Shot followed shot rapidly, the fire of the pirates ceased, then Wilkinson gave the word, and the sailors leapt up and with a cheer rushed forward. Save for a few women the houses were entirely deserted, but some fifty men were seen running down the seaward face.

A couple of volleys were poured into these, and then, placing a dozen of the men on guard, the midshipmen entered the houses. The shells had worked great damage. Over a score of men lay dead within them, and as many others wounded. The women had been in the cellars, and they were glad to find that none of them had been hurt. These cellars were very extensive, each house having one. Several of them were[Pg 267] crammed with goods of all sorts, evidently the proceeds of prizes, and of such varied description that they judged that each house formed a storehouse to one vessel, as otherwise the more valuable goods would have been collected together, instead of sails, ship-gear, bales of valuable silks and embroideries from Constantinople, Broussa, Smyrna, Chios, Alexandria, and Syria being mixed promiscuously together.

Here too were a quantity of European manufactures, showing that it was not only native craft that had suffered from their depredations. There were numbers of barrels of Greek wine, puncheons of rum, cases of bottled wines of different kinds evidently taken from English ships, great quantities of Smyrna figs, and of currants, Egyptian dates, and sacks of flour.

"This will bring us in a nice lot of prize-money, Blagrove," Wilkinson said, after they had roughly examined the contents of the great subterranean storehouses. Presently a still larger find was made. There was, close to the houses, what appeared to be a well. One of the sailors let down a bucket, and hauling it up found, to his surprise, that it was salt water. The well was deep, but certainly not deep enough to reach down to the sea level, and he carried the bucket to Wilkinson and pointed out where he had got the water from.

"There is something curious about this," the latter said. "Lower me down in the bucket, lads." As he descended he saw that the well was an ancient one, and probably at one time had been carried very much lower than at present. In some places the masonry had fallen in. At one of these points there was an opening cut into the rock. He called to those above to hoist him up again, and procuring a lamp at one of the houses, he and Edgar descended together. Entering the passage they found that it widened into a great[Pg 268] chamber some forty feet square and thirty high, which was literally crammed with goods.

"I should never have given the fellows credit for having taken the trouble to cut out such a place as this," Wilkinson said.

"I have no doubt that it is ancient work," Edgar remarked. "I should say that at some time, perhaps when the Genoese were masters here, a castle may have stood above, and this was cut either as a storehouse or as a place of confinement for prisoners, or one where the garrison might hide themselves, with provisions enough to last for a long time, in case the place was captured. The pirates may have discovered it in going down to see if the well could be cleared out, and saw that it would make a splendid place of concealment."

"But how about the salt water, Edgar?"

"I should say that they cemented the bottom or rammed it with clay to make it water-tight, and that as fresh water was scarce they brought up sea water, so that anyone who happened to look down would see that there was water in it. If, as was probable, it would be the Turks who captured the place, they would, when they found that it was salt, not trouble their heads further about the matter. Possibly even these pirates may know nothing of the existence of this store, which may have lain here since the last time the Turks broke up this nest of pirates, and who, you may be sure, left none of them alive to tell the tale. Well, this is a find."

A thorough search was now made of the island, but it was found that the whole of the pirates had made their escape in boats. These had rowed away from the seaward face of the island, so that they were unseen by those on board the brig. Before taking any step to carry away the goods, the[Pg 269] other islets were all visited and found to be deserted. Five or six more magazines of spoil were discovered. These were emptied of their most valuable contents, and the houses all burned to the ground. This operation took two days, and it required six more to transfer the contents of the cellars and great store cavern to the brig. Boats had come off on the first day of their arrival from various villages in the bay, conveying one or more of the principal inhabitants, who assured Wilkinson that they had no connection whatever with the pirates, and that they were extremely glad that their nest had been destroyed.

Wilkinson had little doubt that, although they might not have been concerned in the deeds committed by these men, they must have been in constant communication with them, and have supplied them with fruit and fresh meat and vegetables. However, he told them that he should report their assurances to the Turkish authorities, who would, when they had a ship of war available, doubtless send down and inquire into the whole circumstances, an intimation which caused them considerable alarm, as they had no doubt that, if no worse befell them, they would be made to pay heavy fines.

"The only way that you have to show your earnestness in the matter," Wilkinson said, "is to organize yourselves. You have no doubt plenty of boats, and the first time that a pirate comes in here row out from all your villages, attack and burn it, and don't leave a man alive to tell the tale. In that way the pirates will very soon learn that they'd better choose some other spot for their rendezvous, and the authorities will be well content with your conduct."

The amount of spoil taken was so great that the *Tigress*, when she set sail again, was nearly a foot deeper in the water than when she entered the bay. The prisoners had been the subject of much discussion. It was agreed that[Pg 270] they were probably no worse than their comrades who had escaped, and they did not like the thought of handing them over to be executed. They were, therefore, on the third day after the arrival of the brig, brought up on deck. Three dozen lashes were administered to each, then they were given one of the boats in which they had attacked the ship, and told to go.

CHAPTER XV.
CRUISING.

Before sailing, the yellow band was painted out, for the pirates who escaped would probably carry the news of what had happened over the whole archipelago. Ten men were put on board each of the prizes, and the *Tigress* sailed up through the islands and escorted them to Smyrna, where the pasha, after hearing an account of their capture, at once gave permission for them to be sold as prizes, and as the news of the retreat of the French had given a considerable impetus to trade, they fetched good prices. As soon as this was arranged, the *Tigress* sailed away again. For some months they cruised among the islands, putting into every little bay and inlet, boarding every craft found there, and searching her thoroughly to see if there was any property belonging to plundered vessels on board.

Once or twice she came upon two or three large craft together, and had some hard fighting before she captured or sank them; but, as a rule, the crews rowed ashore as soon as they saw the real nature of the new-comer. Some thirty craft were sent as prizes into Smyrna or Rhodes, and there sold, as many more were sunk or burned. They had, in no case, found spoil at all equal to that which had been cap[Pg 271]tured at Astropalaia, but the total was nevertheless considerable. Once or twice they were attacked by boats when anchored in quiet bays, but as a vigilant watch was always kept they beat off their assailants with heavy loss. The rig of the brig was frequently altered. Sometimes she was turned into a schooner with yards on her foremast, sometimes into a fore-and-aft craft; and as the time went on and captures became fewer and fewer, it was evident that she had established a thorough scare throughout the archipelago, and that for the time the pirates had taken to peaceful avocations, and were indeed completely crippled by the loss of so large a number of their craft.

The *Tigress* had but one awkward incident during the voyage. The day was bright and clear. The two Turks had been, as was their custom, squatting together on the deck, smoking their pipes. Wilkinson and Edgar were pacing together up and down, when the latter said:

"Look at these two native craft; they have both let their lateen sails run down. I am sure I don't know why; there is not a cloud in the sky, except that little white one over there."

They were passing the Turks at the moment, and Edgar said to one of them:

"The two craft over there have just let their sails run down. What can that mean?"

The Turk leapt to his feet with a quickness very unusual to him.

"It is a white squall!" he shouted. "Down with every stitch of canvas, sir. Quick, for your lives! the squall will be upon us in five minutes."

It was Wilkinson's first experience of the terribly sudden squall of the Levant, but he had heard of them and knew their danger, and he shouted at the top of his voice:[Pg 272]

"All hands take in sail! Quick, lads, for your lives!"

The boatswain's whistle rang loudly in the air, and he repeated the order at the top of his voice. The men on deck, who had been engaged on various small jobs since they came up from dinner, looked astounded at the order, but without hesitation ran up the ratlines at the top of their speed, while the watch below looked equally surprised as they glanced upwards and around at the deep blue of the sky.

"Quick, quick!" the Turk exclaimed. "Let go all sheets and halliards!"

Wilkinson shouted, "Do the sails up anyhow, men."

Although the sky was unchanged they could see the light cloud Edgar had noticed advancing towards them at an extraordinary rate of speed, while a white line on the sea kept pace with it.

"Hard up with the helm—hard up!" Wilkinson shouted. "Hold on a moment with those head sails; that will do, that will do. Let go the halliards; down staysails and jib."

The sailors, now conscious of the coming danger, worked desperately. The light upper sails were secured, the courses had been clewed up, but the topsails were still but half-lashed when Wilkinson shouted again:

"Down for your lives! Down on the weather side; slip down by the back-stays. You men to leeward, hold on—all hold on," he shouted a few seconds later.

There was a dull roaring sound, rising to a shriek as the squall struck the vessel.

Most of the men had gained the deck in safety, but many of those coming down by the ratlines were still some distance from the deck. It was well for them that they were on the weather side; had they been to leeward they would have been torn from their grasp, whereas they were now[Pg 273] pinned to the rigging. Two sounds like the explosion of cannon were heard. The main and foretopsails both blew out of their gaskets, bellied for an instant, and then burst from the bolt-ropes and flew away, and were speedily lost to sight. So great was the pressure that the brig was driven bodily down until the water was almost level with the rail at the bow, and it looked for a moment as if she would go down by the head.

One of the jibs was run up, but only to be blown away before it was sheeted home. Another was tried, the sheet being kept very slack. This held, her head lifted, and in a minute the *Tigress* was flying along dead before the wind. The storm-jib was brought up, hooked on, and hoisted. This, being of very heavy canvas, could be trusted, and as soon as it was set the other was hauled down.

"Thank God, that is over!" Wilkinson said, "and we have not lost a hand."

By this time all the men had gained the deck.

"How long will this last?" Edgar shouted in one of the Turks' ears.

"Perhaps one hour; perhaps four."

"Let us have a look at the chart," Wilkinson said. "When we last looked there was a group of rocks ten miles ahead, and at the rate we are going the *Tigress*will be smashed into matchwood if she keeps on this course for long."

Edgar nodded.

"We must get trysails on the main and foremast," Wilkinson went on, "and manage to lay her course a couple of points to the west. I wish we had those upper spars down on deck, but it is of no use talking of that now."

Wilkinson went down to the sail-room with the boatswain and four seamen to bring up the two heaviest and strongest of the triangular sails.[Pg 274]

"We must sheet them home before we hoist them," he said, as they returned on deck. "We should never be able to haul the sheets in when the sails once fill."

Twenty men went aft with them and commenced the task. The fore-trysail was bent to some of the mast-hoops, and the sheet fastened to a cavel on the port side.

"Port your helm a little, my man," Wilkinson said. "That will do, just enough to keep the wind on the starboard quarter. Keep her at that, keep her at that." Edgar had the sail ready to hoist. "Slacken the tack a little. Now, half a dozen of you tail on here, and get ready to haul it down as soon as the sail is up to its full height and the halliards secured. Now, lads, tail on to the halliards. Away with her."

The sailors ran forward with the rope, but as the sail rose the strain was so great that once or twice they were brought to a standstill. At last the boatswain shouted:

"That is enough. Come back a little, but keep a firm grip of it. That is right!" he shouted, as he twisted the slack of the rope over the cleet. "Now, lads, down with the tack; down with it! Belay!"

The main-trysail was hoisted as successfully. Small as were the sails, and slight the angle with the wind, the pressure brought the ship down nearly to her covering-board. Wilkinson and the boatswain took their places by the wheel.

"Keep her full, lads, but not a bit more. She will do at that. By Jove, Blagrove," he said, as Edgar came aft and glanced at the compass, "that was a narrow squeak! If you hadn't noticed those native craft lower their sails and called our attention to it, we should have turned turtle as sure as fate. We have got her snug now. If we were right as to our position at noon we shall clear those rocks nicely."

"I don't think we can have been far wrong, by the posi[Pg 275]tion of the islands. At the same time I will go up to the foretop," Edgar said; "I shall be able to make them out some distance away, for, if you remember, two of them are thirty or forty feet above the water."

"Mind how you go," Wilkinson said. "You had better take one of the men up with you; you can hold each other on then."

Edgar went forward and told one of the best of the hands to go aloft with him.

"All right, your honour!"

"It will be a tight job, but I daresay we can do it. Get a couple of lines seven or eight feet long; we will fasten them under our arms, and if a puff comes harder than usual we can twist the end round a shroud or ratline."

In a couple of minutes both were roped and ready to mount. It was hard work, and several times they had to use the rope to prevent their being torn from their hold. But at last they reached the top, and fastened themselves securely there. The scene was a singular one. Overhead was a cloudless sky, somewhat paler in tint than it had been before the squall burst. Below was a white mass of foam, which, from the height on which they stood, seemed almost pressed level by the force of the wind. On deck they had been drenched with the sheets of spray torn off the heads of the waves as soon as they began to lift themselves, but here they were above this, and there was nothing to prevent their looking round in all directions.

"There are the rocks, sir," the top-man said, after they had been some twenty minutes in their position, "over the lee bow, about two points off our course."

"I see them now," Edgar said. "I thought we should have made them out by the white foam round them, but it is white everywhere."[Pg 276]

He shouted down to the deck, but it was some time before he could make his voice heard above the roar of the squall. He pointed aft when at last one looked up. The sailor ran aft to the helm, and called Wilkinson's attention to Edgar. The latter pointed in the direction of the rocks. Wilkinson waved his hand, and Edgar, then leaving the sailor on watch, made his way down to the deck.

"We shall go within half a mile of them," he said, when he joined his comrade.

"It is lucky that we looked at the chart as soon as we did," Wilkinson shouted back, "for even with this rag of sail I should not have liked to bring her nearer to the wind than we are now."

"I don't think it is blowing quite as hard as it was," Edgar said. "I certainly got down more easily than I went up."

"I was thinking so myself, Blagrove, though there is not much difference. I don't care, now that we are clear of those rocks, how long it keeps on. Directly we pass them we can keep her off the wind again, and there is nothing in our course then for over forty miles, and then it is only a small island with deep water all round. I have just been taking another look at the chart."

By another hour the strength of the wind had considerably abated, the fore-staysail was reefed and hoisted, and before sunset sail was on her again, and the hands were aloft preparing to get up fresh topsails.

At the end of six months, on their going into Rhodes they found that a small gun-boat had arrived with orders from Sir Sidney Smith for them to rejoin him.

"You have done exceedingly well," the latter said in his letter. "The pashas both of Smyrna and Rhodes have written to me expressing their admiration at the work that[Pg 277] you have accomplished, and indeed your report of the number of pirate vessels taken or destroyed speaks for itself."

They were not sorry at the receipt of the order. During the past month they had only made two or three captures, and these were craft of small size, and they were well content to give up their independent life, and return to regular duty. A week later they made out the *Tigre* lying off the Damietta mouth of the Nile. The man-of-war signalled to them to anchor near her. As soon as they did so Wilkinson went on board.

"I am glad to see you back, Mr. Wilkinson," Sir Sidney said cordially. "You have fully justified my confidence in your energy and discretion. The pashas write to me saying that piracy seems to be completely suppressed, and that it is two months since either of them received a complaint of a vessel being chased or missing. Therefore, as I wanted you here, where we have not half enough ships for the work, I thought it as well to recall you. Your craft seems," he went on, as he surveyed the *Tigress* through his glass, "a good deal lower in the water than she was?"

"Yes, sir, she is down nearly two feet and a half. I reported to you that we gained a considerable amount of booty at Astropalaia, and of course we have added gradually to that, but never had anything like so good a haul. The hold up to the level of the main deck is full."

"Full of what, Mr. Wilkinson?"

"Miscellaneous cargo, sir—dried fruit, Manchester goods, and Eastern goods of all sorts. I have not taken an exact inventory of them, sir, for we were generally pressed for time, and I thought that the things were less likely to be damaged if I did not open the bales. I really do not know exactly what we have got, but there is certainly a good deal of silk and a quantity of embroidered things."[Pg 278]

"That sounds well, anyhow," Sir Sidney said, smiling, "but I am afraid that it will not turn out so well for you personally as it ought to do. You see the craft herself was a prize of the *Tigre*, and her officers and crew are still borne on our books; therefore, although you were detached on altogether independent work, you still rank as a tender of the *Tigre*, and we all share with you, and indeed all your names have been sent in on the list of those entitled to share in the prizes that we have made here. As these have been generally laden partly with ammunition and partly with luxuries for the use of the army, they were for the most part valuable, and up to this time we calculate that a sum of fifty or sixty thousand pounds will be shared."

"We quite understood, sir, that we should share with the *Tigre* in all that we captured. It would have been too bad if, in addition to our luck in having an independent cruise on board the *Tigress*, we were to get an advantage over our comrades in the way of prize-money. We have, as I told you in my last report, received twelve thousand five hundred pounds, the result of the sale of the thirty-two craft we sent into Smyrna and Rhodes. It is in gold, and I thought that it would be better for you to send off a boat for it than for me to bring it myself now. What are we to do with the cargo, sir?"

"I must think that over, Mr. Wilkinson. You have not lost many hands, I hope, while you were away?"

"No, sir, we have not done any very hard fighting. We had two men shot in the attack of the pirates' hold at Astropalaia, and more than half the crew have been wounded more or less seriously, but fortunately all got over it."

"That is very satisfactory, Mr. Wilkinson. In giving me a full report of your work, give a list of the casualties in each case. Some of the people at the Admiralty seem to[Pg 279] have an idea that the credit of any affair depends largely on the size of the butcher's bill, whereas, in point of fact, it should be exactly the other way, for not unfrequently heavy loss means that measures were badly taken by the officers in command, whereas a light one shows that the arrangements were all excellent, and the work carried out without a hitch. I shall be glad if you and Mr. Blagrove will dine with me. It is not very regular for you both to leave the ship together, but there are no signs whatever of change of wind, and one can reckon with some certainty here upon the weather for at any rate twenty-four hours in advance. If you should see any change before you come off, or any fall in the glass, Mr. Blagrove must stay on board."

Wilkinson now joined his comrades, who were gathered a short distance away waiting until he had finished his talk with Sir Sidney. "Come down below, Wilkinson, and give us the news. We heard that you had taken some prizes from the pirates; we want to hear all about it. Is Blagrove all right?"

They were soon gathered in the cockpit. "I have not much time to stay," Wilkinson said, "and, before I tell you my story, I want to hear your news, for beyond a few rumours current at Smyrna and Rhodes, we really know hardly anything of what has taken place since we left you at Acre."

"We have had rather a dull time," one of them said; "the only excitement was a fight between the Turks, aided by our boats, and the French. When we returned here, we found that instead of being fifteen thousand strong, as promised, the Turks on board their transports under Mustapha Pasha were but five thousand strong, which was raised to seven thousand by the two thousand we brought with us[Pg 280] from Acre. On the 15th of July they landed, attacked the redoubt and castle of Aboukir with great pluck, and carried it by assault. A week later, we heard that Bonaparte was at Ramanieh, and had no doubt that the Turks would soon have him on them. Sir Sidney tried hard to get them to erect a strong line of works across the spit of ground on which the fort stands.

"Had they done so they could, with the assistance of our boats and their own gun-boats, have maintained their ground. The chief set to work at once to endeavour to get things into shape. The Chiflick regiment, that we had brought with us from Acre, was posted in the village at the end of the spit. The Turkish gun-boats were ordered to take their places directly the assault began on each side of the isthmus, so as to sweep it with their fire, but when that time came the beggars would not move, and did not arrive until it was all over.

"The Turks in the village were attacked several times, but made a magnificent defence. We helped them with our guns as much as we could, but could render them very little assistance. At last we saw that an attack was to be made in earnest; peremptory orders were sent to the Turkish gun-boats to go in and take up their stations, and our boats all went in to the west side of the spit. Nothing could be worse than the arrangements of the Turks. They had sent very little provisions and next to no water on shore, and their troops were nearly half-mad with thirst, and more than half-mutinous. However, they moved forward to the village, and they there repulsed three attacks made by the French columns. Probably no more attacks would have been made, if it had not been for their beastly custom of cutting off the heads of the fallen. Lots of them ran out of the village to do this, and this so infuriated the French[Pg 281] that they came on again with such a rush that they entered the village with the flying Turks.

"The confusion was terrible, and the Turks were driven out. The spit of sand was covered with fugitives, hundreds threw themselves into the water and swam out to us. The castle, which, as you know, is a little bit of a place, was crowded almost to suffocation, and thousands could not get in. The fire of our boat guns kept the French back for a time, and when at last the Turkish gun-boats got into position, they had to fall back and make advances against the castle in a regular way. Unfortunately Mustapha Pasha had been taken in the village, and the garrison had no one to command them, still they resisted for two days, and then surrendered, being almost mad with thirst, for, although we spared as much water as we could, it was impossible for us to find sufficient for six or seven thousand extra men.

"Our marines saved the castle the first day, Colonel Douglas landing and taking command and restoring order, for the Turks were fighting fiercely among themselves when we got in, and during the night he managed to send off about a thousand of them to their ships. The whole business was brought about owing to Mustapha Pasha not acting in accordance with the advice that Sir Sidney had sent him to act against either Damietta or Rosetta, as our ships would station themselves in the Bay of Aboukir, and so threaten Alexandria that the French would not care to weaken their force there by sending any considerable number of men to act against the Turks. There, that is all that has happened. Now let us hear your yarn."

Wilkinson gave a brief account of the trip of the *Tigress*.

"You see," he said, "we have not done much fighting; indeed, with the exception of the first scrimmage at Astro[Pg 282]palaia we can scarcely have said to have had anything worth calling fighting at all. We picked up a lot of small piratical craft, destroyed the majority of them, and sold the others at Smyrna or Rhodes. We got altogether twelve thousand five hundred for them, and as, of course, that will be shared by the *Tigre*, we have done pretty well our share in the way of earning prize-money for the ship. More, indeed, for the *Tigre's* share of the prizes that you have taken here won't come to more than fifteen or twenty thousand at the outside. Besides that, we have got some booty on board the *Tigress*, but what it is worth I have no idea, for we simply bundled the things down below without opening anything. Still, no doubt it will be enough to give you a few pounds a head."

As soon as he could get away Wilkinson returned to the brig. That evening, at the admiral's table, he gave a much more detailed account of their doings than he had done in his reports. When he had finished, Sir Sidney Smith said:

"That attack upon the pirates' hold was extremely well managed, Mr. Wilkinson, and does you and Mr. Blagrove great credit. You were very brief in your account of it, and only said that a considerable amount of booty, which had evidently been taken from plundered ships, was found concealed, and that the more valuable portion was shipped on the *Tigress*. I will come on board in the morning, and you can have a few of those bales brought up on to the main deck, and we can see what is in them."

A dozen bales were opened the next day; two contained European goods, the rest Eastern manufactures, silks and embroideries, Turkish, Syrian, and Persian carpets and rugs.

"That is enough!" Sir Sidney said. "Now, can you roughly give me an idea what proportion of European goods,[Pg 283] dried fruits, and what we may call generally Eastern goods, you have?"

"There are about twenty tons of fruit, sir, thirty tons of European bales, and fifty or sixty tons of Eastern goods. Of these, I should say that two-thirds are carpets and rugs, we could pretty well tell these from the others by the size and feel of the bales; the rest are, judging from the few we opened, cloth for female garments—muslin, silks, scarves, sashes, and embroidered goods.

"It is extraordinary how so great a collection could have been made."

"There have been a great many vessels employed in the making of it, sir, and we may say that we have here the pick from at least a hundred, perhaps several times that number, of captured craft of several sizes. No doubt the pirates would, in all cases, put aside goods of this kind, for although of no use to themselves, and no doubt very difficult to sell, they would store them away under the idea that some time or other an opportunity would occur of turning them into money."

"Well, there is no doubt that you have an extremely rich prize. I should be afraid to give even an approximate calculation of what all this is worth. Some of our East-Indiamen bring very valuable cargoes home; but I should doubt whether any one ship ever carried as much costly merchandise as you have stored here. I will think over how they had best be got to England. The things will require careful handling, for if they were consigned to an ordinary prize agent they might be sold anyhow and for half their value."

On the following day the two midshipmen were signalled to come on board the *Tigre*.

"I have been thinking your matter over, gentlemen,"[Pg 284] Sir Sidney said when they had entered his cabin. "I have power to appoint a prize agent in England. As a matter of fact I have not done so. Coming out here, as I did, on a diplomatic mission, I had no thought of taking prizes. Those we have picked up here I simply sent to the agent at Gibraltar, which, by the way, is one of the very worst places one can send them to, as the vessels are sold at ridiculous prices. Ordinarily Malta would be the port we should have sent them to from here, but as it is still in the possession of the French, Gibraltar is the only port in the Mediterranean. Of course they might be sent to England; but there is the difficulty of detaching men and officers, and the risk of their being captured by French privateers, so that practically we are driven to Gibraltar.

"Of course the prize court will have the disposal of the cargo, but I will write to the head of the court, who is a personal friend of mine, asking him to intrust the sale of the Eastern goods to your father, Mr. Blagrove, saying that as he has been for years engaged in trade in the East, and must therefore be acquainted with the value of these things, is in the habit of sending Egyptian silks and so on to London for sale, he must know the channels in which they could be best disposed of. Of course the dried fruits and the English goods could be sold by the court, but it would never do to throw such a quantity of Eastern goods on the market at once. Among the prizes that have been taken is a smart brig of about the same size as the *Tigress*. She was caught making for Alexandria with powder and ball for the French army. Fortunately for us her captain was not a first-class navigator, and so missed his mark by about ten miles, and found himself, to his consternation and our satisfaction, close under our guns.

"I was going to send her to Gibraltar to be sold. I do[Pg 285] not think that we can do better than buy her to carry home your cargo. I will call a court of four officers to put on her the price they consider it probable that she will fetch, which, I should say, if she were sold at Gibraltar, would not be over eight or nine hundred pounds. You, Mr. Blagrove, can buy her in the name of your father, and I will take your bill at three months upon him. Then there is the question of the crew. As to the officers, I can send you home, Mr. Wilkinson, with despatches. I have not had an opportunity of forwarding any for some weeks now; and to you, Mr. Blagrove, I can give three months' leave on urgent private business. As to men, we have small craft coming over here constantly from Sicily with fruit and fresh provisions, and I have no doubt that, with the offer of good wages, you would be able to pick up ten or twelve men without much difficulty.

"On board our ships there are, I should say, at least twenty men who have been invalided by boards of doctors as being unfit for service, either from the effects of wounds or climate, and this would be a good opportunity for sending them home. Many of them are still fit for easy work, and would, at any rate, counterbalance your Italian crew. Of course I should formally take a passage for them in Mr. Blagrove's ship. The prize mounts six guns, but I would advise you to keep well out of the way of French privateers. Of course the final result of the sale of the merchandise would have to be paid by your father, Mr. Blagrove, into the prize court for division among those entitled to it.

"With the ship, as your father's property, the case is different; that is his private venture. He will, of course, charge freight on the merchandise, and he will get two or three pounds a head for taking the invalids home. As he will certainly get double the price the brig would fetch at[Pg 286] Gibraltar, that and the freight would a good deal more than clear all expenses, and he will of course have the usual prize-agent's commission on the sales he effects. What do you think of that plan?"

Both the midshipmen were highly pleased with the proposal, and thanked their commander very heartily for his kindness. A board of officers assembled on the following day and assessed the value of the French brig at £850, and Edgar formally bought her in his father's name for that sum, and drew a bill upon him for payment in three months.

He had several times heard from him since he had entered on board the *Tigre*, and in the first letter Mr. Blagrove gave a hearty approval of the course that he had adopted, and said that a year or two at sea would give him a thorough knowledge of ships and be a considerable advantage to him in their business. The receipt of Edgar's first letter, and of a heavy budget containing the account of his doings in Egypt from the day on which he was left behind to that on which he sailed, had been an immense relief to them all, for hitherto they had been in absolute ignorance of what had taken place. His father, however, thought that he had, even according to his own account, run a very needless risk in taking part in the rising at Cairo, although he saw that, having for the time become so thoroughly associated with the Arabs, it would have been difficult for him to avoid acting with them when there was danger in so doing.

[Pg 287]

CHAPTER XVI.
A VISIT HOME.

The new purchase, which was named the *Suzanne*, was towed alongside the *Tigress*, and the crew began at once to get up the cargo and transfer it to her hold. More method was observed in restowing the cargo than had before been possible. The dried fruit, as the heaviest of the goods, was placed in the middle of the brig; the European goods, whose brands and packing enabled them to be easily distinguished from the rest, were placed forward; and the Eastern bales packed aft. This was done under the direction of the petty officers.

During the four days that it took to complete the work, Edgar boarded several of the Italian craft, and succeeded in inducing ten active young sailors to join him, by the offer of a rate of pay several times higher than that they earned in their native craft, and of a free passage back on the first opportunity. Condor was appointed to the command of the *Tigress*, as two supernumerary lieutenants and four midshipmen had been sent out from home to the *Tigre*, and two midshipmen received acting orders as his lieutenants. There was much satisfaction among the junior officers of the *Tigre* when they heard from Wilkinson the nature of the spoil he had gathered, and all sorts of guesses were hazarded as to its value.

"I cannot help you there in the least," he said. "I know that Turkish and Eastern carpets fetch a big price at home; and of course silk, and gold and silver embroideries, are valuable; but, as I only know the contents of about a hundred bales, I have no more idea of what the total is likely to come to than you have."[Pg 288]

"You did not get any money, Wilkinson, or jewels?"

"Neither one nor the other. I suppose that the money was divided when captured, and the jewels either given to the women or sold. They were things that might be disposed of anywhere. At any rate we found none of them, and the only cash is, as I told you, the twelve thousand five hundred pounds that the prizes fetched, out of which our share is not likely to be more than twenty or thirty pounds each. Still, that is not to be despised."

"It will come to more than that," one of the party said. "I have calculated it up, and though I have not the exact rules—"

"Well, if you haven't got the exact rules, Macleod, your calculations are not worth more than our guesses. It won't be much more than forty pounds anyhow, and I suppose a bit more than that for our share of the prizes captured here. Of course they were worth a good deal more, but then there are all the ships-of-war to share. If our prize turns out as well as I hope, it will come to a good bit more, as it is only to be divided among the *Tigre's* crew."

"You and Blagrove are going home in the prize, are you not?"

"Yes, I carry Sir Sidney's despatches; Blagrove gets three months' leave."

"Who is going to command the craft that you have bought for your father, Blagrove?"

"I have persuaded the captain of that store-ship that came in yesterday to let me have his second officer for two or three months. She is likely to be here some time; and if we have luck, and his mate gets a return passage soon after he arrives in England, he may be back again in six weeks. From another ship of the same sort I got a young fellow for mate. The ships are chartered by government, and will[Pg 289] likely enough be here for months, as they will furnish stores not only to the ships on the coast, but to any that may come down here from the fleet blockading Toulon. In fact they will act as general shore-ships, until they have cleared out their cargo."

"Then he will be your captain?"

"He will be entered on the ship's books as captain," Edgar replied with a laugh; "but I fancy that Wilkinson and myself will not care to be idle on the voyage."

Three days after the cargo was transferred, twenty invalids were placed on board. Two or three had lost limbs, but the rest were men who had been pulled down by fever and could not shake it off so long as they were on the coast. On the following morning the anchor was got up and the *Suzanne* sailed for England. The nominal captain was a smart young sailor, who was glad indeed of the opportunity, for three or four months of enforced idleness on the Egyptian coast was not at all to his taste. The extra pay that he would receive was a consideration, but the fact that he was to be nominally—for Edgar had explained the situation to him—in command was the great inducement.

He had fortunately passed his examination and obtained his certificate as captain before sailing on the present voyage. Had it not been for this he could not have accepted Edgar's offer. The voyage was a rapid one. They stopped for two days at Gibraltar to take in water. They had some little trouble with the prize-agent there, for of course the ship's papers showed that she had been a prize, and she should have been sent there to be condemned and sold. Sir Sidney Smith, however, had written, saying that as the ships on the station were already short-handed, he could not spare a prize crew, and that he had therefore only the choice of burning the prize or of selling her there, and that a court[Pg 290] of officers from the various ships-of-war had fixed her value at £850, and a purchaser having been found at that price, he had deemed it expedient to sell her, and now forwarded his bill for the amount, to be divided in the usual course by the prize officials at Gibraltar, as if they had sold her themselves. He stated that as she had been loaded with munitions of war for the French army, no question could arise as to the lawfulness of her capture.

The officials shook their heads over the irregularity, but as the defence of Acre had made a great sensation in England, and a vote of thanks had been passed by both Houses of Parliament, and by many of the corporate bodies in England, to Sir Sidney and those serving under him, they agreed to set the matter right; and thereupon, on the evidence given by Wilkinson and Edgar as to the circumstances of the capture, they formally condemned the ship and authorized the sale that had been effected. That point satisfactorily settled, they sailed at once, shaped their course, after issuing from the Straits, a hundred miles west of the usual ship track, and met with no suspicious sail until they entered the Chops of the Channel. Then one or two craft that looked like French privateers were observed; but the *Suzanne* was a fast vessel and kept her distance from them, holding her course up Channel, and one morning, soon after daybreak, dropped anchor among a number of other merchantmen on the Mother bank off Ryde.

Directly the anchor was down the gig was lowered, and Wilkinson, Edgar, and the captain were rowed into Portsmouth, the brig being left in charge of the mate. The former went to the dockyard and reported to the admiral that he had brought home despatches from Sir Sidney Smith for the Admiralty.

"In what ship have you brought them?"[Pg 291]

"As there was no ship of war likely to be sailing, a passage was taken for me in a trader, a prize that had been sold, and was being brought home."

"Very well, sir. You will, of course, post with it at once for London. Have any particular events happened there?"

"No, sir. Beyond the fact that a few prizes have been picked up there is nothing doing. But I understood from Sir Sidney that there had been no opportunity of sending home reports for a month, and that therefore he thought it best to take the opportunity of forwarding his despatches by a private ship. She is also bringing home some goods captured from pirates in the Levant by the *Tigre's* tender, the *Tigress*, which I had the honour to command. There are also twenty men on board invalided home."

"Very well, Mr. Wilkinson. I have nothing further to say to you, and you will doubtless wish to start without delay. I will send off for the sick men at once."

The captain returned on board to take the brig round to London. The two friends reached town late that night, and Wilkinson went straight to the Admiralty with the despatches. He was at once taken to the room where one of the junior officials was on duty.

"Despatches from Sir Sidney Smith, sir," Wilkinson said.

"Anything important?"

"I believe not. There was an opportunity for sending them, and Sir Sidney availed himself of it."

"Then it will not be worth while to wake up the admiral at this time of night?"

"I should say certainly not. But I thought it my duty to bring them here at once."

The other nodded.

"Where do you put up, Mr. Wilkinson?"[Pg 292]

"At the Golden Cross."

"Very well. If you are wanted you can be sent for in the morning. You had best call here about eleven, so that you can answer any questions that the admirals may ask."

In the morning the midshipman went across. Half an hour later his name was called out, and he was at once shown into a room in which two of the naval lords were sitting.

"You are the bearer of the despatches from Sir Sidney Smith, Mr. Wilkinson?"

"Yes, sir."

"He has sent us the report you gave him of your cruise in the brig *Tigress* among the Greek and Turkish islands. There can be no doubt that you did your work exceedingly well, as is shown by the long list of prizes captured or destroyed. He mentions that he has received also reports from the Pasha of Smyrna and the Governor of Rhodes, speaking in high terms of the services that you have rendered, and saying that for the time piracy appears to have entirely ceased and the seas to be open to peaceful traders. What time have you to serve?"

"I have another six months, sir."

"Well, I think, if you feel prepared, it would be as well for you to take advantage of your being at home to pass, and we will take care that you shall get your promotion as soon as you have served your full time. You would like a couple of months' leave, no doubt, before you return. Would you rather wait before going in to be examined, or would you prefer going in at once?"

"I would rather go in at once, sir. I should enjoy my holiday much better if it was over."

"I do not think it will take very long," the admiral said with a smile. "After having been in command of a ten-[Pg 293]gun brig for six months you should be able to satisfy the requirements of the examiners without difficulty. You will be good enough to wait in the ante-room."

The delay was not long. In ten minutes the official messenger requested him to follow him, and took him to a room where three naval captains were sitting. The one in the centre looked up from the papers that he was examining.

"Good-morning, Mr. Wilkinson! I see by these papers that you have for six months been in command of the ten-gun brig *Tigress*, cruising for pirates among the Turkish and Greek islands."

"Yes, sir."

"I suppose during that time you met once or twice with bad weather?"

"We had one tremendous squall, sir."

"It came suddenly upon you?"

"Yes, sir. Our first intimation of it was that we saw two native craft suddenly lower their sails."

"Let us know exactly the measures that you took and the orders you gave."

Wilkinson described what had passed from the time that the first order was given until the violence of the squall abated.

"That will do as far as seamanship is concerned," the officer said.

Another now asked him a few questions as to navigation, and these being answered correctly, the president, after a word with the others, said:

"That will do, Mr. Wilkinson. You have answered creditably, and, indeed, the mere fact that Sir Sidney Smith should have considered you fit to command the *Tigress* in so difficult and dangerous a work as cruising among those[Pg 294] islands is in itself a better guarantee of your fitness for promotion than the most rigid examination could be."

A few further questions were asked, and then Wilkinson was congratulated upon having passed successfully. He then went to the prize court, saw the President, and presented Sir Sidney Smith's note to him. He read it through, and then glanced at a copy of the bill of lading which had been taken when the cargo was transferred.

"You do not know the contents of all those bales and casks, Mr. Wilkinson?"

"No, sir. The greater portion of them have never been opened. Some, of course, one could recognize from the nature of the packing, and I put them down as nearly as I could guess—Manchester goods, woollen, hardware, and so on; but, as we wanted to be off, and it was better that the things should remain in their original packing, we did not trouble to open them, and they were received as cargo consigned to you."

"The Eastern goods you know nothing about, I suppose?"

"Nothing whatever."

"Well, when the brig arrives in the river the captain will, of course, call here, and I will give him instructions where to land them."

"I understand," he went on, looking again at the letter, "that Mr. Blagrove, to whom Sir Sidney asks me to intrust the sale of these goods, is an expert in this special line?"

"Yes, sir; he has been for many years established as a merchant in Alexandria, and Sir Sidney thought that he would not only be able to estimate accurately the value of the goods, but would know exactly where to place them, and would, by bringing them gradually forward, get far larger sums for them than if they were thrown all at once upon the market."[Pg 295]

"I see the vessel is his property, Mr. Wilkinson?"

"It is so, sir, his son purchased it in his name. He is a fellow-midshipman of mine in the *Tigre*, and was with me in the craft with which we captured all these goods and the vessels that have been sold for twelve thousand five hundred. This I have brought up with me in gold, and will pay into the hands of anybody you may appoint, to be added to the proceeds of the sales, for division by the court."

"Have you any idea of the value of these Eastern goods?"

"Not in the slightest, sir; only a few of the bales were opened in the presence of Sir Sidney Smith. He himself said that it would be better not to open more, as there were no facilities for repacking."

"I think that it was a very good idea of Sir Sidney's to suggest that it would be for the advantage of all concerned to vary the usual course, and to place these goods in the hands of an expert instead of selling them by auction. I should like to see Mr. Blagrove. I suppose you know his address. Is he in town?"

"He is living in Dulwich, sir."

"Well, will you let him know that if he calls upon me to-morrow morning I will give him full authority to act in the matter, and then we can settle whether to stow that portion of the cargo in our warehouses or whether to make other arrangements. I will myself write to Sir Sidney Smith to thank him for his suggestion with respect to the sale of these goods, and to say that I have so arranged it. The question of freight is, of course, a matter altogether separate, and I shall give Mr. Blagrove a cheque for the amount arranged between his representative and Sir Sidney Smith at the rate of three pounds per ton when he brings[Pg 296] me the receipt of the officer in charge of the warehouse of his having received the stores in good order from the ship."

Edgar had, on reaching London, stopped at the Golden Cross for the night, and the first thing in the morning taken a hackney-coach and driven at once to Dulwich, where his father had taken a house close to that of his brother. It was now the first week in December. Edgar drove up to the entrance to the garden in which the house stood, paid the coachman, and then rang the bell. The servant opened it, and looked somewhat surprised at seeing a young naval officer standing there.

"Are Mr. and Mrs. Blagrove in?" he asked.

"Yes, sir, they are both in."

"All right!" he said; "show me to the room where they are. You need not announce me; I am their son."

The girl at once led the way into the house, and Edgar walked into the room, where the party were seated at breakfast. Mr. Blagrove was sitting with his back to the door, and did not see him come in. His mother and sisters looked up in surprise as he entered unannounced. It was two years since they had seen him, and they scarcely recognized in the tall young officer the lad whom they had last seen at Alexandria on their departure for England. Mr. Blagrove, on seeing their eyes fixed on the door, turned round, and leapt to his feet.

"My dear Edgar," he exclaimed as he warmly embraced him, "where have you sprung from? Your last letter was from Smyrna three months ago. Mother," he went on, turning round, "let me introduce your boy to you."

For some minutes there was little coherent conversation.

"Now, sit down, Edgar," Mr. Blagrove said at last, "and[Pg 297] let us hear what unexpected chance has brought you home. I suppose, as you are in uniform, that you have not left the service."

"Not at all, sir; I am home on three months' leave, having come home in the _Suzanne_, a brig belonging to yourself."

"Belonging to me!" Mr. Blagrove said in astonishment. "What on earth do you mean?"

"I bought her in your name, father, and you will have a bill presented in the course of a couple of months or so for eight hundred and fifty pounds. At any rate you will not be a loser by her. There will be from six to seven hundred pounds, I cannot say how much exactly, for the cargo was not weighed, but it is somewhat over two hundred tons at three pounds a ton, and there is, besides, a hundred pounds for the passage-money of twenty invalid sailors, so you see you get the ship for practically about a hundred pounds, to which there will have to be added the payment of a captain, mate, and ten Italian sailors. She was valued by a court of naval officers at eight hundred and fifty pounds, that being the price they considered that she might fetch if sold there. I should say that she is worth quite double that. She is about three hundred tons, and carried six guns, so at any rate you are likely to make a thousand by the transaction.

"Then I have to inform you that, at Sir Sidney Smith's request, which I have no doubt will be complied with, you will be appointed, by the president of the prize court, agent for the sale of what Eastern goods there are on board her. The cargo is made up of European goods, dried fruits, and Eastern goods. They are what we captured from the pirates, and Sir Sidney Smith suggested that it would be as well to intrust to one who knew the value of the Eastern[Pg 298] goods the work of selling them privately, instead of putting them up to auction, and he requested that the agency should be given to you. Wilkinson, who has come home with me, is going to see the president of the prize court this morning, and he is to come up here afterwards. Of course Sir Sidney did it chiefly to oblige me, but he thought that the goods would really fetch more if sold in that way. He said, of course, that you would get a commission on the sale, and as you said in the last letter that I received that you were getting very sick of having nothing to do, I thought you might like the job."

"Certainly I should like it, Edgar, and that purchase of the ship seems a very satisfactory one, though, of course, the profit will be yours and not mine, as I had nothing to do with it."

"Oh, yes, it is your business, father; she is bought with your money, and I am glad that I have been able to do something for the firm. I shall soon be getting my prize money, which will keep me in cash for a very long time."

"We won't argue about that now, Edgar. At any rate I shall be glad to see to the sale of these Eastern goods, though, of course, it will be but a small thing."

"I don't know, father. I think that it will be rather a large thing. At any rate there is something between eighty and a hundred tons of them."

"Between eighty and a hundred tons!" his father replied. "You mean with the dried fruits, of course."

"Not at all, father! The fruits will be sold in the ordinary way in the prize court."

"Then, what can these things be?"

"I should say the great proportion of them are carpets—Turkish, Persian, and Syrian."

"A hundred tons of such carpets as those, Edgar, would[Pg 299] be worth a very large sum, indeed; surely you must be mistaken?"

"It's the accumulation of years of piracy, father; perhaps from hundreds of ships captured by those scoundrels. But, of course, they are not all carpets. There are silks, muslins, embroidered robes, Egyptian scarves and manufactures, and other sorts of things. We have not opened above a dozen bales out of some twelve hundred, and have, therefore, no idea of the relative value of the others. We were a tender of the *Tigre's*, our craft being a prize taken by her, and all of us, officers and men, being borne on her books, the whole ship divides. Still, if the things are worth as much as we think, it will bring us in a handsome sum. And there is, besides, twelve thousand five hundred in cash, the proceeds of the sale of the vessels we captured; and we also share with the other ships under Sir Sidney Smith's command in the value of the vessels and cargoes they have captured as they tried to reach an Egyptian port. They say they were worth something like forty thousand, of which the *Tigre's* share will be about half."

"Well, Edgar, if there are a hundred tons of such goods as you describe, your cargo must be a valuable one indeed. Of course I can tell nothing about it until I see them opened. At any rate it will give me occupation, and I should say a good paying occupation, for some time."

"I suppose you got that letter, father, that I sent from Constantinople, from Mr. Muller?"

"Yes, and a very satisfactory one it was. It reconciled me to some extent to staying here. It was not pleasant to think that one was living upon one's capital, but I found from his statement that my share of the business he was doing would fully cover my expenses here. And now, let us hear something more about your doings. Your letter from Con[Pg 300]stantinople told us about your adventures in Egypt; then we had one written the day after the French had retreated from before Acre, and the one that we received from Smyrna two months since; but that was a short one, and beyond saying that you had been very lucky in capturing and destroying a number of pirates, and that you were enjoying your cruise very much, you did not give us any detail. You may as well tell us that part first."

Early in the afternoon Wilkinson arrived. As Edgar had spoken warmly of his kindness to him when he had first joined the *Tigre*, and of the friendship that had sprung up between them, he was very cordially received by Mr. and Mrs. Blagrove. The former was well pleased when he heard the details of the interview with the president of the prize court, and said that he would go up and see him in the morning.

"I will hire a warehouse for a month or two," he said. "It will be much more satisfactory than working in a place where a lot of other business is being transacted. The bales will all have to be opened and examined, the goods classed and assorted, and I shall have to bring people down there to examine them. The expense will be nothing in comparison to the advantage of having a quiet place to one's self."

On the following morning Mr. Blagrove went up and had a very satisfactory talk with the president of the prize court. The *Suzanne* arrived four days later, having made a fast run from Portsmouth. By that time Mr. Blagrove had engaged a warehouse, where, in a short time, the whole of the goods of which he was to dispose were safely stored. Wilkinson went down on the day after his arrival to his people in Devonshire, and Edgar established himself as assistant to his father. As bale after bale was opened, the[Pg 301] latter was astonished at the beauty and value of some of the contents. A few only of the bales contained common country cloths, and it was evident that such goods of this sort as had fallen into the hands of the pirates had been sold at once, as there was a ready market for them at the towns and villages of the islands and the mainland. Many of the carpets were of great size. Some of the very large ones Mr. Blagrove valued at fully £500, and there were scores worth from £50 to £100. Some of the silks and embroideries he pronounced to be almost priceless.

"They must," he said, "have been specially woven and worked for the ladies of the Sultan's harem."

When, after a month's stay, Edgar prepared to rejoin with his friend Wilkinson, not more than one-third of the contents of the warehouse had been sold, but these had fetched over £40,000, and his father had no doubt that he should obtain a proportionate sum for the remainder. The

Italian sailors who had aided to bring the *Suzanne* home had been sent off a week after her arrival by a vessel bound for Naples, and the brig herself had, as soon as the cargo was all cleared out, fetched £1800 by auction, being almost a new vessel.

"I have no doubt," Mr. Blagrove said, "that ere long a British army will be sent out, and the French compelled to leave Egypt. If I thought that the war was likely to go on for some time as at present, I should say that you had better leave the service. As it is, you would not be doing much good if you stayed here, and so may as well hold on."

It was the first day of March, 1800, when the vessel with supplies for the troops, in which Wilkinson and Edgar had taken their passage, joined the fleet off Alexandria, and until the beginning of December they took part in the somewhat tedious work of blockading the Egyptian coast.[Pg 302] In spite of their efforts the fleet were not always successful, for from time to time one or other of the ships was forced to sail to Cyprus to obtain fresh supplies, although quite a fleet of small vessels was employed in bringing water, fresh meat, and vegetables for the use of the fleet, as the health of the seamen would have suffered much from living for so long a period upon salt meat.

In November news was received that the army under Sir Ralph Abercrombie, which had for so long been engaged in watching Cadiz, was to sail upon an expedition for the reconquest of Egypt. It was stated that the expedition would, in the first place, sail for Syria, there to join the army that the Sultan assured the English government was in readiness to advance. Sir Sidney Smith was ordered to sail at once for that coast, to ascertain the real state of things, and to decide upon the spot where the fleet had best assemble, for, from its long absence from England, there were many repairs needed, and it was desirable that the situation should be such that the ships could be careened, and a portion at least of the weeds that had accumulated be scraped off.

His absence was in one respect unfortunate, for some of the other blockading ships were, after a very heavy gale, obliged to go to Cyprus to repair damages; and two French men-of-war heavily laden with troops and ammunition managed to run safely in to Alexandria, thereby increasing the strength of the French army by four thousand seasoned soldiers, and by an ample supply of ammunition. It was a great disappointment to the crews when, on their return to their stations off the coast, they found that the French had taken advantage of their absence, and that the result of their eighteen months of incessant vigil had been wasted.

Wilkinson had by this time served his full time, and[Pg 303] Condor having been appointed to the *Theseus*, Sir Sidney Smith again gave the command of the *Tigress* to him, with the rank of acting lieutenant, which would, he was sure, be confirmed.

"I suppose you would like to have Mr. Blagrove with you?"

"Certainly, sir. There is no one I would rather have."

"It is a pity that he has not served his time yet," Sir Sidney said. "He is a most active young officer, and his knowledge of so many languages is of immense advantage. I would gladly give him an independent command, but as there are so many midshipmen senior to him, I could not do so. You know the coast of Anatolia probably better than anyone else here. Which harbour would you recommend as the most suitable for the entry of a large fleet? It must be well sheltered, and the shore should offer facilities for heeling the vessels over as far as possible in order to clean them. I know that at Rhodes there is not enough water for first-class men-of-war."

"By far the best place I know, sir, is the Bay of Marmorice. It is on the mainland almost opposite Rhodes, and within a day's easy sail. We went into it quite by accident, for the entrance might be passed without notice, but we had been chasing a suspicious craft, and saw her disappear, and, following her, found ourselves in a great landlocked harbour, big enough to hold a hundred ships-of-war, and absolutely sheltered. It is by far the finest harbour that I have ever seen."

"I am sailing for Rhodes in the first place. Lord Keith, who commands the fleet, has written to request me to meet him there; and if your report is correct, it will save me the trouble of examining the whole line of coast between Rhodes and Acre."

Edgar was glad to be again on board the *Tigress*. The[Pg 304] account of the sale of the goods she had captured had now been received; the total amounted to £133,000, of which £110,000 had been paid in to the prize court by Mr. Blagrove, the other £23,000 had been the proceeds of the fruits and other goods. There were in addition the sums received for vessels sold. The astonishment of the officers of the *Tigre* was great indeed when they heard the result, for very little had been said about the value of the cargo, and the sum realized was at least three times as great as the most sanguine had hoped.

"It was an excellent plan getting your father to undertake the business," Sir Sidney Smith said to Edgar, when the latter informed him that he had received a communication from his father saying how much the goods he had sold had realized. "I don't suppose they would have fetched a third of that amount had they been sold in the ordinary way by auction by the prize court. I am sure that we must all feel greatly obliged to him."

"And he must feel greatly obliged to you, Sir Sidney; for, as he told me, his commission had been fixed at three per cent, so he has, after paying his expenses, done a fine stroke of business for himself."

"He has managed extremely well, Mr. Blagrove, and it has been a fortunate affair for us all."

CHAPTER XVII.
ABERCROMBIE'S EXPEDITION.

On arriving at Rhodes Sir Sidney Smith left the *Tigre*, and in the *Tigress* sailed across to the Bay of Marmorice, preferring to explore it, in the first place, in a craft drawing[Pg 305] but little water. He was delighted with the harbour, and after a day spent in sounding in various parts of it, found that there was ample depth of water for the larger ships, and that there were spots where these could lie alongside, run the upper-deck guns directly ashore, and careen the ships over to a point that would enable them to be freed of a considerable proportion of their weeds and barnacles. Returning to Rhodes, he then started in the *Tigre* for Syria. He took Edgar with him as interpreter, replacing him temporarily by another midshipman, and leaving Wilkinson with a report from himself to Lord Keith strongly recommending Marmorice as being suitable in all respects for a rendezvous for the fleet and transports.

On the 28th of December the first division of the fleet arrived, and was at once ordered to proceed to Marmorice, the *Tigress* sailing ahead to show the way. The second division arrived four days later. Tents were at once erected ashore. The sick were landed and encamped; whole regiments were also put under canvas, while the ships which carried them were careened and cleaned. Sir Sidney Smith had already returned with the news that there was practically nothing that could be called an army in Syria, and his report was so discouraging that General Abercrombie and Lord Keith resolved that it would be far better to land the army in Egypt than to disembark at Jaffa and take the long and fatiguing march across the desert, merely in order to gain the aid of a few thousand useless Turkish troops.

Great disappointment was occasioned by the remounts for the cavalry that had been purchased at Constantinople, for when these arrived they were such wretched animals that they were for the most part found to be absolutely useless, and the greater portion were either shot or sold for a dollar each. On the 8th of February one of the most terrible hail-[Pg 306]storms that ever was experienced, took place, and lasted for forty-eight hours. The thunder rolled without intermission; the hailstones were as big as large walnuts, and lay two feet deep in the camp. The scene of confusion there was terrible; horses broke loose and rushed wildly about seeking shelter from the hail. The men dared not venture out, so terrible was the force with which the lumps of ice came down. Ships drove at their anchors, and many lost their upper spars, and the *Swiftsure* was struck by lightning.

The weather continued violent for some time, and it was not until the 23rd of February that the ships weighed anchor, and, numbering a hundred and seventy-five, set sail, and made their way out of the harbour. The expedition on which the troops were about to embark was a most adventurous one. They had by this time learned that the French had received very considerable reinforcements, and that the force was a much larger one than had been reported. The Turkish army with which they were to operate was non-existent, and the only gleam of satisfaction was that Bonaparte himself had managed to get through the blockading force in a small craft, and had arrived in France, and that, therefore, the French army would not have the benefit of his leading, or be animated by his presence among them.

Edgar found himself brought unexpectedly into notice. The fleet was entirely unprovided with reliable maps of Egypt, and none of the officers had any previous knowledge of it beyond the port of Alexandria. Sir

Sidney Smith was able to give every information regarding the coast, but had never set foot on shore.

"It is most unfortunate," General Abercrombie said, when he, Lord Keith, and Sir Sidney Smith were discussing the matter. "Here we are about to land in a country of which we know absolutely nothing. If we had, as originally[Pg 307] intended, landed at Jaffa and marched through El A'rich with the Turks, we should have had the benefit of their knowledge and that of the Arabs of the country. As it is, we are totally ignorant of its features, while the enemy are thoroughly acquainted with them. It is like a blind man fighting in the dark against one who can see perfectly."

"By the way," Sir Sidney exclaimed suddenly, "I have a young officer who knows the country well. He has been a resident at Alexandria for years, and, riding about, knows every foot of the country within many miles of it. He has been up to Cairo, was with the Arabs who harassed the French march, was present at the battle of the Pyramids, and at the fighting in Cairo, and knows the position of all the French forts round that city. He was on his way to England when I overhauled the craft he was in, on my way out, and as he speaks Arabic perfectly, to say nothing of French and Italian, I offered him a berth as midshipman and to act as my interpreter. In the latter capacity he was invaluable both in Constantinople and at the siege of Jaffa. He is, moreover, a most gallant young officer, and was second in command of the *Tigress* when she did such good service in eradicating piracy among the islands, capturing and destroying over a hundred piratical craft."

"That is good news indeed!" the general said. "Will you send for him now? His knowledge would be invaluable to me."

A boat was sent off at once to the *Tigre* with an order for Edgar to come on board the flagship immediately. Much surprised, but supposing that he was wanted to act as interpreter between Sir Sidney and some Turkish official who had come on board, he at once took his place in the gig and was rowed to the flagship. As soon as he reached the deck[Pg 308] an officer told him that he was wanted in the admiral's cabin. There he was again surprised at seeing not only the admiral, but General Abercrombie and Sir Sidney Smith.

"This is Mr. Blagrove, Lord Keith," Sir Sidney said. "I can speak most highly of him, as a most gallant and able young officer, and as a master of four or five languages. In the capacity of interpreter he has rendered signal services."

"Take a seat, sir," the admiral said. "How long has he served, Sir Sidney?"

"About two years and two months, sir, and therefore I have been unable to recognize the services that he has rendered me in his double capacity, beyond mentioning them in my reports."

"I hear, Mr. Blagrove," Lord Keith went on, "that you are intimately acquainted with the country round Alexandria, have visited Cairo, and know the city and its defences. How did you go to Cairo?"

"I rode, sir, in company with a party of Arabs with whom I was living after the sudden and unexpected departure of my father when the French fleet first appeared in sight. I may say I went up and down twice, for we went back to fetch the women of the tribe."

"Sir Ralph Abercrombie will be glad to learn from you all the information that you can give him respecting the country round Alexandria, and also what you can tell him of the route between that place and Cairo. As we were in the Mediterranean when we received orders to undertake the invasion of Egypt, we have no maps of the country, and practically know nothing whatever about it. However, of course, in the first place the most important part of the affair is to learn the positions round Alexandria."

"I shall be very glad to answer any questions, sir."[Pg 309]

The general then began to examine him. "Can you draw, sir?"

"I have no knowledge of military drawing," Edgar replied, "but I could point out the position of the villages."

The general pushed a large sheet of paper towards him.

"The position of the villages will, of course, be useful," he said, "as these are points that would be naturally defended; but what is of most importance is the position of the sand-hills and other eminences, the points at which artillery would command the surrounding country, prepare the way for a force advancing to attack the French, or to check columns advancing against us, the line which the enemy would be most likely to occupy, those by which we might best attack him in front or turn his position."

Edgar looked at the paper in doubt.

"I am afraid, sir, that is beyond me altogether; but if you will tell me where the landing would probably be effected, I could go on from that spot and indicate the various risings and falls of the ground."

"Of course you know the Castle of Aboukir?"

"Certainly, sir. I was on the sand-hills for two days, within half a mile of it, watching the approach of Lord Nelson's fleet and the battle of Aboukir."

"Good!" the general said; "we shall probably land near there."

"The sand-hills rise sharply from the water's edge, and a short distance behind there are several points on which the French would probably place batteries to oppose the landing."

He sketched the line of coast, drew a few lines indicating the trend of the sand-hills, and marked the special eminences. Then step by step he showed the line where the French would probably post themselves, were a successful[Pg 310] landing effected, between the heights of Ramleh and the sea, described the country, and, as far as he could, the lay of the land.

"How about water?" the general asked after he had questioned Edgar for more than half an hour.

"There are wells at several points," he said, "but for the most part they are too near the French position for them to be useful to you until you have driven them into the town. There is, however, a well here," and he marked a spot about a mile from the landing-place. "I cannot tell you its exact position. There is a peasant's hut there. He was speaking to us while we were watching the battle, and he told us that he so hated the French that he had filled up his well so that they should not fetch water from it for the garrison of the castle. I have no doubt that I could find the hut, and the man will, I am sure, show you where the well has been, and it will probably take but little trouble to clear it out. The Arabs, however, told me that wherever you find clumps of trees you will be sure to find water at no great depth."

"That is very valuable information," the general said. "It is bad enough to have to depend upon the fleet for provisions; but the difficulties of transporting water sufficient for some 12,000 men, with the cavalry and artillery horses, would be enormous.

"Thank you, Mr. Blagrove. I must have some more conversation with you."

Edgar bowed and retired.

"You must let me have that young fellow," the general said to Sir Sidney Smith. "He is evidently thoroughly acquainted with the country. As he knows nothing of military drawing, one cannot get the full advantage of his information here; but if I had him on shore with me his[Pg 311] knowledge would be invaluable, for he could then point out to me the nature of the country beyond the points we can see."

"I should be very happy to lend him to you, Sir Ralph, and I am sure he will be glad to go, for really a midshipman's pay is absurd as a consideration for the services that he has rendered as interpreter. Fortunately his father was a merchant at Alexandria, and money is of no great importance to him, and he really entered the navy only for the pleasure of seeing service, and to pass the time until the departure of the French would enable his father to return to his business. Of course if he had served his time and passed I should most strongly recommend him for promotion to lieutenant at once. As it is, I am powerless."

"There are exceptions to every rule," Lord Keith said, "and as commander-in-chief in the Mediterranean, I think that I might overstep the line. Could he pass?"

"I have no doubt whatever that he could do so," Sir Sidney said. "Certainly he could in practical knowledge of seamanship, after being second in command of a ten-gun brig for six months among the islands, the commander being a midshipman only a few months older than himself. Owing to the loss of so many officers at Acre, I was unable to spare one of higher rank, and the complaints of piracy were so urgent and frequent, that I felt it absolutely necessary to send a ship up to try and put a stop to it. I had some misgivings at the time, but my choice was more than justified, as was shown by the number of craft captured; and when I say that the plunder taken sold for over one hundred and thirty thousand pounds, it speaks well for both their skill and activity, for navigation among those islands is a very ticklish business."

"I will call a board to-morrow to examine him," the ad[Pg 312]miral said, "and will at once, if he passes, appoint him as acting lieutenant, and send home a report, if you will get one drawn up, Sir Sidney, as to his exceptional services, and saying that I was partly influenced in taking so exceptional a step by the consideration that Sir Ralph Abercrombie had asked that he should be appointed to his staff, both from his knowledge of the country and of the Arab and Turkish languages."

The next morning the flagship signalled to the *Tigre*. The flag midshipman, after spelling out the message and reporting to Sir Sidney, ran forward to Edgar.

"You are to go on board the admiral's ship at once; the signal has been made for you."

On reaching the ship he was conducted down to the wardroom, where, to his surprise, three naval captains were seated at a table.

"Please to sit down, Mr. Blagrove," the one in the centre said, "we want to ask you a few questions."

Supposing that he was about to be asked more about Egypt, or perhaps the depth of water in the port of Alexandria, Edgar prepared to answer, and the first questions justified his anticipations, for he was questioned minutely as to the point for which a ship would head to round the dangerous reef extending from the outer point of the western port. Then he was asked as to the depth of water between this and the shore, the guns that could be brought to bear upon it, and the depths at various points in the harbour itself. All these he was able to answer at once. Then he was asked various questions as to harbours in the Turkish and Greek islands, and as he had constantly consulted the charts during his cruise in the *Tigress*, he was able to reply readily on all these points. The next question surprised him.[Pg 313]

"Now, Mr. Blagrove, if caught by a sudden and heavy squall, when under full sail, among these islands, and having but three or four minutes to strip the ship, what orders would you give?"

As he had in his mind every order that Wilkinson had given on the approach of the squall, he was able to repeat them with accuracy.

"You are cutting them rather short, Mr. Blagrove."

"Yes, sir; but the time is very short. When cruising there we were struck by a squall less than three minutes after we had notice of its coming, and everything had to be done at once and with the greatest possible speed. As it was, the men were not out of the rigging when the squall struck us."

"Supposing you had had ten minutes' notice, how would you have proceeded?"

Edgar gave the orders as laid down in the text-book, for after the narrow escape they had had, he and Wilkinson had especially learnt these by heart.

"Very good indeed, Mr. Blagrove."

Two or three questions in navigation were then asked, and these were also answered well, as they had found it absolutely necessary to be able to find their exact position when cruising in such dangerous waters.

"Thank you, sir," the officer said when the last question had been answered; "we shall have much pleasure in certifying that you have passed your examination in a most creditable manner."

Edgar looked a little bewildered.

"Sir Sidney Smith perhaps did not inform you, Mr. Blagrove, that, by Lord Keith's orders, you were to be examined to-day, and that we have sat as a board for that purpose?"[Pg 314]

"No, indeed, sir, I had no thought of such a thing. I shall not have served my time for nearly three years."

"I suppose Lord Keith had some special reason for having you examined now. It was a good opportunity, you see. You will please remain on deck for a few minutes while we draw out the certificate."

He was soon called in again and presented with a certificate, saying that he had passed the examination most satisfactorily.

"You will now go to the admiral's cabin," the president said; "he desires to speak to you."

Still greatly puzzled why he should be examined so long before his time, Edgar sent in his name to the admiral, and was at once shown in. Sir Sidney Smith was with him.

"I am very glad to hear from the examining board that you have passed your examination with great credit, Mr. Blagrove," the admiral said. "Sir Sidney Smith has spoken to me in very high terms of the services you have rendered him, and the general commanding the troops has requested that you should be told off to his staff, where your knowledge of the country will be of great service to him. Under these very exceptional circumstances I have taken the exceptional step of having you examined at once, and as you have passed with flying colours I now hand you your appointment as acting lieutenant. The appointment is, of course, a temporary one, but when I explain to the Admiralty my reasons for making it, and inclose the report of your services that Sir Sidney Smith has handed to me, I have no doubt that the step will be confirmed. I may say that one reason for my doing this at the present moment is that as you will be on Sir Ralph Abercrombie's staff, I think that, as the navy is to be represented, it should be[Pg 315] represented by an officer with at least the rank of lieutenant, so as to give him a proper status. I congratulate you, Lieutenant Blagrove, on the promotion that you have, in my opinion and in that of your immediate superior, most worthily won."

Thereupon he shook Edgar warmly by the hand. Sir Sidney Smith did the same, and with a smile stopped Edgar's disjointed words of thanks and pointed to the door. Some of the middies of the flagship nudged each other and smiled at his pale face as he walked to the gangway.

"He has been getting a wigging and no mistake," one said to another. "He looked all right when he went in, for I noticed him as he came on deck; but he has evidently got into some awful scrape, and will be court-martialled and sent home, I should say, or his captain would have kept the affair in his own hands instead of bringing him up before the admiral."

"Anything the matter, Mr. Blagrove?" Mr. Knight, who was still second lieutenant on the *Tigre*, asked him, as he came on board. "'Tis not often that a midshipman is signalled for by an admiral's flagship, and you are looking rather shaky."

"No, sir, there is nothing wrong, but I do feel a little queer. When I got there I was taken down to the wardroom, where three captains were sitting. They asked me a number of questions about the port of Alexandria, the depth of water, the batteries, and so on. Of course I knew about that from going so often on board ship in the harbour and from sailing in and out. Then, to my surprise, they asked me what I should do if the ship I was in command of was caught in a sudden squall. As we had been caught in a white squall in the islands, of course I was able to answer. They asked me some other questions as to navigation, and[Pg 316] I could not for the life of me make out what they were doing, and was thunderstruck when they told me that they were a board, and that I had passed my examination with great credit. When they gave me the certificate I was taken to the admiral's cabin;" and he then repeated the substance of what the admiral had said.

"I congratulate you, Blagrove. You are a lucky young dog; but I don't think that luck is the proper word, for you owe it entirely, first to your knowledge of languages, then to your own behaviour and pluck. It is rare indeed, I can tell you, that a midshipman of two years' standing is passed and promoted. I have no doubt that, as the admiral said, your going on Abercrombie's staff had a good deal to do with it, because, for the credit of the navy, one would not like to be represented by a midshipman on such service. Well, you must borrow an epaulette;" for at that time a naval officer did not mount two epaulettes until he had obtained the rank of commander.

At first Edgar's story was altogether disbelieved in the cockpit, where his arrival was anxiously expected, as all were curious to learn what he had been signalled for. When at last they understood that he was in earnest, he was very warmly congratulated. Three of them were senior to him; but he was so generally liked, and his acquirements in the way of languages so fully acknowledged, that there was no feeling of jealousy, especially as they felt sure that, when the campaign was over, Sir Sidney Smith would get him appointed to another ship. Two of them that evening got a boat and rowed to several other men-of-war, and at last succeeded in buying an epaulette from an officer who had bought the kit of another who had died some time before, and this they formally presented to Edgar that evening.[Pg 317]

While at Marmorice Bay the latter had almost daily interviews with the general. At these the quarter-master and adjutant-generals and several other superior officers were often present, and he was asked innumerable questions as to the country between Alexandria and Cairo, the probabilities of obtaining animals for the baggage-waggons and artillery, the amount of provisions that could be obtained from the country, the length of the marches and the nature of the ground, and whether the Arabs were likely to render any efficient assistance. All these questions he answered to the best of his power, saying, however, that it would be absolutely necessary to depend to a large extent on the boats for provisions as the French had done, for that comparatively few horses could be obtained, as the French had purchased all that they could lay their hands on.

Then to an engineer officer he described the position of the old and newly-erected works at Cairo, saying that the latter were intended solely to overawe the town, and that some of them were open works in the rear, although no doubt they would be much strengthened, and some of the guns turned outward, as soon as news was received of the landing of the British army. He pointed out that many of the guns must, however, be retained in their present position, in case the population should rise as soon as the army approached, and that the guns were in most cases small, as the French had brought no battering-train with them.

"There is no doubt," the general said, "that Damietta and Rosetta must be taken before we advance, and that a strong force of our gun-boats and armed ships' boats must convoy the native craft laden with provisions and stores, for from what you describe of the country, and the difficulty of obtaining animals, it is clear that we shall have to depend upon the river for food."[Pg 318]

On the 24th the great fleet sailed, and on the 1st of March anchored in Aboukir Bay. The weather was boisterous and a landing was impossible. The next morning, to their mortification, a French frigate was seen to enter Alexandria. She had passed near several of the blockading squadron, but was in some way furnished with a British naval signal-book, and answered all the signals made to her without attracting the slightest suspicion. During that night a French brig also ran in. Not until the 8th did the sea moderate sufficiently for a disembarkation to be attempted. This delay of seven days was most unfortunate, as it enabled the French general to make every preparation for opposing the landing.

On the morning of the 8th the brigade of Guards, and part of the 1st brigade, amounting in all to 5500 men, under the command of Major-general Coote, embarked in boats, and at three started for the spot where they were to gather for the landing. But the ships were widely scattered, and it was not until nine o'clock that the boats were all marshalled in order.

In the meantime the remainder of the 1st and the 2nd brigades were taken to the ships close inshore, so that no time might be lost after the boats had landed the other division.

Edgar had the night before been rowed to the ship on which were the general and his staff, and accompanied them to the vessel near the shore on which he took his post. On either flank of the transport's boats were posted three gun-vessels and two of the fleet's launches. Two bomb-vessels were placed close to them, and three sloops-of-war were moored with their broadsides to the shore.

Sir Sidney Smith had charge of the launches which contained the field-artillery. As the signal-gun fired, the oars[Pg 319] all dipped in the water together, and the men burst into a tremendous cheer.

For a moment the French remained passive; 2000 men were posted on the top of the sand-hills, which here formed a crescent. In the centre rose two hills, to a height of 180 feet, apparently inaccessible. Twelve guns were posted on the sand-hills, and the Castle of Aboukir was able to assist with the fire of its guns. So strong was the position that the French had hardly deemed it possible that the British would decide to attack them here; but as the boats dashed forward, every man rowing as if his life depended upon his efforts, they could no longer doubt the intentions of the British, and a tremendous fire of grape and musketry, shot and shell, was opened.

Some of the boats were sunk, but most of those on board were saved by the others, and the greater part of the line, without a check, pressed on until they reached the beach. The 23rd and 40th, whose boats were the first to land, rushed up the height without stopping to fire a shot, and, charging the two French battalions with the bayonet, carried it and two hills in the rear, taking three pieces of cannon posted there. The 42nd Regiment formed up as if on parade, and mounted the sand-hills under the fire of two pieces of artillery and a battalion of infantry. The moment they reached the crest 200 French cavalry advanced to charge, but fell back under the heavy fire opened upon them.

They rallied behind the hills, and charged down upon the Guards as the latter were beginning to land. The 58th, however, poured a volley into them, and gained time for the Guards to form up, when the cavalry again rode off. The 54th and the Royals, being in heavy transport boats, arrived a little later, but were in time to check a French column advancing through a hollow against the left flank of[Pg 320] the Guards. The British were now in full possession of the heights, and the French everywhere fell back, keeping up, however, a fire from another range of sand-hills for an hour and a half, when, as the troops got into motion against them, they retreated, having lost 300 men and eight pieces of cannon.

The advance of the boats had been anxiously watched by Sir Ralph Abercrombie's staff from the deck of the *Mondovi*. It seemed to Edgar well-nigh impossible that any of these could reach the shore, so torn up was the water by shot, shell, and bullets. A hearty cheer broke from all on board as the men in the boats that first arrived were seen to jump out on to the shore. These were repeated again and again as the 23rd, 40th, and 42nd won their way up the hill, and the French could be seen hastily retiring. But it was not until the Guards and the three other regiments were seen formed up in order ashore—for the French might, for aught it was known, be preparing to take the offensive and recover the ground that they had lost—that it was felt that full success had attended the operation. The moment they had landed their freight the boats returned to their ships, and by evening the navy succeeded, with the greatest exertions, in conveying the whole of the remainder of the force to the shore.

As soon as the fight was over, the troops were set to dig for water wherever there were clumps of trees, and succeeded in finding it in several places. Edgar was requested by the general to ride with a troop of cavalry to find out the hut where the peasant who had spoken to him lived. He took them almost straight to the spot. The peasant was there, but had difficulty in recognizing in the young officer, the apparent Arab with whom he had spoken on the day of the battle of Aboukir. However, on being told that the French[Pg 321] had been defeated, and that the British intended to drive them out of the country altogether, he at once pointed out where the well stood.

Some of the troopers had been provided with shovels. All dismounted and worked by turns, and late in the evening the officer in command of the party rode into camp with the welcome news that a large supply of water could be drawn from the well. The army advanced some little distance the next day, and established itself on the narrow strip of land between the sea and the Lake of Aboukir; while the stores were brought ashore and a hospital established on the beach. On the 12th the force moved four miles farther, and on the following day marched to attack the French, who were encamped on a ridge. They had received reinforcements from Cairo, bringing up their strength to 6000 men. They had some thirty guns, and the ground, which sloped regularly and smoothly down, afforded a natural glacis, which would be swept by their fire.

The army marched in two columns against the French right, their advance being supported by the guns of some of the ships' launches, which had entered the Lake of Aboukir. The French guns played rapidly, and the 92nd, which was the leading regiment, pushed forward, while the French cavalry, which charged the 90th, were received with a heavy fire and driven back. The columns now formed into line, and, pressing steadily forward, the French were compelled to abandon their position, and to retreat to the works on the heights before the town itself. Unfortunately, the British general, from the ease with which he had turned the enemy from their first position, thought that he might carry the second by a sudden attack. But, although the troops fought gallantly, they were unable to win the position,[Pg 322] which was strong and well armed, and after some hours' fighting they were called off. Their loss during the day had been about 1100 killed and wounded, while that of the French was not more than half this number.

The ground on which the army now took up its position was a strong one. The right was on high ground, and extended to the ruins of a Roman palace within fifty yards of the sea. The left was on the canal that supplied Alexandria with water; here two batteries were ordered to be constructed, the lake protected its rear from attack. The distance from the sea to the lake was about a mile, and the position occupied was high and commanding. In front of this line was a plain on which cavalry could act, and beyond this was the French position, a high and steep ridge, extending from the sea to the canal. The army laboured unceasingly at the work of constructing batteries, and bringing up guns and provisions. Water was fortunately found in abundance, and the nights being cold, tents were landed and set up. The castle of Aboukir had been left unattacked as the army moved forward, but was now besieged and surrendered on the eighteenth.

CHAPTER XVIII.
THE BATTLE OF ALEXANDRIA.

On the afternoon following the capture of Aboukir Castle, an Arab was seen riding at full speed towards the British left. He was pursued by some French cavalry, and another party endeavoured to cut him off. The general happened to be at the time watching the troops at work completing the batteries on that flank.[Pg 323]

"That Arab is well mounted," he said, as he and those around him watched the chase. "I believe he will get through if he is not shot," for, at this moment, the cavalry behind him, seeing that he was leaving them fast, began to use their carbines. Waving his gun over his head, and from time to time giving a yell of derision and defiance, the Arab swept round towards his right, and so passed ahead of the troop that had endeavoured to cut him off, then bore round again, until he reached the bank of the canal, and galloped along it, slackening his pace as a musketry fire was opened from the battery, and the French cavalry turned and rode away. The Arab rode across the bridge over the canal, and then cantered up to the battery. As he was crossing the bridge, the idea that had for a minute or two previously been in Edgar's mind rose to a certainty.

"It is Sidi!" he exclaimed.

The general turned and looked at him interrogatively.

"It is the young chief of the Beni Ouafy, the tribe I was with when I was here, sir; we call each other brother, and indeed are that in feeling. We have saved each other's life more than once."

"Go and meet him then, and bring him here," the general said. "You spoke frequently of him when describing your journeys to and from Cairo."

Sidi had checked his horse as he approached the battery, not seeing any entrance to it, and was pausing, irresolute which way to turn, when Edgar leapt from an embrasure and ran towards him. The Arab did not in the least recognize his friend in the naval officer who advanced to meet him. He had supposed him to be in England, and, indeed, as it was now some months over two years since they had parted, and Edgar had grown and widened out[Pg 324] into a fine manly figure, Sidi would hardly have recognized him had he come across him suddenly in a civilian dress. He was astounded, when, on coming close to him, Edgar held out both hands and cried:

"Sidi, my brother!"

The voice was unchanged. Sidi, with the shout of "All praise be to Allah!" flung himself from his saddle, grasped Edgar's hands, and stood there speechless with joy and emotion, and with tears standing in his eyes. Edgar himself was much moved.

"Is all well with you, Sidi?" he asked; "the chief and your mother?"

"It is well with us all," Sidi answered. "We talk of you always, but had not hoped to see you so soon. Little did I dream that I should not know you when we met, though, when we heard that your people had landed and had beaten the French, we thought that the time might not be very far off when the Franks would go, and you might return. So you are an officer, one of the ship officers?"

"Yes, Sidi. We met a ship-of-war as I sailed from here, and since I could speak Arabic and Turkish I was made an officer, and was at the siege of Acre, where we beat off the French; but we will talk of all that afterwards. Our general saw you coming, and thinking that you might have news for us, requested me to bring you to him."

"I have news," Sidi said.

"Do not tell me now, it is best that you should tell him first."

Walking side by side, Sidi leading his horse, they went round to the entrance to the battery. As they entered, Edgar told one of the general's orderlies to hold the horse, and then took Sidi up to Sir Ralph Abercrombie.[Pg 325]

"This is the English general, Sidi," he said. Sir Ralph held out his hand to the young sheik, who raised it to his forehead.

"Our hearts are rejoiced," he said, "that you have come at last to fight for us against the Franks. I bring you news, my lord. Late yesterday their general, Menou, with a large force, arrived at Damanhour. I have been among them. There must be five thousand men. His intentions are to march to-day and to attack with all his force to-morrow morning."

"This is important news, indeed!" the general said, as Edgar translated the message. "Ask him if he speaks merely from report or from his own knowledge."

Sidi then said that some of the tribe had early that morning started with a number of sheep, intending to bring them round into the British camp. They were surprised by a body of French cavalry coming from Damanhour. Several of the tribesmen were killed, but two escaped, being well mounted, and brought the news to their camp. On the way they met him, he having started some hours later, knowing that he could easily overtake them before they reached the British camp. Seeing the importance of the matter, he told them to tell his father that he should try and find out how many of the French were at Damanhour, and take the news to the British. He had then ridden toward that place, and remembering how he had passed unsuspected before, had left his horse there, had obtained the loan of a peasant's dress, had bought half a dozen sheep, and had driven them into the town.

He found it crowded with the French. Having sold his sheep, he had wandered about among the soldiers, and had entered into conversation with some of the natives who had been engaged at Cairo as drivers of the baggage-carts.[Pg 326] From them he had learned that the French general-in-chief, Menou, who had succeeded Kleber on the latter's assassination at Cairo, was himself there, and that he intended to attack at once with the troops he had brought, and with those in the city. As soon as he obtained this news he returned to the village, changed his dress, mounted, and rode off at full speed.

The party that had been seen chasing him was a cavalry squadron, whom he had come upon suddenly while they were dismounted and sitting down in the shade of a grove, and who, judging that he was making for the British camp, had started in pursuit. Knowing well enough that they could not catch him, he had amused himself by keeping but a short distance in advance, and had not put his horse to its full speed until he saw the mounted party coming out from the French lines to cut him off.

The general listened attentively to Edgar as he translated the story.

"Please to question him again, Lieutenant Blagrove, as to the report that Menou intends to attack us as soon as he gets here. It is, as you see, of the greatest importance. Late as it is this afternoon, and formidable as are the French lines, I should endeavour to carry them as soon as the troops can form up, for it would be hopeless to try to do so to-morrow when Menou arrives. If, on the other hand, he really means to take the offensive, I should prefer remaining in our present position, for I think that we could maintain it against the whole of the French army, and that more easily than we could carry their line of defences held by only the troops at present in front of us."

Edgar questioned Sidi again. The latter said that he had heard the same story from three different persons. The French had arrived late the evening before, and when[Pg 327] he left, the bugles were sounding and they were beginning to fall in for their march, and would probably reach Alexandria by ten at night. The men had said that it was the talk among the soldiers that they should take the English by surprise at daybreak and drive them into the sea.

"That certainly seems to decide it," the general said. "They have made a mistake indeed, if they think that they will catch us napping."

Orders were at once issued for a number of the troops to set to work to complete the defences. Another battery was, during the night, erected in front of the Roman ruins. A redoubt in front of the position of the Guards was strengthened, and other points seen to.

At three o'clock in the morning the army was, as usual, under arms. Half an hour later there was a sudden outburst of firing on the extreme left. The firing continued, but it did not increase in strength, as would have been the case had a serious attack been made, and General Moore, who was the general officer of the night, remained on the right, against which portion of the line he believed the real attack would be delivered. It was still dark, and all waited anxiously for some sign of the spot against which the storm was to burst.

Suddenly loud shouts were heard in advance of the right. A roar of musketry immediately broke out. Covered by the inequalities of the ground, the French had crept up unobserved by the sentries until close at hand, and the moment the alarm was given, sprang forward in great force, and the advanced pickets fell back on the main position at once. A heavy column of French advanced against a ruined wall, behind which the 58th were lying. The wall was of considerable length, and in many places had fallen and left wide openings. Here the 58th were[Pg 328] posted. Their colonel made his men hold their fire until the enemy were close to them, when volley after volley was poured into them, so well aimed and deadly that the enemy retired quickly into a hollow in their rear, then wheeled round to the right, and while one column marched straight at the newly-formed battery, another endeavoured to force its way round its left and take it in rear.

The 28th Regiment stationed there opened a heavy fire on the force attacking them in front, but the flanking column, now joined by a third, forced its way in behind the battery. While some attacked it in the rear, the rest penetrated into the ruins held by the 58th. Its colonel wheeled back the left wing of the regiment, and after two or three volleys, fell on the French with the bayonet. At this moment the 23rd came up in support, and the 42nd advanced from the left, and, keeping on the outside of the ruins, cut off the troops which had entered, and after suffering heavy loss they were compelled to surrender.

The 28th had remained firmly at the front line of the redoubt, and they and the 58th had hitherto been supporting simultaneously attacks in front, flank, and rear. The arrival of the 42nd for a time relieved them, but as the latter regiment approached the right of the redoubt, the enemy's cavalry, which had passed round by its left, charged them furiously and broke them. The Highlanders, however, gathered in groups, and fought desperately until relieved by the fire of the flank companies of the 40th, and the cavalry, passing on, were about to charge this small force, when the foreign brigade came up from the second line and poured such a heavy fire into the French cavalry that they fled.

As soon as the fire broke out, General Abercrombie, with his staff, mounted and proceeded towards the point where[Pg 329] the battle was raging. On the way he detached his aides-de-camp with orders to different brigades, and while thus alone with an escort of dragoons, some of the French cavalry dashed at him and he was thrown from his horse. A French officer rode up to cut him down, but he sprang at him, seized his sword, and wrested it from his hand. At that instant the officer was bayoneted by one of the 42nd.

While this incident was proceeding Sir Ralph received a musket-ball in the thigh, and also a severe contusion on the breast, probably by a splinter of stone struck by a cannon-ball. In the heat of the action he was unconscious of the first wound, but felt much pain from the contusion. At this moment Sir Sidney Smith rode up; he had accidentally broken his sword, and the general discerning it, at once presented him with the one that he had wrested from the[Pg 330] French officer. He then took up his station in the battery, from which he could obtain a view of the whole scene of the battle, for by this time it was daylight. The contest still raged. Another body of cavalry charged the foreign brigade, but were received with so heavy a fire that they did not press the charge home. The French infantry were now no longer in column, but spread out everywhere in skirmishing order. The ammunition of the English on the right was by this time totally exhausted, and but one cartridge remained for each of the guns in the battery.

The chief point of attack was now the centre. Here a column of grenadiers, supported by a heavy line of infantry, advanced to the assault, but the Guards stoutly maintained themselves until General Coote, with his brigade, came up, and the French were then driven back. All this time the French guns kept up an incessant cannonade on the British position. The attack on the British left, which had been but a feint, was never seriously pursued, but was confined to a scattered fire of musketry and a distant cannonade. General Hutchinson, who commanded here, kept his force in hand; for, had he moved to the assistance of the centre and right, a serious attack might have been made on him, and the flank being thus turned, the position would have been taken in rear.

On the right the French as well as the British had exhausted their ammunition, and the singular spectacle was presented of two hostile forces pelting each other with stones, by which many heavy blows were given on both sides, and some killed, among them a sergeant of the 28th. The grenadiers and a company of the 40th presently moved out against the assailants, and the French then fell back. General Menou, finding that all his attacks had failed, now called off his troops. Fortunately for them the[Pg 331] artillery ammunition was now exhausted, but they lost a good many men by the fire of some British cutters, which had during the whole action maintained their position a short distance in advance of the British right, and greatly aided the defenders of the redoubt by their fire.

By ten o'clock the action was over. Until the firing ceased altogether Sir Ralph Abercrombie remained in the battery paying no attention to his wounds, and, indeed, the officers who came and went with orders were ignorant that he had been hit. Now, however, faint with loss of blood, he could maintain his position no longer, and was placed in a hammock and carried down to the shore, and rowed off to the flagship. As soon as the French had withdrawn, attention was paid to the wounded. The total loss was 6 officers and 230 men killed, 60 officers and 1190 men wounded. The French loss was heavier. 1700 French, killed and wounded, were found on the battlefield, and 1040 of these were buried on the field. Taking the general proportion of wounded and killed, the French loss, including the prisoners, amounted to 4000 men; one French standard and two guns were captured.

The total British force was under 10,000 men, of whom but half were seriously engaged. The French were about 11,000 strong, of whom all, save the 800 who made the feint on the British left, took part in the fighting. On the 25th the Capitan Pasha, with 6000 men, arrived in the bay, and landed and encamped. Three days later the army was saddened by the news of the death of Sir Ralph Abercrombie. He was succeeded in his command by General Hutchinson. For some time Edgar had an idle time of it. The French had failed in their attack, but they had not been defeated, and their position was too strong to be attacked. The Capitan Pasha had with him an excellent[Pg 332] interpreter, and therefore his services were not required in that capacity.

The night before the battle he stopped up all night talking with Sidi, relating all that had happened since he had left him, and hearing from him what had taken place on land. This was little enough. A great number of the Arabs had gathered in readiness to sweep down upon the French when they attacked the Turkish army at Aboukir, but when the latter had, with terrible slaughter, been driven into the castle, they had scattered to their homes. The next day the young Arab witnessed with delight the repulse of the French attack, and at the conclusion of the fight rode away to tell his father of Edgar's return, and of the events that he had witnessed. The sheik had come back with him on the following day, accompanied by some of his followers, and their tents were pitched on a sand-hill a short distance in the rear of the British lines.

Until April 13th nothing was done. The army was too small to undertake any operations, and was forced to remain in its position, as it might at any moment be again attacked.

In the pocket of General Roiz, who had been killed in the battle, was found a letter from General Menou, expressing fear that the English would cut the Canal of Alexandria and let the waters of it and Lake Aboukir into the old bed of Lake Mareotis. It was evident that an immense advantage would be gained by this. Our own left would be secure against attack. The French would be nearly cut off from the interior, and the British army be enabled to undertake fresh operations. General Hutchinson, however, hesitated for a long time before taking the step. A tract of rich country would be overwhelmed, and none of the Arabs could say how far the inundations would reach. However, the step was evidently so much to the advantage of the[Pg 333] army that at last he gave the order, and on the 13th of April the work began, and that evening the water rushed out from Lake Aboukir through two cuts. Others were opened the next day. The rush of water quickly widened these, and soon the inundation spread over a large tract of country behind Alexandria.

A considerable force was at once detached to support Colonel Spencer, who was menacing Rosetta, and marched to El Hamed. Sir Sidney Smith ascended the Nile with an armed flotilla as far as El Aft, and on the 19th aided the Turks in capturing Fort St. Julian, a strong place between Rosetta and the mouth of the Nile. After the fall of St. Julian, Rosetta was taken possession of with but little difficulty. Soon after this, to the deep regret of the navy, Sir Sidney Smith was recalled to his ship. The Grand Vizier had a serious grudge against him. This arose from a capitulation that had, shortly after the retreat of the French from Acre, been agreed upon between the Turkish authorities and the French, by which the latter were to be permitted to evacuate Egypt.

Sir Sidney Smith had not been consulted, but considering, and justly, that the advantages were great, had signed it. Lord Keith, as commander-in-chief, had refused to ratify the treaty, and the English government, who were in high spirits at the blow struck at the French at Acre, agreed with his action. Sir Sidney Smith, as soon as he received Lord Keith's despatch, sent a mounted messenger to Cairo to inform General Kleber that the terms of the convention were rejected. The despatch reached the French just as they were preparing to evacuate Cairo. Unfortunately, the Grand Vizier, who, with his army, was but a short distance away from the town, did not receive a similar intimation, and approaching the city with his troops, but[Pg 334] without guns, was attacked by the French, and suffered a disastrous defeat.

The Turks had not forgiven Sir Sidney Smith for this misfortune, but the latter had not supposed for a moment that the Turks themselves would have neglected to apprise the Grand Vizier of the news, and only thought of warning the French. The Grand Vizier now demanded that Sir Sidney Smith should not take part in any operations in which he and the Turkish army were concerned, or retain the command of the naval flotilla that he had created, and with which he had performed such excellent service in opening the Nile for the ascent of the gun-boats and the native craft laden with stores for the supply of the troops that were to advance against Cairo. General Hutchinson, very weakly and unworthily, and to the indignation and regret both of the army and fleet, at once gave way, and Admiral Keith, instead of supporting his subordinate, who had gained such renown and credit, and had shown such brilliant talent, acquiesced, and appointed Captain Stevenson of the *Europa* to succeed Sir Sidney in command of the flotilla that was to ascend the Nile to Cairo.

This surrender of one of our most distinguished officers to the prejudices of a Turkish commander was, in all respects, a disgraceful one, but from Sir Sidney Smith's first appointment Admiral Keith had exhibited a great jealousy of his obtaining a command that rendered him to some extent independent, and had lost no opportunity of showing his feeling. Indeed, there can be little doubt that the discourteous manner in which he repudiated, without any authority from the English government, the convention that would have saved all the effusion of blood and cost of the British expedition was the result of his jealousy of the fame acquired by Sir Sidney Smith. The latter, greatly[Pg 335] hurt at the unjust and humiliating manner in which he had been treated, at once returned to the *Tigre*, where the delight of the crew at being again under his command was at least some alleviation to the pain he felt.

Edgar, who had obtained leave of absence for a week, and who had ridden with the sheik for a stay of a few days at his camp, had not heard of the slight inflicted upon his kind friend until his return. He at once went on board the *Tigre* and sent in his name to his commander.

"I have come, Sir Sidney," he said when he was shown into the latter's cabin, "to say that I desire to be recalled from service on shore. After the manner in which you have been deprived of your command, I feel that I could not remain for a day upon the staff of General Hutchinson."

Sir Sidney smiled.

"You are too impetuous, Blagrove. I have received too many assurances from the officers of the fleet to doubt what their feelings are at the course that has been taken, but that can make no difference in their duty. It is to do their best in the various positions they occupy, without allowing the question whether they consider that an individual has been unjustly treated to influence them in any way. The service comes before everything. It is distinctly for the benefit of the service that General Hutchinson should have the advantage of your knowledge of the country and of its languages, and, moreover, you really received your promotion in no small degree owing to the fact that you were going to act as a sort of interpreter and guide to the general commanding the expedition, and although unhappily Sir Ralph Abercrombie's death has caused a change in that command, that in no way alters the arrangements.

"In the next place I think that you would be foolish to resign, because there can be no doubt that there will very[Pg 336] shortly be an advance against Cairo. The inundations and the strong defences that the troops have been throwing up will enable a comparatively small number to hold the garrison here in check. The Capitan Pasha's men have fought bravely at Rosetta, and the Grand Vizier's army is making its way down to join him. From what they say these are a mere rabble, but with five thousand or six thousand of our troops and Capitan Pasha's force, we ought to be able to make a good fight, even without the Vizier's people. At any rate, you would like afterwards to have gone to Cairo with our troops, and there is no doubt that your knowledge of the country will be very valuable. It would be a pity not to see the thing through when you have been in it from the very beginning.

"Lastly, Mr. Blagrove, I should be sorry, indeed, that any naval officer should evince any feeling whatever with regard to a matter purely personal to myself. I should therefore take it as a particular favour to me that you should continue to hold the appointment to which you have been posted."

"Thank you, Sir Sidney," Edgar said; "of course I will in that case retain the appointment. Now that I think of it, indeed, I feel that it was an impertinence to manifest in any way my feeling at General Hutchinson's conduct; my excuse must be that I only returned from my trip with the sheik half an hour since, and on hearing the news was so stirred that I ran down to the landing-place and came off on the impulse of the moment. You have shown me such extreme kindness, sir, that at the time it seemed to me a matter almost personal to myself."

"Do not apologize," Sir Sidney Smith said kindly; "the feeling did you credit as a man, though as an officer personal feelings cannot be permitted to sway the actions.[Pg 337] Now go ashore again and report yourself as returned from leave."

The advance up the Nile did not take place for some little time, as great preparations were necessary. Fortunately large numbers of native craft had been captured from the French, and stores were landed and placed on board these for the use of the troops. Colonel Stewart was in command of the British advanced force which accompanied the Capitan Pasha's division. A large force of gun-boats and rowing-boats were furnished by the fleet, and following the river banks the expedition proceeded up the river. The French resistance was very feeble. Detached parties were taken or driven off, but there was no fighting of a serious character. For a time Edgar remained with General Hutchinson before Alexandria, then he accompanied him to Rosetta, and, joining the main British division, came up with the Turkish army, that had now been joined by that of the Vizier, and the whole advanced towards Cairo.

They met with no real resistance on the march. There can be little doubt that the French generals were hampered by the intense longing among the troops to return to France. Their disasters in Syria had to some extent been retrieved by the defeat of the Turks at Aboukir, but the appearance of the great fleet of men-of-war and transports on the coast, followed by the failure of Menou to drive, as was confidently expected, his assailants back to their ships, produced a profound effect. The report that Alexandria had been almost cut off from the rest of Egypt by the inundation of Lake Mareotis, and that to regain the city an army would have to force its way along the narrow neck of land between the lakes Mareotis and Aboukir, seemed to diminish still further their hope of ever getting away.

The news, therefore, that a great force of British and[Pg 338] Turks, supported by gun-boats, and accompanied by an immense flotilla carrying stores, was ascending the Nile, reduced them almost to despair, and so unwilling were they to fight, that when, on the approach of the Vizier's army to Cairo, it was met by four thousand French, these suffered themselves to be repulsed by the rabble and fell back to Cairo.

They were well aware that if they surrendered they would be guaranteed a passage back to France. Better terms than this they could not hope to obtain after the most vigorous resistance, involving a great and useless loss of life. Therefore as soon as the whole allied force approached Cairo, negotiations were begun, and on the 28th of June (1801) these were concluded, and one of the gates of the town occupied by the Capitan Pasha's body-guards, and a fort by the 30th Regiment, and on the 10th the French evacuated the city, and the next day the Turkish troops took possession of it.

In the meantime fighting had been going on almost incessantly in front of Alexandria. General Coote, who was in command of the besieging force, gradually gained ground. The French lines were forced backward, and on September 2nd, finding the contest altogether hopeless, and most of the British troops from Cairo having returned, reinforced by a British native Indian army, the garrison capitulated. The number of troops, including the sick, who surrendered in Alexandria, were 10,528, while the force that surrendered at Cairo, which, like the other, was embarked in British ships and taken to France, was 13,672; included among them were 1900 sailors who had for the most part been landed after the battle of Aboukir, while some had been drawn from the French war-ships that had succeeded in running the blockade.[Pg 339]

The Indian force arrived in time to witness the surrender of Alexandria, but the fact that the work was practically accomplished by the 12,000 men who landed under General Abercrombie, aided after their work was half done by a Turkish force of no great value, renders the operation one of the most brilliant in our military history, and redounds equal credit upon the gallant soldier who died in the hour of victory, on his successor whose operations were most skilfully conducted, and on the British officers and soldiers who endured no ordinary amount of privation and labour under a burning sun.

Upon the advance to Cairo Edgar had been accompanied by the sheik and his son with a score of their followers. The information that they were enabled to give the general was of the greatest importance and value. The sheik was intimately acquainted with every foot of the ground, and on the force halting in the afternoon he was able to inform the quartermaster-general of the most likely spot for the next camping-ground, and of the distance and nature of the country to be traversed. At daybreak he would start ahead with his party, ascertain from the inhabitants of the villages whether any bodies of the enemy were in the neighbourhood, and arrange with them to forward such supplies of food and vegetables as remained at their disposal for sale, to the spot selected for the camping-ground that afternoon.

The supplies were but small, for the French had well-nigh made the whole country below Cairo a desert. Nevertheless, such as could be produced were gladly purchased by the commissariat for the use of the troops, and owing to the custom prevalent throughout the East of storing grain in covered pits, the supply obtained as forage for the horses largely exceeded expectations, for the peasants re[Pg 340]garded the British as deliverers from their oppressors, and upon being assured by the sheik that they paid well for everything that they required, the pits that had escaped the French searchers were thrown open at once. General Hutchinson, on his return to carry out the siege of Alexandria to a conclusion, reported to Admiral Keith his very warm appreciation of the services that Lieutenant Blagrove had rendered him. Long before that time the admiral had received from England a confirmation of the acting rank he had given Edgar. As soon as the capitulation was signed, although it had been stipulated that the British troops were not to go into the town until the French took their departure, many officers did so, as General Menou freely gave permission to enter to anyone who applied for it. Edgar was one of the first of these, and, riding in, alighted at his father's house.

CHAPTER XIX.
QUIET AND REST.

Mr. Muller came forward to meet his visitor as he entered, thinking it probable that this naval officer had come in reference to some arrangements to be made with regard to the transports that would carry the French army away. It was three years since he had last seen Edgar, and the latter had grown from a boy into a young man, and the uniform had altered him beyond recognition, for no news had been received from England since he had left, and Mr. Muller had supposed that he was all this time there with his father. Edgar smiled as he saw the absence of recognition in his face.[Pg 341]

"Don't you know me, Mr. Muller?" he asked. "I have no doubt changed a good deal since you saw me last in the dress of an Arab."

"Mr. Edgar Blagrove!" the latter exclaimed in astonishment. "Your disguises are endless, sir, and I think that this is the best of them, though why you should have adopted it I do not know."

"It happens that it is not a disguise at all this time. I am what I seem to be, a naval lieutenant. I have been serving in the navy ever since I joined it, ten days after I sailed from here, and was through the siege of Acre with Sir Sidney Smith. As you see, I have had the good fortune to be promoted. I have been serving ashore since we first landed here, and have been up to Cairo with the force that marched there as a sort of guide and interpreter."

"I am sure I congratulate you heartily. But you don't intend to stop in the navy, do you?"

"No, I think not. Of course I like the life, and have been so fortunate in getting early promotion and in being mentioned in despatches that I ought to rise very rapidly if I stayed in it, and I am sure that Sir Sidney Smith would interest himself for me. But I do not think that it would be fair to my father. He has reckoned on taking the management of the business at home, and that I should be established here with you, and probably it would be the best thing for me in the long run. The war with France cannot last many years, and when peace comes there will, of course, be a great reduction of the navy, and an immense number of officers put upon half-pay, without much chance of again obtaining employment. My time during the last three years will not have been misspent. As a lieutenant in the service who had obtained exceptionally rapid promotion I should be able to secure orders for stores or repairs to any[Pg 342] men-of-war who might put in, and the knowledge I have gained of ships, their fittings, rigging, and so on, would render me far more useful to you in superintending the harbour work than I would have been had I not had that experience."

"Certainly, Mr. Blagrove. I myself have, as you know, always been in charge of the office here, and as far as books and accounts go I think I know my work thoroughly, but in the last three years I have felt that my want of knowledge of the practical side of the business has been a serious drawback. I have been able to have the repairs necessary to French transports and so on carried out, for the two shipwrights are good workmen, and after it was done I could, of course, calculate what had been the cost, and charge it with a percentage for profit; but, as a rule, captains want an estimate before we begin, and I was unable to give one.

"On a few occasions I did so after consulting the shipwrights, but I burnt my fingers badly in each case, for it turned out that the defects were much more serious than met the eye; so after that, I refused to give an estimate at all, and lost some business in consequence, for a French firm here snapped up all the work they could get, and were always ready to give an estimate, though I believe in nine cases out of ten they either did not carry out their work thoroughly or else when half-way through were obliged to ask for considerable increase on the ground that the amount to be done far exceeded what they supposed. This has been so notorious that for the past year we have had our hands full, and I believe that they intended to leave even if the French occupation had continued. Indeed, they came to me three months ago and asked if I should be inclined to buy their yard and appliances and stock. I refused at[Pg 343] that time, but I am of opinion that the matter is well worth thinking over. Since trade increased again we have been very cramped for room. Of course it formed but a small portion of your father's business, but I think that in future it could be made at least as important a part as the inland trade, and certainly with you at the head it could be largely extended."

"That would quite suit me. As you know, I have always been fond of ships, and now, after being three years at sea, am naturally more fond of them than before; and although I could make myself very happy in looking after the work of a ship-yard and superintending the business afloat, I should feel altogether like a fish out of water if I were to be kept to book-keeping inside. I know that there is a ship sailing for England to-night with despatches. I will sit down at once and write to my father, and say that I am ready to leave the navy at once and fall to work here. He is certain to come out as soon as he hears the news that the place has surrendered, and that the French are going.

"I will tell him what you say about the other ship-yard, and ask him to go to the Admiralty. I have no doubt that the president of the prize court, who had some business with my father, and has since been on very friendly terms with him, will give him a good introduction, and may possibly go with him to urge that as I am going to undertake the superintendence of a ship-yard here, and that we hope to be of service to ships of war putting in for repairs, they will consent to my going on half-pay instead of retiring altogether. It would certainly strengthen my position here so far as our ships of war are concerned. I daresay that you will be sending off too."

"Yes; I have kept everything written up and copies made so that I could send them off should an opportunity[Pg 344] offer; and a couple of hours' work will enable me to bring matters pretty well up to date."

"I suppose, except for the ship work, everything has been of late very dull?"

"Very dull indeed. We have had literally no goods whatever from the interior. Of course production has fallen off very greatly, and the sale of Egyptian products at Cairo, to the troops, has been considerable. Then, too, the disturbed state of the country has prevented the manufacturers from sending valuable goods down here, so that practically that part of the business has been at a standstill, and I have not attempted to accumulate a stock. However I have lately purchased many large lots from native traders here who feared that their shops might be pillaged in the event of a riot, and especially lately when they were afraid that if your people took the town by storm there might be a general sack. So as I was certain that the French must go before long, and I got all these goods at a bargain, I have bought freely. Then I have not done badly with goods run in by French ships that managed to slip through the blockade, and which were laden with speculative cargoes of luxuries for the army. As we are almost the only European house open, and I was able to pay cash, I bought things up largely, and realized very good profits by supplying the native shops here and the officers of the garrison, and also sent a great deal of wine and goods of that sort up to Cairo, getting leave from the commandant here for them to go up under the guard of any body of troops that happened to be proceeding there, so that altogether the firm had not done badly, all things considered."

"Are you short of cash now, Mr. Muller? for if so I can give you a draft on my father, who has some money of mine in his hands, for a thousand pounds, the result partly[Pg 345] of prize-money, partly of a speculation I made in the purchase of a prize which I went home in. I bought it in his name, but he insists that as it was purely my speculation he should put the profit to my account."

"Thank you; I do not require it. I have had no opportunity of sending the money home for the last three years, and have therefore an abundance of funds for all purposes."

"I suppose that you must be very short of timber, cordage, and ship stores?"

"Not so much so as you would think. I am indeed very short of timber, and would gladly take the whole cargo of a ship laden with it should it arrive, but in other respects I am well off, for I boarded every transport and merchantman before they left the port, and bought up all their spare stores, which they were glad enough to part with on reasonable terms, for there was no advantage in carrying them back to France, and of course I could well afford to pay a considerable advance on the prices they would obtain there. I hope that you will stay here for the night, Mr. Blagrove, for I am anxious to hear all that you have been doing. I can offer you nothing but horse-flesh for dinner, for the town is in a state of starvation."

"I cannot do that. I have only leave till five o'clock, and indeed I only obtained permission to enter the town for two hours, and the French might object were I to stop here to-night."

Edgar wrote a long letter to his father. An hour after he had done so he left, taking it and the trader's packet away with him. These he placed in the headquarter-staff mail-bag. The letters were to be taken the next morning by the *Carmine*, which carried Sir Sidney Smith and Colonel Abercrombie, who were in charge of the naval and military[Pg 346] official despatches, giving an account of the successful termination of the campaign, to England. Lord Keith was most anxious that the men-of-war should get away from the coast before bad weather set in, and accordingly 5000 of the troops, under the command of General

Craddock, embarked on board the ships of war, and sailed on the 12th of September, and two days later the first division of French marched to Aboukir, and embarked on board transports.

Keith was in command of the fleet, and on the way fell in with a ship bringing despatches which had been sent out in anticipation of an early fall of Alexandria. The fleet was ordered to rendezvous at Malta. General Coote, with 6000 of the troops, were to be taken to Gibraltar. General Moore was ordered to England. General Hutchinson had leave to return home, and Lord Cavan was to remain in command in Egypt. Edgar had, two days after his visit to the city, been appointed as third lieutenant to one of the frigates that sailed with the first division of the army, and convoyed it to Gibraltar. It arrived there at the end of September, but as no orders had been received as to the destination of the force, the sick were landed, to be cared for in the hospitals, and the rest of the troops remained on board ship until the middle of November, when a vessel brought the news that a general peace had been virtually concluded.

England gave up all her conquests with the exception of Ceylon and Trinadad, while France was permitted to retain all hers. The treaty of Amiens, which was finally signed in the following March, was one of the most humiliating ever made by England. With it came an order for the ships at Gibraltar to carry the greater portion of the troops retained on board, to England. The wind was favourable,[Pg 347] and on the last day of the month the fleet cast anchor in Spithead. It was soon known that almost the whole fleet were to be paid off and the ships laid up at once. The men were pleased at the news, for most of the vessels had been engaged in arduous service in the Mediterranean for years, and the men were glad at the prospect of an opportunity of a turn ashore, until they had got rid of the prize-money that had accrued to them.

The officers, on the other hand, were depressed at the news. To them it meant that they might be years before they again obtained employment, that all chances of gaining distinction or promotion were at an end, and that they would be reduced to live on their scanty half-pay for an indefinite time. Mr. Addington indeed, who was now in power, thought only of retrenchment, and although it was evident to every thinking person that such a peace could only be of short duration, he crippled the country by paying off the greater portion of her ships-of-war; and when in May in the following year war again broke out, and Pitt returned to power, the whole work of getting the navy into fighting order had to be done over again. Two days after the fleet anchored at Spithead, Edgar was delighted to see his father on board a shore-boat that came alongside.

"Everything has turned out well," he said as soon as the first greeting was over. "On the very day that I got your letter, I had an intimation that the war was likely to come to an end shortly. I thought it better, therefore, to wait before moving in your matter until things were definitely settled, as it was infinitely better that you should be put on half-pay because the war had come to an end than to apply to give up active service while the war lasted."

"Certainly, father. There can be no doubt of that."

"Of course I got the letter that you wrote when you were[Pg 348] at Gibraltar, saying what ship you were on, and learned from my friend Captain Harrington of the prize court, that unless some hitch occurred in the negotiations, the fleet there, with the troops on board, would at once be ordered home, and on arrival would be paid off. There was, therefore, no occasion for me to make any application in the matter. The troops are, I see, landing to-day, and I suppose that in a week at latest the ships will be taken to the harbour and you will all be paid off."

"Nothing could be better, father."

"At any rate, there would be no chance whatever of your obtaining employment until the war breaks out again. When it does, my friend Harrington says that he has no doubt that he will be able to obtain for you an official post at Alexandria, with special instructions to aid in the provisioning and general repairs of any ships-of-war that may put in there, and that indeed he has no doubt that he will be able to get you the post of vice-consul there at once, for this, as you know, is as a rule given to merchants of standing, and as Sir Sidney Smith is in London, he would no doubt be able to support you in the matter. Of course there will be a consul-general in Egypt, and a vice-consul at each of the ports. So far, no appointments of the kind have been made, and, as he says, from your knowledge of the country, with our firm being long established as merchants there, with your knowing so many languages and your naval record, there can be little doubt that, if you apply, and are backed by Sir Sidney Smith, you will get the appointment at once."

"That would be capital, father. I hope that Muller's account of the work of the last three years has been satisfactory?"

"Perfectly so. We have done much better than I could[Pg 349] have expected under the circumstances; and indeed the profits of the last three years have been nearly as large as those of the years before the French landed."

Four days later the order arrived for the ship to pay off, and Edgar at once posted up to town, for the number of officers wanting to go up was so large that it was impossible to secure a place by a coach to London for a week to come. The next day he called upon Sir Sidney Smith and stated to him the plans he had formed.

"They could not get a better man for the place," the admiral said warmly, for he had now been promoted to that rank. "If you will bring me your formal application for the post of vice-consul at Alexandria, I will myself take it to the proper quarter. Put your qualification as a resident merchant and as a linguist as strongly as you like. I will urge your naval record, and myself testify to your abilities as a linguist and to the services which you have rendered."

A week later Edgar received his formal appointment as His Majesty's vice-consul at the port of Alexandria, and was given a fortnight's leave before starting to take up his work. Wilkinson, who had also been ordered home and placed upon half-pay, stayed with Mr. Blagrove during the time Edgar was at home, and was much more communicative as to the work his comrade had done than the latter had himself been.

"I can tell you," he said, "that for a midshipman to be promoted after only two years and a half service is an almost unknown thing in the navy, and shows what was thought by Lord Keith and Sir Sidney of his work."

Mr. Blagrove returned to Alexandria with his son, having before he started freighted a ship with timber, principally oak, of the kinds and sizes that would most frequently be[Pg 350] in demand for the execution of repairs, together with an apparatus for steaming and bending them. He had already, directly after receiving Edgar's letter from Gibraltar, sent out directions to Mr. Muller to take over the yard and premises of the French firm. The old name had not been replaced at the entrance of the offices, but now read Blagrove, Son, & Muller, while over the door of the premises recently acquired was now placed the words, "British Vice-consulate," and an office here was set apart for consular business, an Italian clerk, who spoke English well, being established there. As there were still some thousands of British soldiers in Alexandria, among whom were many officers who had been personally acquainted with Edgar while he had served on the staff of the general, his position was a very pleasant one. The Egyptian governor of the city, a Turkish general, who had been with the army of the Capitan Pasha, and to whom Edgar had frequently carried communications, also received him warmly.

"I am glad, indeed, to have a British vice-consul here," he said, "who speaks our language so perfectly, and who is a British officer. So often these posts are given to small traders, who, instead of endeavouring to smooth over difficulties, seem to delight in causing them. Whenever you have any complaint to make, sir, I hope that you will come direct to me, and I will see that right is done."

After spending a month at Alexandria, Mr. Blagrove returned to England, perfectly satisfied that matters would go on well, with his steady-going partner controlling the commercial part of the business, and Edgar taking the management of the shipping side. The business indeed flourished greatly, and when, some time afterwards, the Turks were forced to join in the European coalition against England, the firm was enabled to continue their business[Pg 351] without molestation, as the Capitan Pasha himself took him under his special protection. Four years after his appointment Edgar returned to England on a short visit, and was present at the marriage of one of his sisters with Wilkinson, who had returned home wounded after the battle of Trafalgar; though only a month at home, he persuaded a friend of his sisters to return as his wife to Alexandria.

Ten years later Mr. Muller died. Mr. Blagrove, who was now getting on in years, wished to have Edgar at home with him; and as moreover the climate was telling upon the latter's wife, the business was wound up and the premises and good-will disposed of for a considerable sum of money to another firm doing business there. Scarce a week had passed during Edgar's stay in Alexandria without either the sheik or Sidi riding into Alexandria to see him. He on his part purchased a large tent from a Turkish general who had been recalled to Constantinople. This was large and commodious, divided by hangings into two or three compartments. It was set up in the Beni Ouafy's oasis, and there he and his wife sometimes went out with their two children and spent a few days. It was with the deepest regret that he and his Arab friends bade farewell to each other when he finally left for England.

Before sailing he made an advantageous arrangement with the firm that had purchased the business, that his father should act as their agent in London, and by the influence of Sir Sidney Smith he himself obtained an appointment in the Admiralty. As his father's savings during many years, and his own share of the property during the time that he had been partner amounted to a considerable sum, he cared less for the increase of his income by going on full pay again than for the employment that it afforded him. His father and mother died within a few months of each[Pg 352] other in 1825. His second sister had been married some fifteen years before to a London merchant.

At the general reduction of the navy after the great war, Wilkinson was retired with the rank of commander, and he and his wife settled down in a pretty house within a few hundred yards of that of Edgar at Hampstead, and the two friends often talked over their experience at Acre, and of the cruise in search of pirates among the islands of the Archipelago.